GLENCOE
PHYSICS
Principles and Problems

• • • • • • • • • • • •

Study Guide
Teacher Edition

GLENCOE
McGraw-Hill

New York, New York   Columbus, Ohio   Woodland Hills, California   Peoria, Illinois

GLENCOE
PHYSICS
Principles and Problems

Student Edition

Teacher Wraparound Edition

Teacher Classroom Resources

Transparency Package with Transparency
Masters

Laboratory Manual SE and TE

Physics Lab and Pocket Lab Worksheets

Study Guide SE and TE

Chapter Assessment

Tech Prep Applications

Critical Thinking

Reteaching

Enrichment

Physics Skills

Advanced Concepts in Physics

Supplemental Problems

Problems and Solutions Manual

Spanish Resources

Lesson Plans with block scheduling

Technology

Computer Test Bank (Win/Mac)

MindJogger Videoquizzes

Electronic Teacher Classroom Resources
(ETCR)

Website at *science.glencoe.com*

Physics for the Computer Age CD-ROM
(Win/Mac)

The Glencoe Science Professional Development Series

Graphing Calculators in the Science Classroom

Cooperative Learning in the Science Classroom

Alternate Assessment in the Science Classroom

Performance Assessment in the Science
Classroom

Lab and Safety Skills in the Science Classroom

Glencoe/McGraw-Hill

A Division of The McGraw·Hill Companies

Send all inquiries to:
Glencoe/McGraw-Hill
8787 Orion Place
Columbus, Ohio 43240

ISBN 0-02-825494-5
Printed in the United States of America.

5 6 7 8 9 045 05 04 03 02

Contents

To the Teacher

This *Study Guide* for *Physics: Principles and Problems* is a tool that will help your students learn physics—its vocabulary and concepts. It includes six pages of questions and exercises for each chapter of the textbook. Items are presented in a variety of objective formats: fill-in-the-blanks, matching, true/false, interpreting diagrams and data, multiple choice, short-answer questions, and so on. The first *Study Guide* worksheet for each chapter is a review of vocabulary. Subsequent worksheets closely follow the organization of the textbook, providing review items for each textbook section and references to specific content.

Students will find these *Study Guide* worksheets helpful for previewing and/or reviewing chapter material. As a preview, the sheets help students focus on the concepts at the time you assign the reading. Students can then complete each *Study Guide* section after reading the corresponding textbook section. Some students will have more success completing the sheets in smaller chunks. For this reason, question sets in the *Study Guide* are referenced to specific readings in the textbook. When complete, the collection of these worksheets will prove to be an excellent review instrument for chapter tests and comprehensive exams.

1 Study Guide

Use with Chapter 1.

What is physics?

Vocabulary Review

Write the term that correctly completes each statement. Use each term once.

physics   quintessence   technology

planets   scientific method

1. _____ The study of matter and energy is _____.

2. _____ A _____ is a systematic way to observe, experiment, and analyze the world.

3. _____ The _____ are five bright objects that move relative to the constellations.

4. _____ Greek philosophers thought that celestial bodies are made of the element _____.

5. _____ The application of science to solve a practical problem is _____.

Section 1.1: Physics: The Search for Understanding

In your textbook, read about the work that physicists do.
Write the term that correctly completes each statement. Use each term once.

experiments   observations   theories

explanation   phenomena   universe

models   predictions

Physicists make **(1)** _____, do **(2)** _____, and create

(3) _____ or **(4)** _____ to answer questions. Like all scien-

tists, their goal is to obtain a compelling **(5)** _____ that describes many different

(6) _____, makes **(7)** _____, and leads to a better under-

standing of the **(8)** _____.

1 Study Guide

· · · · · · · · · · · · · · · ·

In your textbook, read about early astronomy.
For each term on the left, write the letter of the matching item.

_____ **9.** wanderer

_____ **10.** one of the elements that the ancient Greeks
thought composed matter

_____ **11.** the element that the ancient Greeks thought
composed celestial objects

_____ **12.** the Roman name of the god of war

_____ **13.** the result of an element traveling in a straight
line toward its own natural place

a. Mars

b. water

c. planet

d. quintessence

e. motion

In your textbook, read about Galileo.
For each of the statements below, write true *or rewrite the italicized part to make the statement true.*

14. Galileo estimated the heights of the mountains of the moon by their *volumes.*

_____

15. Galileo discovered that the planet *Mars* has four moons.

_____

16. Galileo discovered that the planet *Venus* has phases.

_____

17. Galileo argued that the planets circle *the sun.*

_____

18. Galileo wrote most of his scientific works in his native *Latin,* so that they could be read by an
educated person.

_____

19. According to Galileo, the first step of studying a problem in an organized way is *observing.*

_____

20. Galileo is considered to be the father of modern *space exploration.*

_____

Physics: Principles and Problems

1 Study Guide

● ● ● ● ● ● ● ● ● ● ● ● ● ●

In your textbook, read about scientific methods.
Label the following steps in the order in which scientists study problems.

_____ **21.** Draw a conclusion.

_____ **22.** Combine experimentation with careful measurements and analyses of results.

_____ **23.** Subject the conclusion to additional tests to determine if it is valid.

In your textbook, read about observations of Mars.
Answer the following question.

24. List four features attributed to Mars by astronomers and the general public that made it seem like Earth.

_____

_____

_____

_____

_____

_____

In your textbook, read about missions to Mars.
In the table below, enter each mission's launch date and check the appropriate accomplishment box.

Table 1				
Mission	**Launch Date**	**Result/Goal**		
		Fly-by	**Orbit**	**Land**
Mariner 4 (U.S.)				
Mariner 6 (U.S.)				
Mariner 9 (U.S.)				
Mars 3 (USSR)				
Mars 5 (USSR)				
Viking 1 (U.S.)				
Viking 2 (U.S.)				
Global Surveyor (U.S.)				
Mars Pathfinder (U.S.)				
Mars Surveyor Orbiter (U.S.)				
Mars Surveyor Lander (U.S.)				

1 Study Guide

In your textbook, read about the makeup of the Mars exploration teams.

Under each heading, list four careers that are represented on a Mars exploration team.

Scientific   Engineering   Other

_____   _____   _____

_____   _____   _____

_____   _____   _____

_____   _____   _____

In your textbook, read about the importance of physics.

Describe how physics is involved in each aspect of a Mars exploration mission.

25. Propulsion and guidance

_____

_____

_____

_____

_____

_____

26. Onboard energy systems

_____

_____

_____

_____

27. Communications

_____

_____

_____

_____

_____

1 Study Guide

· · · · · · · · · · · · · ·

In your textbook, read about physics success stories.
For each term on the left, write the letter of the matching item.

_____ **28.** will allow performing functions on a
submicroscopic level

_____ **29.** a result of research in heat transfer, thin films,
plasma sources, vacuum technology , and new materials

_____ **30.** once thought worthless but now used in many
endeavors including data storage, medicine, and
telecommunications

_____ **31.** developed from wartime research in radar and
miniature electronics

_____ **32.** aids in quality control

_____ **33.** developed from research into thin films,
magnetic materials, and semiconductors

_____ **34.** helps reduce automotive costs

a. laser

b. microwave oven

c. personal computer

d. nanotechnology

e. lighter weight composite
materials and polymers

f. energy efficient houses

g. computerized vision
system

2 Study Guide

Use with Chapter 2.

A Mathematical Toolkit

Vocabulary Review

Write the term that correctly completes each statement. Use each term once.

accuracy	kilogram	precision	significant digits
base units	linear relationship	quadratic relationship	slope
derived units	meter	scientific notation	*y*-intercept
factor-label method	metric system	second	
inverse relationship	parallax	SI	

1. _____ The apparent shift in the position of an object when it is viewed from various angles is _____.

2. _____ The SI base unit of mass is the _____.

3. _____ A way to convert a quantity in one unit to a quantity in another unit, using a relationship between the two units, is the _____.

4. _____ The SI base unit of length is the _____.

5. _____ Expressing numbers in exponential notation is _____.

6. _____ On a graph, the rise divided by the run is the _____ of the line.

7. _____ The system of measurement established by French scientists in 1795 is the _____.

8. _____ A relationship that produces a graph with a straight line is a(n) _____.

9. _____ The degree of exactness of a measurement is _____.

10. _____ The units of quantities measured against standards are the _____.

11. _____ A relationship in which one variable varies with the square of the other variable is a(n) _____.

12. _____ On a graph, the point where the line crosses the *y*-axis is the _____.

13. _____ The Système Internationale d'Unités, _____, is a system of measurement established by an international committee.

14. _____ A relationship in which one variable varies with the inverse of the other is a(n) _____.

15. _____ Units that are combinations of base units are _____.

16. _____ In any measurement, the digits that are valid are _____.

17. _____ The SI base unit of time is the _____.

18. _____ The extent to which a measured value agrees with the standard value of the quantity is _____.

2 Study Guide

• • • • • • • • • • • • • •

Section 2.1: The Measures of Science

In your textbook, read about SI.

For each base quantity on the left, write the matching base unit and the matching symbol.

			Base Unit	Symbol
1.	_____ _____	length	ampere	cd
2.	_____ _____	mass	candela	kg
3.	_____ _____	time	kelvin	m
4.	_____ _____	temperature	kilogram	mol
5.	_____ _____	amount of a substance	meter	s
6.	_____ _____	electric current	mole	A
7.	_____ _____	luminous intensity	second	K

Answer the following questions, using complete sentences.

8. What is the current definition of a meter?

_____

_____

_____

_____

9. How is a second currently defined?

_____

_____

_____

_____

10. What is the current definition of a kilogram?

_____

_____

_____

_____

2 Study Guide

In your textbook, read about SI prefixes.
Complete the table.

		Table 1	
Prefix	**Symbol**	**Multiplier**	**Scientific Notation**
11.		1/1 000 000 000 000 000	
12. pico			
13.			10^{-9}
14. micro			
15.		1/1000	
16.		1000	
17. mega			
18.			10^{9}
19.	T		

Write the term that correctly completes each statement.

20. In scientific notation, the numerical part of a quantity is written as _____.

21. In 10^{n}, n is an _____.

22. In changing the numerical part of a measurement to scientific notation, the number of places you move the decimal point to the left is expressed as a _____ exponent.

23. In changing the numerical part of a measurement to scientific notation, the number of places you move the decimal point to the right is expressed as a _____ exponent.

2 Study Guide

• • • • • • • • • • • • • •

Section 2.2: Measurement Uncertainties

In your textbook, read about accuracy and precision.
Refer to the diagram below. Circle the letter of the choice that best completes each statement.

1. Measurements that have the same precision are those of students _____.

   a. A and B   **b.** A and C   **c.** A and D   **d.** B and D

2. Measurements that have the least precision are those of student _____.

   a. A   **b.** B   **c.** C   **d.** D

3. Measurements that have the greatest precision are those of student _____.

   a. A   **b.** B   **c.** C   **d.** D

4. Measurements that have the same accuracy are those of students _____.

   a. A and B   **b.** A and C   **c.** A and D   **d.** B and D

5. Measurements that have the least accuracy are those of student _____.

   a. A   **b.** B   **c.** C   **d.** D

6. Measurements that have the greatest accuracy are those of students _____.

   a. A and B   **b.** A and C   **c.** A and D   **d.** B and D

7. The most precise and accurate measurements are those of student _____.

   a. A   **b.** B   **c.** C   **d.** D

8. To assure the greatest precision and accuracy in reading an instrument such as a thermometer, you should read the instrument _____.

   a. below eye level   **b.** above eye level   **c.** at eye level

2 Study Guide

• • • • • • • • • • • • • • •

In your textbook, read about significant digits.

Write the letter of each rule that is used to determine the correct number of significant digits in each measurement below. Then write the measurement in scientific notation.

Measurement	Rules Used	Scientific Notation	Rules
9. 321 m	_____	_____	**a.** Nonzero digits are always significant.
10. 1201 s	_____	_____	
11. 1.0 m/s	_____	_____	**b.** All final zeros after the decimal point are significant.
12. 0.01 K	_____	_____	**c.** Zeros between two other significant digits are always significant.
13. 70.010 Mg	_____	_____	
14. 53 000 000 cm	_____	_____	**d.** Zeros used solely as placeholders are not significant.
15. 0.200 A	_____	_____	
16. 40 000 L	_____	_____	
17. 0.680 kg	_____	_____	

In your textbook, read about arithmetic with significant digits.

Explain how the number of significant digits was determined for the answer to each problem.

18.
    21.65 mm
    14.00 mm
 + 1.2 mm
    37.9   mm

_____

_____

_____

19.
    0.62 m
 × 3.57 m
   2.2 m^2

_____

_____

_____

20. $\dfrac{5013 \text{ m}}{2.6 \text{ s}} = 1900 \text{ m/s}$

_____

_____

_____

2 Study Guide

· · · · · · · · · · · · · · ·

Section 2.3: **Visualizing Data**

In your textbook, read about graphing data.
Read the paragraph below. Refer to the table to answer the questions that follow.

A student cuts an aluminum rod into four random pieces. She then measures the volume and mass of each piece. The data she records is shown. To determine how the mass of each piece varies with its volume, she constructs a graph.

1. What is the range of the data of the independent variable?

   _____

2. What would be a convenient range for the *x*-axis?

   _____

3. What is the range of the data of the dependent variable?

   _____

4. What would be a convenient range for the *y*-axis?

   _____

Table 1	
Volume (mL)	**Mass (g)**
9.2	24.93
18.3	49.15
34.5	93.19
48.2	131.92

In your textbook, read about linear and nonlinear relationships.
For each term on the left, write the letter of the matching item.

_____	5. the equation of a linear relationship	**a.** hyperbola
_____	6. the shape of the graph of a linear relationship	**b.** parabola
_____	7. the equation of an inverse relationship	**c.** straight line
_____	8. the shape of the graph of an inverse relationship	**d.** $y = mx + b$
_____	9. the equation of a quadratic relationship	**e.** $y = ax^2 + bx + c$
_____	10. the shape of the graph of a quadratic relationship	**f.** $y = \dfrac{a}{x}$

3 Study Guide

Describing Motion

Vocabulary Review

Write the term that correctly completes each statement. Use each term once.

average acceleration	motion diagram	position vector
average speed	operational definition	problem-solving strategy
average velocity	origin	scalar quantity
coordinate system	particle model	time interval
displacement	physical model	vector quantity
distance	pictorial model	

1. _____ A series of images of an object that records the object's position after equal time intervals is a(n) _____.

2. _____ A quantity that has magnitude and direction is a(n) _____.

3. _____ The _____ replaces an object by a single point.

4. _____ The zero point of a variable and the direction in which the values of the variable increase is indicated in a(n) _____.

5. _____ An arrow that is proportional to the distance an object is from the origin and points in the direction of the object is a(n) _____.

6. _____ The magnitude of the average-velocity vector is _____.

7. _____ A step-wise procedure for solving problems is a(n) _____.

8. _____ A change in time is a(n) _____.

9. _____ A quantity defined in terms of the procedure used to identify it is a(n)_____.

10. _____ The change in position of an object is its _____.

11. _____ The point in a coordinate system at which the variables have the value of zero is the _____.

12. _____ The length of the displacement vector represents the _____ between the two positions.

13. _____ A model that uses symbols to represent variables is a(n) _____.

14. _____ The ratio of the displacement to the time interval in which the displacement takes place is the _____.

15. _____ A motion diagram is an example of a(n) _____.

16. _____ The _____ is the ratio of the change in velocity to the time interval in which the change took place.

17. _____ A quantity that has only magnitude is a(n) _____.

3 Study Guide

Section 3.1: Picturing Motion

In your textbook, read about motion diagrams.

Refer to the diagrams below, showing frames from a camcorder at 2-s intervals. Circle the letter of the choice that best completes each statement.

1. In set I, the object that is moving is _____.

   a. A   **b.** B   **c.** C

2. Set II shows that object B is _____.

   a. at rest   **c.** slowing down

   b. increasing its speed   **d.** traveling at constant speed

3. Set _____ shows object B is slowing down.

   a. I   **b.** II   **c.** III   **d.** IV

4. Set _____ shows object B at rest.

   a. I   **b.** II   **c.** III   **d.** IV

5. Set _____ shows object B traveling at a constant speed.

   a. I   **b.** II   **c.** III   **d.** IV

3 Study Guide

Section 3.2: Where and When?

In your textbook, read about coordinate systems.

Refer to the diagrams below, showing the location of an object represented by a circle. Complete the table by writing the position vector of each object.

A

B

Table 1	
Diagram	**Position Vector**
A	
B	
C	
D	
E	

C

D

E

In your textbook, read about vectors, scalars, time intervals, and displacements.

For each term on the left, write the letter of the matching term.

_____ **1.** symbol that represents time interval

_____ **2.** Greek letter delta used to mean change

_____ **3.** definition of time interval

_____ **4.** one way of representing the vector quantity

        acceleration

_____ **5.** symbol that represents position

_____ **6.** magnitude of the displacement vector

_____ **7.** definition of displacement

_____ **8.** one way of representing the vector quantity velocity

_____ **9.** symbol that represents displacement

_____ **10.** symbol that represents the scalar quantity mass

a. distance

b. m

c. Δt

d. $\vec{a}$

e. Δd

f. Δ

g. v

h. d

i. $t_1 - t_0$

j. $d_1 - d_0$

3 Study Guide

••••••••••••••

In your textbook, read about time intervals and displacements.

In the space provided, draw and label the vectors d_0 and d_1 for the given information. Then draw and label the vector Δd and determine its magnitude.

11. $d_0 = +4$ m $\qquad d_1 = +10$ m

12. $d_0 = +2$ m $\qquad d_1 = +9$ m

13. $d_0 = -4$ m $\qquad d_1 = -6$ m

In your textbook, read about time intervals and displacements.

Refer to the motion diagram below, showing the locations of an object during a 12-s interval. Answer the following questions.

14. What is the magnitude of the position vector at $t = 0$ s?

_____

15. At what time does the object have a position of $+8.0$ m?

_____

16. What is displacement of the object in the time interval $t_6 - t_5$?

_____

17. In what time intervals does the object have a constant speed?

_____

18. What is happening to the motion of the object in the time interval $t_{12} - t_9$?

_____

19. What distance does the object travel in the time interval $t_{12} - t_0$?

_____

_____

Section 3.3: Velocity and Acceleration

In your textbook, read about velocity.

For each of the statements below, write true *or rewrite the italicized part to make the statement true.*

1. _____ The ratio $\Delta d/\Delta t$ is called the *average velocity*.

2. _____ The symbol $\bar{v}$ represents the *average acceleration*.

3. _____ The magnitude of the average-velocity vector is the quantity average *distance traveled*.

4. _____ Automobile speeds are usually measured in miles per hour (mph) or *kilometers per hour (km/h)*.

5. _____ The equation $d_0 + \bar{v}\,\Delta t$ represents the *position* of an object after the time interval Δt.

6. _____ The quantity $\bar{v}\,\Delta t$ represents the change in *speed* of an object during the time interval Δt.

In your textbook, read about interpreting velocity vectors and acceleration.

Refer to the motion diagram below, showing the position at 1-s intervals of a car traveling to the right along the positive x–axis. In the space provided, draw the displacement, velocity, and acceleration vectors for each time interval. Answer the following questions.

•   •   •   •   •   •   •   •   •   •

Displacement

Velocity

Acceleration

7. What is happening to the motion of the car during the time intervals in which both the velocity and the acceleration vectors are in the positive direction?

_____

8. What is happening to the motion of the car during the time intervals in which the velocity vectors are positive and the acceleration vectors are negative?

_____

3 Study Guide

In your textbook, read about problem-solving strategies.

Read the following problem and refer to the diagram below. Circle the letter of the choice that best completes the statement or answers the question.

A car traveling at a constant 7 m/s takes 5 s to pass through a school zone and then accelerates at 2 m/s^2 for 3 s. How far does the car travel in the 8 s?

d_1
v_1

d_2
v_2

a_{12}

d_3
v_3

a_{23}

$+x$

1. The diagram above represents a(n) _____ of the problem.

   a. physical model

   b. operational definition

   c. pictorial model

   d. particle model

2. A likely choice for the origin of the coordinate system would be at a point _____.

   a. where the car enters the school zone

   b. halfway through the school zone

   c. at the beginning of the school zone

   d. at the end of the school zone

3. Which of the following motion diagrams represents the problem?

   a. ●●●● ● ●●●●

   b. ● ● ● ●●●●●●

   c. ●●●●●●●●●

   d. ●●●●● ● ● ●

4. The problem can be thought of as a two-step problem because the car has _____.

   a. one displacement

   b. constant velocity and an acceleration

   c. equal time intervals

   d. unequal time intervals

5. If d_1 is the position of the car at the beginning of the problem and d_3 is the position of the car at the end of the problem, a good choice of d_2 is the position of the car _____.

   a. at the beginning of the school zone

   b. halfway through the school zone

   c. at the point where the car changes speeds

   d. at the point where the car stops

6. The acceleration a_{12}, between d_1 and d_2, is _____.

   a. increasing   b. decreasing   c. 0 m/s^2 d. +2.0 m/s^2

7. The acceleration a_{23}, between d_2 and d_3, is _____.

   a. increasing   b. decreasing   c. 0 m/s^2 d. +2.0 m/s^2

8. The vector representing acceleration a_{23} _____.

   a. points to the left

   b. points to the right

   c. is equal to zero

   d. is shorter than vector a_{12}

4 Study Guide

Use with Chapter 4.

• • • • • • • • • • •

Vector Addition

Vocabulary Review

Write the term that correctly completes each statement. Use each term once.

algebraic representation   magnitude   vector
components   origin   vector decomposition
direction   Pythagorean relationship   velocity
displacement   resultant vector
graphical representation   scalar quantity

1. _____ An arrow or an arrow-tipped line segment is called a(n) _____ of a vector.

2. _____ A(n) _____ of a vector is represented by an italicized letter in bold-face type.

3. _____ A(n) _____ is a vector that is equal to the sum of two or more vectors.

4. _____ The _____ states that the sum of the squares of the two sides of a right triangle is equal to the square of the hypotenuse.

5. _____ The _____ of a vector is defined as the angle that the vector makes with the x-axis, measured counterclockwise, in a rectangular coordinate system.

6. _____ The process of breaking a vector into its components is sometimes called _____.

7. _____ Two vectors projected on the axes of a coordinate system are called the _____ of the resultant vector.

8. _____ A quantity that has both magnitude and direction is a(n) _____.

9. _____ The _____ of a vector is always a positive quantity.

10. _____ Distance is the magnitude of a vector quantity called _____.

11. _____ A quantity that has only magnitude is a(n) _____.

12. _____ The magnitude of an object's _____ is its speed.

13. _____ The center of a coordinate system is called the _____.

4 Study Guide

Section 4.1: Properties of Vectors

In your textbook, read about representing vector quantities.

For the diagrams below, use the scale to determine the magnitude of each displacement vector. Determine the direction of each displacement using compass points of north, south, east, and west, or the intermediate points such as northeast and southwest. Write the value of the displacement in the space to the left.

1. _____

2. _____

3. _____

4. _____

5. _____

6. _____

7. _____

8. _____

9. _____

10. _____

1. ⊢+++++▶ ⊢ = 1 km

2. ↑ ⊢ = 1 km

3. ↖ ⊢ = 1 km

4. ↓ ⊢ = 1 km

5. ◀+++⊢ ⊢ = 1 km

6. ↘ ⊢ = 1 km

7. ↙ ⊢ = 10 m

8. ⊢++++▶ ⊢ = 2 km

9. ↘ ⊢ = 5 m

10. ◀+++⊢ ⊢ = 100 m

Read the following statement. Circle the letter of the choice that is the best response.

The displacement of a student is 2.0 km north.

11. Which is the correct algebraic representation of the displacement?

   a. d = 2.0 km north

   b. *d* = 2.0 km north

   c. **d** = 2.0 km north

   d. *d* = 2.0 km north

12. Which is the correct algebraic representation of the magnitude of the displacement?

   a. d = 2.0 km

   b. *d* = 2.0 km

   c. **d** = 2.0 km

   d. *d* = 2.0 km

4 Study Guide

In your textbook, read about representing vector quantities.

Each set of displacement vectors below is drawn to the same scale. For each situation, write its letter next to the correct number of the expression.

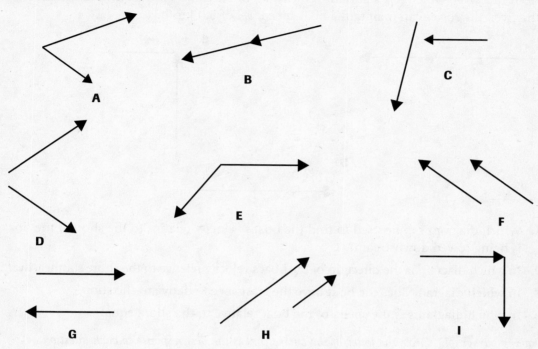

13. _____ Vectors in set have same direction.

14. _____ Vectors in set have same magnitude.

15. _____ Vectors in set are equal.

In your textbook, read about the graphic addition of vectors.

For each of the statements below, write true *or rewrite the italicized part to make the statement true.*

16. _____ The *length* of the arrow representing a vector should be proportional to the magnitude of the quantity being represented.

17. _____ A *ruler* is used to measure the angle that establishes the direction of the vector.

18. _____ When adding two vectors, the first vector is drawn and the *tip* of the second vector is placed at the tip of the first vector.

19. _____ When adding vectors, the resultant vector is drawn from the *tail* of the first vector to the tip of the last vector.

20. _____ The resultant vector is *dependent* on the order in which the vectors are added.

4 Study Guide

In your textbook, read about relative velocities.

Read the following paragraph. Write the letter of the diagram that is the best response to each question.

A boat is placed in a river, which has a current velocity, v_c, of 3.0 km/h east, relative to the shore. Relative to the river, the rower can maintain a boat speed, v_b, of 6.0 km/h.

_____ **21.** Which diagram can be used to find the boat's velocity relative to the shore if the boat is being rowed downstream?

_____ **22.** In which diagram is the direction of the boat's velocity relative to the shore southeastward?

_____ **23.** In which diagram does the boat have the least speed relative to the shore?

_____ **24.** In which diagrams is the speed of the boat relative to the shore equal?

Read the following paragraph. Circle the letter of the choice that is the best response to each question.

In questions 21–24, the resultant vector represents the velocity of the boat, v_s, relative to the shore. Algebraically,

$$v_s = v_b + v_c.$$

If a rower wants to get to a certain point by a certain time, he or she knows what v_s is. What the rower must determine is v_b, that is, how fast and in what direction he or she must row relative to the river. Solving the above equation for v_b gives

$$v_b = v_s - v_c.$$

25. The equation for v_b can be written as which of the following equations?

    a. $v_b = v_c - v_s$ **c.** $v_b = -(v_s + v_c)$

    b. $v_b = v_s + (-v_c)$ **d.** $v_b = -(v_s - v_c)$

26. Which diagram illustrates the velocity at which a boat must be rowed relative to the river if the rower wants to maintain a heading of 45.0° northeast relative to the shore? The river has a current velocity of 3.0 m/s east relative to the shore.

   a.   **b.**   **c.**   **d.**

4 Study Guide

Section 4.2: Components of Vectors

In your textbook, read about coordinate systems.

Refer to the diagram below. Circle the letter of the choice that best completes each statement.

1. In the coordinate system shown, the positive *y*-axis is located _____ counterclockwise from the positive *x*-axis.

    a. 0°   **c.** 180°

    b. 90°   **d.** 270°

2. The *y*-axis crosses the *x*-axis at the _____.

    a. angle θ **c.** quadrant

    b. origin   **d.** vertex

3. Vectors *E* and *F* lie in quadrant _____.

    a. I   **c.** III

    b. II   **d.** IV

4. Vector _____ has a positive horizontal component and a positive vertical component.

    a. *A*   **c.** *D*

    b. *B*   **d.** *E*

5. The sine of an angle is defined as
$$\sin \theta = \frac{\text{opposite side}}{\text{hypotenuse}}.$$
   The sine of the angle that vector *B* makes with the *x*-axis is _____.

    a. $\sin \theta = \dfrac{B_x}{B}$ **b.** $\sin \theta = \dfrac{B}{B_x}$ **c.** $\sin \theta = \dfrac{B_x}{B_y}$ **d.** $\sin \theta = \dfrac{B_y}{B}$

6. The cosine of an angle is defined as
$$\cos \theta = \frac{\text{adjacent side}}{\text{hypotenuse}}.$$
   The cosine of the angle that vector *D* makes with the *x*-axis is _____.

    a. $\cos \theta = \dfrac{D_x}{D}$ **b.** $\cos \theta = \dfrac{D}{D_x}$ **c.** $\cos \theta = \dfrac{D_x}{D_y}$ **d.** $\cos \theta = \dfrac{D_y}{D}$

7. Vector _____ has no horizontal component.

    a. *A*   **b.** *B*   **c.** *C*   **d.** *G*

8. The horizontal component of vector *F* has a value of _____.

    a. *F*   **b.** $F \sin \theta$ **c.** $F \cos \theta$ **d.** $\dfrac{F}{\cos \theta}$

9. The vertical component of vector *F* has a value of _____.

    a. *F*   **b.** $F \sin\theta$ **c.** $F \cos\theta$ **d.** $\dfrac{F}{\cos \theta}$

10. Both components of vector _____ are negative.

    a. *B*   **b.** *D*   **c.** *E*   **d.** *G*

4 Study Guide

In your textbook, read about addition of vectors using components.

The diagram shows the displacement of a hiker. The data table shows the magnitudes of the vertical and horizontal components of each displacement.

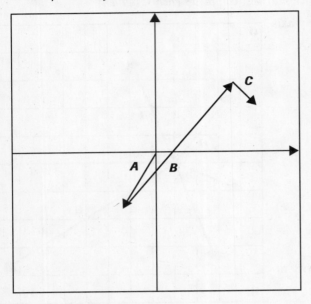

Table 1	
Component	**Magnitude (km)**
A_x	1.4
A_y	3.8
B_x	4.0
B_y	6.9
C_x	1.5
C_y	1.3

Circle the letter of the choice that is the best response.

11. What is the value of R_x, which represents the sum of the horizontal components of the displacements?

   a. $R_x = 1.4$ km $+ 4.0$ km $+ 1.5$ km $= 6.9$ km

   b. $R_x = (-1.4$ km$) + (-4.0$ km$) + (-1.5$ km$) = -6.9$ km

   c. $R_x = (-1.4$ km$) + 4.0$ km $+ 1.5$ km $= 4.1$ km

   d. $R_x = 1.4$ km $+ (-4.0$ km$) + (-1.5$ km$) = -4.1$ km

12. What is the value of R_y, which represents the sum of the vertical components of the displacements?

   a. $R_y = 3.8$ km $+ 6.9$ km $+ 1.3$ km $= 12.0$ km

   b. $R_y = (-3.8$ km$) + (-6.9$ km$) + (-1.3$ km$) = -12.0$ km

   c. $R_y = (-3.8$ km$) + 6.9$ km $+ (-1.3$ km$) = 1.8$ km

   d. $R_y = 3.8$ km $+ (-6.9$ km$) + (-1.3$ km$) = -4.4$ km

13. What is the magnitude of the resultant R?

   a. $R < 0$ km   **b.** $R = 0$ km   **c.** $R > 0$ km

14. What is the magnitude and direction of the displacement vector Y that will return the hiker to the starting point?

   a. $Y = 0$ km   **b.** $Y = R$ **c.** $Y = -R$ **d.** $Y = -2R$

5 Study Guide

Use with Chapter 5.

A Mathematical Model of Motion

Vocabulary Review

Write the term that correctly completes each statement. Use each term once.

acceleration due to gravity   instantaneous velocity   slope

constant acceleration   position-time graph   uniform motion

constant velocity   rise   velocity-time graph

instantaneous acceleration   run

1. _____ A graph that shows how position depends on time is a(n) _____.

2. _____ The vertical separation of any two points on a curve is the _____.

3. _____ On a position-time graph, the slope of a tangent to the curve at a specific time is the _____.

4. _____ In _____ equal displacements occur during successive equal time intervals.

5. _____ An object that has the same average velocity for all time intervals is moving at _____.

6. _____ The constant acceleration that acts on falling bodies is the _____.

7. _____ The ratio of the rise to run is the _____ of a curve.

8. _____ A graph that shows how velocity depends on time is a(n) _____.

9. _____ Motion that can be described by a constant slope on a velocity-time graph is _____.

10. _____ The horizontal separation of any two points on a curve is the _____.

11. _____ On a velocity-time graph, the slope of a tangent to the curve at a specific time is the _____.

5 Study Guide

• • • • • • • • • • • • • • •

Section 5.1: Graphing Motion in One Dimension

In your textbook, read about position-time graphs.
Answer the following questions, using complete sentences.

1. How are the position and time of a moving object related on a position-time graph?

_____

2. If you decide that the duration of an instant on a position-time graph is a finite period of time, where is the object during that period?

_____

3. What does your conclusion in problem 2 indicate about the motion of the object during that period?

_____

4. If the object is moving, what can you conclude about the duration of an instant?

_____

5. What is the duration of an instant?

_____

In your textbook, read about using graphs to determine position and time.
The position-time graph below shows the position of a teacher at various times as she walks across the front of the room. The position 0.0 m represents the left side of the room and movement to the right is positive. Circle the letter of the choice that best completes each statement.

5 Study Guide

• • • • • • • • • • • • • •

6. The teacher was walking to the right during the time interval _____.

   a. 1.0–2.0 s   **b.** 6.0–7.0 s   **c.** 10.0–12.0 s   **d.** 7.0–12.0 s

7. The teacher's displacement for the time interval 0.0–3.0 s is _____.

   a. –3.0 m   **b.** 0.0 m   **c.** +1.0 m   **d.** +3.0 m

8. The teacher's average velocity for the time interval 1.0–3.0 s is _____.

   a. –1.0 m/s   **b.** +1.0 m/s   **c.** +2.0 m/s   **d.** +3.0 m/s

9. The teacher is standing still during the time interval _____.

   a. 1.0–2.0 s   **b.** 6.0–7.0 s   **c.** 10.0–12.0 s   **d.** 12.0–15.0 s

10. The average velocity for the time interval 10.0–12.0 s is _____.

    a. +1.0 m/s   **b.** +0.5 m/s   **c.** 0.0 m/s   **d.** –0.5 m/s

11. The teacher's average velocity for the time interval 0.0–15.0 s is _____.

    a. –2.0 m/s   **b.** 0.0 m/s   **c.** +0.067 m/s   **d.** +0.75 m/s

Sketch a motion diagram for each time interval, using the teacher's position-time graph on page 26.

Time Interval	*Motion Diagram*
12. 0.0–5.0 s	
13. 5.0–7.0 s	
14. 7.0–15.0 s	

In your textbook, read about using position and time equations.

Refer to the equation $d = d_0 + vt$. For each of the statements below, write true *or rewrite the italicized part to make the statement true.*

15. _____ The equation contains *three* quantities.

16. _____ This equation *cannot* be used if the velocity is changing.

17. _____ The quantity d_0 represents the position at *any time*.

18. _____ The quantity in the equation that represents the slope of a position-time graph for this motion is *v*.

19. _____ The displacement of the object is *vt*.

5 Study Guide

• • • • • • • • • • • • • • •

Section 5.2: Graphing Velocity in One Dimension

In your textbook, read about velocity-time graphs and displacement.

Refer to the velocity-time graph of a jogger to complete the two tables.

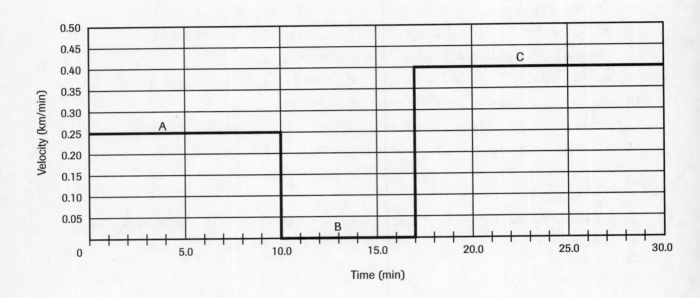

Table 1			
Segment	***v***	**Δ*t***	**Δ*d***
A			
B			
C			

Table 2			
Δ*t*	**Distance Ran**	**Displacement**	**Average Velocity**

5 Study Guide

Name _____

Section 5.3: Acceleration

In your textbook, read about equations of motion for uniform acceleration.

Complete each table with the values of the variables and initial conditions. Write a question mark for the unknown variable. If a variable or an initial condition is not needed to answer the problem, write an X. Then write the equation that you would use to solve the problem. It is not necessary to calculate the answer.

1. A car accelerates from 10 m/s to 15 m/s in 3.0 s. How far does the car travel in this time?

Table 1						
Variables			Initial Conditions			Equation
t	d	v	a	d_0	v_0	

2. A racing car accelerates at 4.5 m/s² from rest. What is the car's velocity after it has traveled 35.0 m?

Table 2						
Variables			Initial Conditions			Equation
t	d	v	a	d_0	v_0	

3. A car initially traveling at 15 m/s accelerates at a constant 4.5 m/s² through a distance of 45 m. How long does it take the car to cover this distance?

Table 3						
Variables			Initial Conditions			Equation
t	d	v	a	d_0	v_0	

4. A ball rolls past a mark on an incline at 0.40 m/s. If the ball has a constant acceleration of 0.20 m/s² what is its velocity 3.0 s after it passes the mark?

Table 4						
Variables			Initial Conditions			Equation
t	d	v	a	d_0	v_0	

Physics: Principles and Problems

5 Study Guide

Section 5.4: Free-Fall

In your textbook, read about free-fall.

Refer to the diagram on the right showing the positions of a ball that was thrown upward at time t_0. Complete the tables by indicating if the direction of the velocity and the direction of the acceleration at each time is + or −, or if the value of the velocity or acceleration equals 0.

○ t_2

○ t_3

○ t_1

○ t_4

○ t_0

1. Downward direction is positive.

   Rank the magnitudes of the velocities v_0, v_1, v_2, v_3, and v_4, in decreasing order.

   _____

   _____

2. Upward direction is positive.

   Rank the magnitudes of the velocities v_0, v_1, v_2, v_3, and v_4, in decreasing order.

   _____

   _____

Table 1					
	Time				
Variable	t_0	t_1	t_2	t_3	t_4
v					
a					

Table 2					
	Time				
Variable	t_0	t_1	t_2	t_3	t_4
v					
a					

Refer to the velocity-time graph of the vertical velocity of a ball from the time it is thrown upward from the top of a building until it reaches the ground. Answer the following questions.

3. Use a red pencil to shade the area under the curve that represents the total upward displacement of the ball.

4. Use a blue pencil to shade the area under the curve that represents the total downward displacement of the ball.

5. How could you use the red and blue areas to determine the height of the building?

   _____

   _____

   _____

   _____

6 Study Guide

Use with Chapter 6.

Forces

Vocabulary Review

Write the term that correctly completes each statement. Use each term once.

agent	force of gravity	mechanical resonance	simple harmonic
amplitude	free-body diagram	net force	motion
apparent weight	inertia	Newton's first law	static friction force
contact force	interaction pair	Newton's second law	system
environment	kinetic friction force	Newton's third law	terminal velocity
equilibrium	long-range force	period	weightlessness
force			

1. _____ In _____, the amplitude of motion is increased by the repeated application of a force when the time between applications is equal to the period of oscillation.

2. _____ The vector sum of two or more forces acting on an object is the _____.

3. _____ The net force on an object in _____ is zero.

4. _____ The horizontal force exerted on one surface by another when the two surfaces are not in relative motion is the _____.

5. _____ The acceleration of a body is directly proportional to the net force on it and inversely proportional to its mass; this is a statement of _____.

6. _____ The force exerted by a scale on an object is the _____.

7. _____ A force that acts on an object by touching it is a(n) _____.

8. _____ The two forces in an interactive pair act on different objects and are equal in magnitude and opposite in direction; this is a statement of _____.

9. _____ The world outside a system is the _____.

10. _____ An attractive force that exists between all objects is the _____.

11. _____ An object that is at rest will remain at rest or an object that is moving will continue to move in a straight line with constant speed, if and only if the net force acting on the object is zero; this is a statement of _____.

12. _____ The horizontal force exerted on one surface by another when surfaces are in relative motion is the _____.

13. _____ A defined object or group of objects is a(n) _____.

6 Study Guide

• • • • • • • • • • • • • •

14. _____ The tendency of an object to resist changes in its motion is _____.

15. _____ The specific, identifiable cause of a force is a(n) _____.

16. _____ The time to repeat one complete cycle is a(n) _____.

17. _____ A force that is exerted without contact is a(n) _____.

18. _____ In any periodic motion, the maximum displacement from equilibrium is the _____.

19. _____ A push or pull is a(n) _____.

20. _____ Two forces that are in opposite directions and have equal magnitudes are a(n) _____.

21. _____ In a(n) _____, a dot represents an object and arrows represent each force acting on it, with their tail on the dot and their points indicating the direction of the force.

22. _____ In _____, the force that restores an object to its equilibrium position is directly proportional to its displacement.

23. _____ The constant velocity that a falling object reaches when the drag force equals the force of gravity is its _____.

24. _____ When an object's apparent weight is zero, the object is in a state of _____.

Section 6.1: **Force and Motion**

In your textbook, read about Newton's second law and combining forces.
For each of the statements below write true *or* false.

_____ 1. Newton's second law can be written as the equation

$$a = \frac{F_{net}}{m}.$$

_____ 2. The acceleration of an object and the net force acting on it are proportional.

_____ 3. Force and acceleration are scalar quantities.

6 Study Guide

In your textbook, read about equilibrium and free-body diagrams.
Refer to the diagrams below. Circle the letter of the choice that best completes the statement or answers the question.

Diagram 1

Diagram 2

4. Which part of diagram 1 best represents the weight force of the bowl sitting on a shelf?

   a. A   **b.** B   **c.** C   **d.** D

5. F_N is a symbol that represents the _____ force.

   a. friction   **b.** tension   **c.** normal   **d.** weight

6. What part of diagram 2 best represents the bowl in equilibrium?

   a. A   **b.** B   **c.** C   **d.** D

7. The magnitude of the net force on the bowl in equilibrium is _____.

   a. F_N **b.** F_g **c.** 0   **d.** $2F_g$

8. The agent of F_N is _____.

   a. the bowl   **b.** Earth   **c.** friction   **d.** the shelf

9. The agent of F_g is _____.

   a. the bowl   **b.** Earth   **c.** friction   **d.** the shelf

Draw a free-body diagram of each situation.

10. A rocket immediately after vertical liftoff

11. A penny sliding at constant velocity on a desktop

12. A penny immediately after sliding off a desktop

6 Study Guide

· · · · · · · · · · · · · ·

Section 6.2: Using Newton's Laws

In your textbook, read about mass, weight, and apparent weight.
For each term on the left, write the letter of the matching item.

_____ **1.** name of gravitational force acting on object

_____ **2.** magnitude of acceleration caused by gravity

_____ **3.** symbol for the acceleration caused by gravity

_____ **4.** symbol for the weight force

_____ **5.** expression for the weight of an object

_____ **6.** unit of weight

_____ **7.** property of an object that does not vary from location to location

_____ **8.** having an apparent weight of zero

a. g

b. newton

c. weight

d. 9.8 m/s^2

e. weightlessness

f. mg

g. F_g

h. mass

In your textbook, read about scales and apparent weight.
*Read the passage below and refer to the diagram next to it.
Circle the letter of the choice that best completes the statement or answers the question.*

A 1.0-kg mass at rest is suspended from a spring scale. The direction of positive forces that are acting or could act on the 1.0-kg mass are shown to the right.

9. The 1.0-kg mass and spring scale are being lifted at a constant speed. The net force on the mass is _____.

    a. 0 N   **c.** −10 N

    b. +10 N   **d.** +20 N

10. The 1.0-kg mass and spring scale are being lifted so that the 1.0-kg mass is being accelerated in the positive upward direction at 1.0 m/s^2. What is the net force acting on the mass?

    a. 0 N   **b.** +1 N   **c.** −1 N   **d.** +20 N

11. In problem 10, what is the relationship among the magnitudes of the forces acting on the mass?

    a. $F_{net} = F_{scale} + F_g$ **c.** $F_{net} = -(F_{scale} + F_g)$

    b. $F_{net} = F_{scale} - F_g$ **d.** $F_{net} = F_g - F_{scale}$

12. In problem 10, what is the spring scale reading?

    a. < 10 N   **b.** 10 N   **c.** >10 N   **d.** 0 N

13. If the scale is accidentally dropped, the net force acting on the 1.0-kg mass is _____.

    a. 0 N   **b.** +10 N   **c.** −10 N   **d.** +20 N

14. If the scale is accidentally dropped, the reading of the spring scale as it falls is _____.

    a. 0 N   **b.** +10 N   **c.** −10 N   **d.** +20 N

                      Physics: Principles and Problems

6 Study Guide

In your textbook, read about the friction force.

For each of the statements below, write true *or rewrite the italicized part to make the statement true.*

15. _____ The force of friction *opposes* the motion of an object sliding on a surface.

16. _____ The force of friction acts in a direction that is *perpendicular* to the surface on which the object slides.

17. _____ The force of friction acts in the *same* direction as the direction of the sliding object.

18. _____ Static friction opposes the *start* of an object's motion.

19. _____ The static friction force *does* depend on the area of the surfaces in contact.

20. _____ The kinetic friction force *does* depend on the speed of the relative motion of the surfaces.

In your textbook, read about periodic motion.

Read the sentence below and answer the following questions, using complete sentences.

A stone attached to a spring is oscillating vertically.

21. What is the direction of the stone's acceleration when it is at the lowest point of its oscillation?

    _____

    _____

22. At what point in its oscillation does the stone have the greatest downward acceleration?

    _____

    _____

23. At what point does the stone have an acceleration of zero in its downward motion?

    _____

    _____

24. At what point does the stone have its maximum upward and downward velocities?

    _____

    _____

25. What causes the stone to move through the midpoint of its oscillation?

    _____

    _____

6 Study Guide

Section 6.3: Interaction Forces

In your textbook, read about interaction pairs.

Refer to the diagram below to complete the table.

Table 1		
Force	**Magnitude**	**Direction**
$F_{\text{book 1 on book 2}}$		
$F_{\text{book 2 on book 1}}$		
$F_{\text{book 2 on desktop}}$		
$F_{\text{desktop on book 2}}$		
$F_{\text{books 1 and 2 on desktop}}$		
$F_{\text{desktop on books 1 and 2}}$		

In your textbook, read about the four fundamental forces.

For each answer given below, write an appropriate question.

1. Answer: an attractive force due to the masses of objects

   Question: _____

2. Answer: the electromagnetic interaction

   Question: _____

3. Answer: two forces that occur within the nucleus of the atom

   Question: _____

   _____

4. Answer: the strong nuclear interaction

   Question: _____

   _____

5. Answer: the force apparent in some kinds of radioactive decay

   Question: _____

7 Study Guide

Use with Chapter 7.

Forces and Motion in Two Dimensions

Vocabulary Review

Write the term that correctly completes each statement. Use each term once.

centripetal acceleration   lever arm   range

centripetal force   maximum height   rigid rotating object

coefficient of kinetic friction normal force   torque

equilibrant   period   trajectory

equilibrium   projectile   uniform circular motion

flight time

1. _____ The perpendicular distance from the axis of rotation to a line along which a force acts is the _____.

2. _____ The path of a projectile is the _____.

3. _____ A force that produces equilibrium is the _____.

4. _____ The horizontal distance traveled by a projectile is the _____.

5. _____ A force that acts toward the center of a circle is the _____.

6. _____ The height of a projectile when its vertical velocity is zero is the _____.

7. _____ A mass that rotates around its own axis is a(n) _____.

8. _____ The time a projectile is in the air is the _____.

9. _____ Acceleration toward the center of a circle is the _____.

10. _____ An object that has been launched by an initial thrust is a(n) _____.

11. _____ A contact force that acts perpendicular to and away from a surface is a(n) _____.

12. _____ The product of a force and the lever arm is the _____.

13. _____ The movement of an object or a point mass at constant speed around a circle with a fixed radius is _____.

14. _____ When the net sum of the forces acting on an object is zero, the object is in _____.

15. _____ The ratio of the force of kinetic friction to the normal force is the _____.

16. _____ The time needed to complete one cycle of motion is a(n) _____.

7 Study Guide

• • • • • • • • • • • • •

Section 7.1: Forces in Two Dimensions

In your textbook, read about the equilibrant.

For each of the statements below, write true *or rewrite the italicized part to make the statement true.*

1. _____ Equilibrium occurs when the resultant of two or more forces equals a net force *greater than* zero.

2. _____ An object in equilibrium is motionless or has a *constant velocity*.

3. _____ The *equilibrant* is a force that places an object in equilibrium when added to the resultant of all the forces on the object.

4. _____ The equilibrant is *equal* in magnitude to the resultant force.

5. _____ The equilibrant acts in the *same direction* as the resultant force.

Refer to the diagram below. Circle the letter of the choice that best completes each statement.

6. Angle θ is _____.

   a. 57.5°   b. 65°   c. 115°   d. 230°

7. The force equation that represents equilibrium is _____.

   a. $F_A - F_B - F_g = 0$ c. $F_A = F_B$

   b. $F_A = 2F_g$ d. $F_A + F_B - F_g = 0$

8. $F_A \cos \theta =$ _____.

   a. $F_A \sin \theta$ b. $-F_B \cos \theta$ c. F_g d. $F_g/2$

9. $F_B \sin \theta =$ _____.

   a. $F_A \cos \theta$ b. $F_B \cos \theta$ c. F_g d. $F_g/2$

10. As θ increases, the tension on each rope _____.

   a. increases   b. decreases   c. remains the same

7 Study Guide

In your textbook, read about motion along an inclined plane.

Draw a free-body diagram representing the situation below. Label angle θ and the horizontal and vertical components of the weight force.

A trunk is placed on a frictionless inclined plane that is at angle θ from the horizontal.

For each situation below, write the letter of the matching item.

_____ **11.** calculation of F_{gx}

_____ **12.** calculation of F_{gy}

_____ **13.** calculation of F_N

_____ **14.** calculation of F_g

_____ **15.** component of weight force that increases as angle θ increases

_____ **16.** component of weight force that decreases as angle θ increases

_____ **17.** calculation of acceleration along incline

a. perpendicular component of weight force

b. mg

c. $-F_g \cos \theta$

d. $-g \sin \theta$

e. $-F_g \sin \theta$

f. parallel component of weight force

g. $-F_{gy}$

18. Draw a free-body diagram representing the situation below. Label the +x-axis in the direction of motion. Label the +y-axis. Then draw and label items a–f.

An 82-N trunk is accelerating along a plank inclined at 26.0° from the horizontal. The coefficient of kinetic friction of the trunk and plank is 0.20.

    a. horizontal component of the weight force

    b. vertical component of the weight force

    c. angle of 26.0°

    d. normal force

    e. force of kinetic friction

    f. net force

7 Study Guide

19. Refer to the free-body diagram you drew in problem 18. Complete the table below. Then answer the following questions. Note: sin 26.0° = 0.44; cos 26.0° = 0.90.

20. What will happen to the acceleration of the trunk if the elevated end of the plank is raised? Why?

_____

_____

_____

_____

_____

Table 1			
Variable	**Value**	**Variable**	**Value**
F_g		F_N	
F_{gx}		F_f	
F_{gy}		F_{net}	

21. What will happen to the motion of the trunk if it reaches a section of the plank where the coefficient of sliding friction makes the frictional force equal to the magnitude of the horizontal component of the weight force?

_____

_____

Section 7.2: Projectile Motion

In your textbook, read about solving projectile-motion problems.

Read each problem and complete the table by writing the value of the variable, an X if the variable is not necessary to answer the problem, or a question mark for the unknown. (Assume that the coordinate system has the +y-axis pointing up.) Briefly explain how you would solve the problem.

1. A ball rolls off a horizontal shelf at 2.0 m/s and falls to the floor 1.8 m below. How far from the shelf does the ball land?

Table 2		
Variable	**Vertical Component**	**Horizontal Component**
acceleration $a = F_{net}/m$	$a_y =$	$a_x =$
velocity $v = v_0 + at$	$v_{y0} =$	$v_{x0} =$
	$v_y =$	$v_x =$
position $d = d_0 + v_0 t + \frac{1}{2}at^2$	$y_0 =$	$x_0 =$
	$y =$	$x =$

_____

_____

_____

_____

7 Study Guide

• • • • • • • • • • • •

2. A javelin leaves the thrower's hand at a velocity of 21 m/s at an angle of 43° above the horizontal. What is the maximum height the javelin will reach? Note: (21 m/s)(sin 43°) = 14 m/s; (21 m/s)(cos 43°) = 15 m/s.

Table 3		
Variable	**Vertical Component**	**Horizontal Component**
acceleration $a = F_{net}/m$	$a_y =$	$a_x =$
velocity $v = v_0 + at$	$v_{y0} =$	$v_{x0} =$
	$v_y =$	$v_x =$
position $d = d_0 + v_0 t + \frac{1}{2}at^2$	$y_0 =$	$x_0 =$
	$y =$	$x =$

_____

_____

_____

_____

3. A person at the edge of a vertical 12-m cliff throws a rock down at a velocity of 8.5 m/s, 55° below the horizontal. How far from the base of the cliff does the rock land? Assume a coordinate system in which the upward direction is positive. Note: (8.5 m/s)(sin 55°) = 7.0 m/s; (8.5 m/s)(cos 55°) = 4.9 m/s.

Table 4		
Variable	**Vertical Component**	**Horizontal Component**
acceleration $a = F_{net}/m$	$a_y =$	$a_x =$
velocity $v = v_0 + at$	$v_{y0} =$	$v_{x0} =$
	$v_y =$	$v_x =$
position $d = d_0 + v_0 t + at^2$	$y_0 =$	$x_0 =$
	$y =$	$x =$

_____

_____

_____

_____

7 Study Guide

Section 7.3: Circular Motion

In your textbook, read about circular motion.
Write the term that correctly completes each statement. Use each term once.

center	directions	length	straight line
centripetal	directly	perpendicular	tangent
constant	inversely	radius	

An object is moving in uniform circular motion if the radius of its path and its speed are

(1) _____. The velocity of an object in uniform circular motion is

(2) _____ to the radius and **(3)** _____ to the circular path.

The velocity vectors have the same **(4)** _____ but different

(5) _____. The direction of the centripetal acceleration vector lies along the

(6) _____ and points toward the **(7)** _____. The cen-

tripetal acceleration is **(8)** _____ proportional to the square of the velocity and

(9) _____ proportional to the radius of the circle. The force that causes the cen-

tripetal acceleration is the **(10)** _____ force. If this force ceases to act on the

object in uniform circular motion, the object will travel in a **(11)** _____ tangent

to the circle.

In your textbook, read about torque.
The diagrams below represent a force of 65 N applied at three different angles to a wrench 0.25 m long and connected to the head of a bolt. In each diagram, construct the lever arm and label it. Then answer the following questions.

A   **B**   **C**

12. In which diagram is the torque the greatest?

_____

13. At what angle θ will the torque be maximal?

_____

14. At what angle θ will the torque be minimal?

_____

Physics: Principles and Problems

8 Study Guide

Use with Chapter 8.

Universal Gravitation

Vocabulary Review

Write the term that correctly completes each statement. Use each term once.

black hole

centripetal acceleration

gravitational field

gravitational mass

inertial mass

inverse square law

Kepler's laws of planetary
motion

law of universal gravitation

Newton's universal
gravitational constant

period

1. _____ The behavior of every planet and satellite is described by _____.

2. _____ The _____ states that the gravitational force between two objects depends directly on the product of their masses and inversely on the square of the distance between the centers of the masses.

3. _____ The _____ of an object is $\frac{F_{net}}{a}$, where F_{net} is the net force exerted on an object and a is its acceleration.

4. _____ The _____ of an object is defined as $\frac{r^2 F_{grav}}{Gm}$ where F_{grav} is the gravitational force exerted on an object by another object of mass m at a distance r, and G is a universal constant.

5. _____ The _____ is a property of the region surrounding an object, is due to the object's mass, and interacts with other objects, resulting in a force of attraction.

6. _____ A massive and dense object in which light leaving the object is totally bent back to the object, resulting in no light escaping is a(n) _____.

7. _____ The time needed to repeat one complete cycle of motion is a(n) _____.

8. _____ The direction of _____ is toward the center of motion.

9. _____ A relationship in which one variable is inversely proportional to the square of another variable is the basis of a(n) _____.

10. _____ _____ is the same number for any two masses anywhere.

8 Study Guide

· · · · · · · · · · · · · ·

Section 8.1: Motions in the Heavens and on Earth

In your textbook, read about observed motion and Kepler's laws.
For each statement below, write true *or rewrite the italicized part to make the statement true.*

1. Tycho Brahe believed that Earth was the center of the universe.

_____

2. Johannes Kepler believed *the sun* was the center of the universe.

_____

3. From studying Brahe's astronomical data, Kepler developed three *physical* laws of planetary motion.

_____

4. Kepler's first law states that the paths of the planets are *ellipses.*

_____

5. In the first law, *the planet* is located at one focus of the planet's orbit.

_____

6. The second law states that an imaginary line extending from the sun to the planet sweeps out equal *distances* in equal times.

_____

7. The third law states that the *product* of the squares of the periods of any two planets revolving about the sun is equal to the cube of the ratio of their average distances from the sun.

_____

8. Kepler's *first, second, and third* laws apply to each planet, moon, or satellite individually.

_____

In your textbook, read about Kepler's laws.
Refer to the diagram to answer the following questions.

9. The shaded portions of planet A's orbit represent areas swept out by an imaginary line from the sun between times t_1 and t_2 and between times t_3 and t_4. If the time intervals $t_2 - t_1$ and $t_4 - t_3$ are equal, what statement can be made about the two shaded areas?

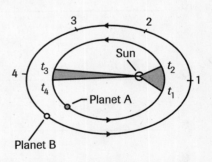

_____

_____

8 Study Guide

10. At which of the indicated points in planet B's orbit is its speed the greatest?

_____

_____

11. Io, one of Jupiter's moons, has a period of 1.8 days. What information would you need to apply Kepler's third law to determine how far Io is from the center of Jupiter?

_____

_____

_____

In your textbook, read about observed motion and universal gravitation.
For each term on the left, write the letter of the matching item.

_____ **12.** German mathematician who developed three laws of planetary motion

_____ **13.** Danish astronomer who recorded the exact positions of the planets and stars for over 20 years

_____ **14.** English physicist who proposed that gravitational attraction keeps planets and satellites in their orbits

_____ **15.** Italian scientist who discovered the moons of Jupiter

a. Brahe

b. Galileo

c. Kepler

d. Newton

In your textbook, read about universal gravitation.
Refer to the diagram and complete the table for the new values of distance and mass.

Table 1			
Distance	**Mass A**	**Mass B**	**Force**
16. d	m_A	$2m_B$	
17. d	$2m_A$	m_B	
18. d	$2m_A$	$2m_B$	
19. $2d$	m_A	m_B	
20. $d/2$	m_A	m_B	

8 Study Guide

• • • • • • • • • • • • •

Read about universal gravitation and weighing the earth.
Answer the following questions, using complete sentences.

21. What apparatus did Cavendish use to find a value for Newton's universal gravitational constant?

_____

_____

_____

_____

22. How did Cavendish get an experimental value for gravitational force, F, to use in Newton's law of gravitational force?

_____

_____

_____

_____

23. The gravitational force between two 1.00-kg masses whose centers are 1.00 m apart is defined as 6.67×10^{-11} N. Show that the value of Newton's universal gravitational constant is 6.67×10^{-11} N·m^2/kg^2.

8 Study Guide

• • • • • • • • • • • • • •

Section 8.2: **Using the Law of Universal Gravitation**

In your textbook, read about the motion of planets and satellites.
Write the term that correctly completes each statement.

If a cannonball is fired horizontally from a cannon high atop a mountain, its

(1) _____ has both horizontal and vertical components. During the first

second of its flight, the cannonball falls **(2)** _____. If fired at the right horizontal

velocity, the cannonball will fall 4.9 m at a point where Earth's surface has curved 4.9 m from the

(3) _____. Thus, the cannonball is at the same **(4)** _____

above Earth as it was initially. The curvature of the cannonball's path will continue to just match the

(5) _____ of Earth. As a result, the cannonball is said to be in

(6) _____. A horizontal speed of 8 km/s will keep the cannonball at the same

altitude, and it will circle Earth as an artificial **(7)** _____.

In your textbook, read about the gravitational field.
Refer to the diagram on the right to answer the following questions.

8. Draw the vector representing the direction and magnitude of the gravitational field at each of the points 1–5. Indicate the scale you used. Label each gravitational field vector with its magnitude.

9. What is the weight of a 10.0-kg mass located at point 4?

_____

In your textbook, read about two kinds of masses.
For each term on the left, write the letter of the matching item.

_____ 10. definition of inertial mass

_____ 11. definition of gravitational mass

_____ 12. property of inertial mass

_____ 13. property of gravitational mass

_____ 14. hypothesis that inertial and gravitational masses are identical

a. resistance to acceleration

b. principle of equivalence

c. $\dfrac{F_{net}}{a}$

d. attraction toward other masses

e. $\dfrac{r^2 F_{grav}}{Gm}$

8 Study Guide

● ● ● ● ● ● ● ● ● ● ● ● ●

In your textbook, read about Einstein's theory of gravity.
Circle the letter of the choice that best completes each statement.

15. The effect of gravity can be explained by the _____

    a. equivalence principle

    b. gravitational field

    c. general theory of relativity

    d. inertial field

16. The origin of gravity is proposed in _____.

    a. the law of universal gravitation

    b. the gravitational field

    c. the general theory of relativity

    d. the inertial field

17. According to Einstein, gravity is _____.

    a. an effect of space

    b. a force

    c. a property of mass

    d. energy

18. The mass of an object causes the space around it to become _____.

    a. more dense

    b. less dense

    c. heated

    d. curved

19. Objects _____ because they follow the shape of the space surrounding a massive object.

    a. are repulsed

    b. become visible

    c. lose mass

    d. undergo accelerations

20. The effect of mass on space _____.

    a. accounts for the deflection of light by massive objects

    b. explains the existence of black holes

    c. models gravitational attraction

    d. all of these

9 Study Guide

Use with Chapter 9.

Momentum and Its Conservation

Vocabulary Review

Write the term that correctly completes each statement. Use each term once.

angular momentum	impulse-momentum theorem	law of conservation of momentum	Newton's third law
closed system			recoil
external forces	internal forces	linear momentum	torque
impulse	isolated system	Newton's second law	vector

1. _____ The acceleration of a body is directly proportional to the net force on it and inversely proportional to its mass; this is a statement of _____.

2. _____ When one object exerts a force on a second object, the second exerts a force on the first that is equal in magnitude but opposite in direction; this is a statement of _____.

3. _____ A quantity that has magnitude and direction is a(n) _____.

4. _____ The product of the average force exerted on an object and the time interval through which it acts is the _____.

5. _____ The product of the mass and velocity of a body is its _____.

6. _____ The _____ states that the impulse on an object is equal to the change of momentum that it causes.

7. _____ The quantity of motion used with objects rotating about a fixed axis is _____.

8. _____ A(n) _____ does not gain or lose mass.

9. _____ Forces within a closed system are _____.

10. _____ All the forces that act on the system from outside the system are _____.

11. _____ A closed system in which the net external force on the system is zero is a(n) _____.

12. _____ The _____ states that the momentum of any closed system with no net external force acting on it does not change.

13. _____ The backward motion of part of an isolated, closed system due to an internal force is _____.

14. _____ The product of force and a lever arm is _____.

9 Study Guide

Section 9.1: Impulse and Momentum

In your textbook, read about relating impulse and momentum.

The diagram below shows the force-time graph of a force acting on an 8.0-kg cart initially at rest on a frictionless surface. Circle the letter of the choice that best completes each statement.

1. The magnitude of the force acting on the cart is _____.

   a. +2.0 N   **c.** +10.0 N

   b. +8.0 N   **d.** +20.0 N

2. The force acted on the cart for a duration of _____.

   a. 2.0 s   **c.** 8.0 s

   b. 6.0 s   **d.** 10.0 s

3. The shaded area of the graph represents _____.

   a. force   **c.** momentum

   b. impulse   **d.** acceleration

4. The shaded area of the graph is represented algebraically by _____.

   a. $F\Delta t$ **c.** $F/\Delta t$

   b. mv **d.** m/v

5. The impulse acting on the cart is _____.

   a. 0 N·s   **c.** +8.0 N·s

   b. +2.0 N·s   **d.** +48 N·s

6. The momentum of the cart is represented algebraically by _____.

   a. $F\Delta t$ **c.** $F/\Delta t$

   b. mv **d.** m/v

7. The change of momentum of the cart is _____.

   a. 0 kg·m/s   **c.** +8.0 kg·m/s

   b. +2.0 m/s   **d.** +48 kg·m/s

8. The final velocity of the cart is _____.

   a. 0 m/s   **c.** 12 m/s

   b. 6.0 m/s   **d.** 48 m/s

9 Study Guide

In your textbook, read about using the impulse-momentum theorem.

Read each of the statements below. In the diagrams, draw and label the velocities of the sport utility van before and after the event described. In the vector diagram section, draw and label the momentum vectors p_1 and p_2, and the impulse vector $F\Delta t$.

9. The van has a velocity of +30 km/h and uniformly comes to a stop in 15 s.

Before   **After**

Vector diagram

10. The van, initially at rest, uniformly reaches a velocity of +30 km/h in 20 s.

Vector diagram

11. In 5 s, the van uniformly backs up to a speed of 5 km/h.

Vector diagram

12. The van has a velocity of −5 km/h and uniformly comes to a stop in 5 s.

Vector diagram

9 Study Guide

In your textbook, read about the impulse-momentum theorem as it applies to air bags.
Answer the following questions, using complete sentences.

13. In what two ways can impulse be increased?

_____

_____

14. In terms of impulse, how does an air bag reduce injuries that would be caused by the steering wheel during an accident?

_____

_____

_____

_____

_____

_____

In your textbook, read about angular momentum.
For each of the statements below, write true *or rewrite the italicized part to make the statement true.*

15. _____ The speed of a rotating object changes only if *torque* is applied to it.

16. _____ The quantity of angular motion that is used with rotating objects is called *linear* momentum.

17. _____ When a *torque* acts on an object, its angular momentum changes.

18. _____ Angular momentum is the product of the object's mass, displacement from the center of rotation, and the component of its velocity *parallel* to that displacement.

19. _____ If the angular momentum of a rotating object is constant and its distance to the center of rotation decreases, then its velocity *decreases*.

20. _____ The torque on the planets orbiting the sun is zero because the gravitational force is directed toward the sun and, therefore, is not *perpendicular* to its velocity.

21. _____ Because the torque on each planet is zero, each planet's angular momentum is *zero*.

22. _____ When a planet's distance from the sun becomes smaller, the planet moves *slower*.

Physics: Principles and Problems

9 Study Guide

Section 9.2: The Conservation of Momentum

In your textbook, read about two-particle collisions.
Read the sentence below and answer the following questions, using complete sentences.

Two balls of unequal mass traveling at different speeds collide head-on and rebound in opposite directions.

1. How does the force that ball A exerts on ball B compare to the force that ball B exerts on ball A?

   _____

2. How do the impulses received by both balls compare?

   _____

3. How do the sums of the momenta of the balls before and after the collision compare?

   _____

Write the term that correctly completes each statement. Use each term once.

change	conditions	interaction	isolated system
closed system	external forces	internal forces	law of conservation of momentum

A system that doesn't gain or lose mass is a(n) **(4)** _____. All the

forces within a closed system are **(5)** _____. All the forces outside the

system are **(6)** _____. When the net external force on a closed system is

zero, the system is a(n) **(7)** _____. The **(8)** _____

states that the momentum of any closed system with no net external forces does not

(9) _____. Using this law, you can connect **(10)** _____

before and after an interaction without knowing any of the details of the

(11) _____.

In your textbook, read about explosions.
Read the paragraph below. Then circle the letter of the choice that best completes each statement.

Two in-line skaters are skating on such a smooth surface that there are no external forces. They both start from rest. Skater A gives skater B a push in the *positive* direction.

12. The momentum of the system before the push is _____.
    a. >0 **b.** 0   **c.** <0

13. The momentum of the system after the push is _____.
    a. >0 **b.** 0   **c.** <0

14. The momentum of skater B after the push, p_{B2}, is _____.
    a. >0 **b.** 0   **c.** <0

9 Study Guide

• • • • • • • • • • • • • •

15. The momentum of skater A after the push, p_{A2}, is _____.

   a. $+p_{B2}$ **b.** 0   **c.** $-p_{B2}$

16. If the velocity of skater B after the push is represented by v_{B2}, the velocity of skater A after the push, v_{A2}, is _____.

   a. $+\left(\dfrac{m_A}{m_B}\right) v_{B2}$ **c.** $-\left(\dfrac{m_B}{m_A}\right) v_{B2}$

   b. 0   **d.** $-\left(\dfrac{m_A}{m_B}\right) v_{B2}$

In your textbook, read about two-dimensional collisions.

Read the paragraph below. Label the momentum diagram, indicating the final momentum of the system p_2, the momenta of both balls after the collision p_{A2} and p_{B2}, and the 50.0° angle.

A 4.0-kg ball, A, is moving at a speed of 3.0 m/s. It collides with a stationary ball, B, of the same mass. After the collision, ball A moves off in a direction of 50.0° to the left of its original direction. Ball B moves off in a direction of 90.0° to the right of ball A's final direction.

For each situation below, write the letter of the matching item.

_____ **17.** initial momentum of the system

_____ **18.** magnitude of final momentum of the system

_____ **19.** magnitude of ball A's momentum after the collision

_____ **20.** magnitude of ball B's momentum after the collision

   a. (12 kg·m/s)(cos 50.0°)

   b. 12 kg·m/s

   c. (12 kg·m/s)(sin 50.0°)

   d. p_A

10 Study Guide

Energy, Work, and Simple Machines

Vocabulary Review

Write the term that correctly completes each statement. Use each term once.

compound machine	kinetic energy	system
efficiency	machine	watt
effort force	mechanical advantage	work
energy	power	work-energy theorem
ideal mechanical advantage	resistance force	
joule	simple machine	

1. _____ The energy resulting from motion of an object is called _____.

2. _____ The _____ states that the work done on an object is equal to the object's change in kinetic energy.

3. _____ The force exerted on a machine is called the _____.

4. _____ The ratio of the output work to the input work is a machine's _____.

5. _____ The SI unit of work is the _____.

6. _____ The unit of power equal to 1 J of energy transferred in 1 s is the _____.

7. _____ A machine exerts _____.

8. _____ The product of the applied force and the distance through which the force is applied is _____.

9. _____ The ability of an object to produce a change in itself or its surroundings is _____.

10. _____ The rate of doing work is _____.

11. _____ A device that changes the magnitude or direction of a force is a(n) _____.

12. _____ The ratio of effort distance to resistance distance is a machine's _____.

13. _____ The ratio of resistance force to effort force is a machine's _____.

14. _____ A device that consists of two or more simple machines linked so that the resistance force of one machine becomes the effort force of the second machine is a(n) _____.

15. _____ A defined group of objects is called a(n) _____.

16. _____ A lever, pulley, wheel and axle, inclined plane, wedge, or screw is a(n) _____.

10 Study Guide

. . . .

Section 10.1: Energy and Work

In your textbook, read about energy.
For each phrase on the left, write the letter of the matching item.

_____ **1.** symbol for kinetic energy

_____ **2.** calculation of kinetic energy

_____ **3.** symbol for work

_____ **4.** calculation of work

_____ **5.** statement that the work done on an object is equal to the object's change in kinetic energy

_____ **6.** equivalent to 1 kg $\cdot \dfrac{m^2}{s^2}$

a. *W*

b. *Fd*

c. $\dfrac{mv^2}{2}$

d. $\Delta K = W$

e. 1 J

f. *K*

In your textbook, read about energy transfer and calculating work.
Circle the letter of the choice that best completes each statement.

7. Through the process of doing work, energy can move between the environment and the system as the result of _____.

   a. forces

   b. matter

   c. momentum

   d. impulse

8. If the environment does work on the system, the quantity of work is _____.

   a. negative

   b. positive

   c. zero

   d. undetermined

9. If the environment does work on the system, the energy of the system _____.

   a. decreases

   b. increases

   c. remains the same

   d. cannot be determined

10. If the system does work on the environment, the energy of the system _____.

   a. decreases

   b. increases

   c. is undetermined

   d. remains the same

11. In the equation *W = Fd*, *Fd* holds only for _____ forces exerted in the direction of displacement.

   a. constant

   b. frictional

   c. gravitational

   d. positive

12. In the equation $W = Fd \cos \theta$, angle θ is the angle between *F* and the _____.

   a. *x*-axis

   b. *y*-axis

   c. direction of the displacement

   d. vertical direction

10 Study Guide

For each situation shown, write its letter next to the number of the correct expression.

13. _____ W > 0

14. _____ W = 0

15. _____ W < 0

The diagram below is the force-displacement graph of a crate that was pushed horizontally. Answer the following questions.

16. What was the magnitude of the force acting on the crate?

    _____

17. How far did the crate move horizontally?

    _____

18. What does the area under the curve of this graph represent?

    _____

    _____

19. How much work was done in moving the crate 0.1 m?

    _____

For each term on the left, write the letter of the matching item.

_____ 20. rate of doing work

_____ 21. unit of power

_____ 22. symbol for power

_____ 23. calculation of power

_____ 24. 1000 watts

a. power

b. $\dfrac{W}{t}$

c. watt

d. kW

e. P

10 Study Guide

Section 10.2: Machines

In your textbook, read about mechanical advantage and efficiency.
For each of the statements below, write true *or rewrite the italicized part to make the statement true.*

1. A *machine* makes doing a task easier.

   _____

2. A machine eases the load by changing either the magnitude or the direction of *energy*.

   _____

3. Work is the transfer of *energy* by mechanical means.

   _____

4. A machine *cannot* create energy.

   _____

5. The force that is exerted on a machine is the *effort force*.

   _____

6. The *product* of the resistance force and the effort force is the mechanical advantage of the machine.

   _____

7. When the mechanical advantage of a machine is greater than one, the machine *decreases* the effort force.

   _____

8. A real machine *cannot* have a mechanical advantage that is less than one.

   _____

9. The *ideal mechanical advantage* of a machine can be used to calculate the distance the effort force moves compared to the distance the resistance force moves.

   _____

10. If a machine transfers all of the energy applied to it, then the output work is *less than* the input work.

    _____

11. The *IMA* of most machines is fixed by their *design*.

    _____

12. The efficiency of a machine is the *ratio* of work output to work input.

    _____

13. An ideal machine has an efficiency *greater than* 100 percent.

    _____

14. A real machine has an efficiency *equal to* 100 percent.

_____

15. The *lower* the efficiency of a machine, the greater the effort force needed to produce the same resistance force.

_____

In your textbook, read about simple machines.

The numbers below correspond to the numbers in the diagram. For each number, write the letter of the matching term from the right column. A term may be used more than once.

16. _____	22. _____	**a.** axle
17. _____	23. _____	**b.** F_e
18. _____	24. _____	**c.** F_r
19. _____	25. _____	**d.** pivot point
20. _____	26. _____	**e.** r_e
21. _____	27. _____	**f.** r_r
		g. wheel

Refer to the machine on the left in the diagram above. Circle the letter of the choice that best completes the statement or answers the question.

28. What is the value of the *MA*?

   a. >1   **c.** <1

   b. =1   **d.** cannot be determined

29. What is the value of the *IMA*?

   a. >1   **c.** <1

   b. =1   **d.** cannot be determined

30. To increase the *IMA* of the machine, you would _____.

   a. increase r_r **c.** decrease r_e

   b. increase r_e **d.** decrease F_r

10 Study Guide

In your textbook, read about compound machines.

Refer to the diagram below. For each term on the left, write the letter of the matching item.

_____ **31.** *MA* of pedal and front sprocket

_____ **32.** *IMA* of pedal and front sprocket

_____ **33.** *MA* of rear sprocket and rear wheel

_____ **34.** *IMA* of rear sprocket and rear wheel

_____ **35.** *MA* of pedal and rear wheel

_____ **36.** *IMA* of pedal and rear wheel

a. $\dfrac{rear\ sprocket\ radius}{wheel\ radius}$

b. $\dfrac{F_{on\ road}}{F_{by\ chain}}$

c. $\dfrac{pedal\ radius}{front\ sprocket\ radius}$

d. $\dfrac{F_{on\ road}}{F_{on\ pedal}}$

e. $\dfrac{pedal\ radius}{wheel\ radius}$

f. $\dfrac{rear\ sprocket\ radius}{front\ sprocket\ radius} \times \dfrac{pedal\ radius}{wheel\ radius}$

g. $\dfrac{F_{on\ chain}}{F_{on\ pedal}}$

Refer to the diagram above. Write the value <1, =1, or >1 to complete the table below.

Table 1		
Machine	**MA Value**	**IMA Value**
pedal and front sprocket	**37.**	**38.**
rear sprocket and rear wheel	**39.**	**40.**
pedal and rear wheel	**41.**	**42.**

Physics: Principles and Problems

11 Study Guide

Use with Chapter 11.

Energy

Vocabulary Review

Write the term that correctly completes each statement. Use each term once.

closed system   inelastic collision   mechanical energy

elastic collision   isolated system   momentum

elastic potential energy   joule   reference level

energy   kinetic energy   work

gravitational potential energy   law of conservation of energy   work-energy theorem

1. _____ The energy of an object resulting from motion is _____.

2. _____ The _____ states that the work done on an object is equal to the object's change in kinetic energy.

3. _____ The energy in a compressed spring is _____.

4. _____ A system that does not gain or lose mass is a(n) _____.

5. _____ A collision in which the kinetic energy doesn't change is a(n) _____.

6. _____ The SI unit of work is the _____.

7. _____ A collision in which kinetic energy decreases is a(n) _____.

8. _____ Energy stored in the Earth-object system as a result of gravitational interaction between the object and Earth is _____.

9. _____ The product of the applied force and the distance through which the force is applied is _____.

10. _____ The ability of an object to produce a change in itself or its surroundings is _____.

11. _____ Within a closed, isolated system, energy can change form, but the total amount of energy is constant; this is a statement of the _____.

12. _____ The sum of the kinetic energy and gravitational potential energy is _____.

13. _____ A closed system in which the net external force on the system is zero is a(n) _____.

14. _____ The position at which the potential energy is defined to be zero is a(n) _____.

15. _____ The product of the mass and velocity of an object is its _____.

11 Study Guide

• • • • • • • • • • • • • • •

Section 11.1: The Many Forms of Energy

In your textbook, read about modeling the work-energy theorem.

The diagram below shows changes to your finances for the first week in October. Circle the choice that best completes the statement or answers the question.

1. How much money did you have on hand on Monday morning, October 1?

   a. $85   **c.** $40

   b. $45   **d.** $0

2. How much money did you have on hand on Tuesday?

   a. $85   **c.** $40

   b. $45   **d.** $0

3. By the end of the day on Wednesday, how much money did you have on hand?

   a. $85   **b.** $45   **c.** $40   **d.** $0

4. On Thursday, what happened to the amount of money you had on hand?

   a. It increased.   **b.** It decreased.   **c.** It remained unchanged.

5. By the end of the day on Saturday, how much money had you spent during the week?

   a. $75   **b.** $50   **c.** $40   **d.** $0

6. How much money did you have on hand on the morning of Monday, October 8?

   a. $75   **b.** $55   **c.** $40   **d.** $0

Read the following situations and draw before-and-after energy diagrams in the space provided.

7. A partially loaded shopping cart has a kinetic energy of 60 J. A short time later the cart's kinetic energy is 60 J.

8. A partially loaded shopping cart has a kinetic energy of 60 J. You do 20 J of work on the cart.

9. You do 50 J of work on a shopping cart at rest.

10. A partially loaded shopping cart has a kinetic energy of 60 J. You do −40 J of work on the cart.

11. You do 70 J of work on a partially loaded shopping cart, giving it a total kinetic energy of 80 J.

12. A partially filled shopping cart has a kinetic energy of 80 J. The work you do on the cart stops it.

11 Study Guide

• • • • • • • • • • • • •

In your textbook, read about kinetic energy.

Circle the letter of the choice that best answers each question. Refer to Table 11-1 on page 250 of your textbook.

13. What accounts for the aircraft carrier having a greater kinetic energy than the orbiting satellite?

    a. mass   **b.** speed   **c.** mass and speed

14. What accounts for the pitched baseball having a greater kinetic energy than the falling nickel?

    a. mass   **b.** speed   **c.** mass and speed

15. What accounts for the bumblebee having more kinetic energy than the snail?

    a. mass   **b.** speed   **c.** mass and speed

16. How much work would have to be done to the truck starting from rest to give it half the listed kinetic energy?

    a. 0 J   **b.** 2.2×10^3 J   **c.** 5.7×10^5 J   **d.** 1.1×10^6 J

17. How fast would the truck be moving if it had half the listed kinetic energy?

    a. –52 km/h   **b.** 0 km/h   **c.** 71 km/h   **d.** 118 km/h

In your textbook, read about gravitational and elastic potential energies.

For each statement below, write true *or rewrite the italicized part to make the statement true.*

18. _____ If a juggler's ball is considered a system, work is done on it by gravity and *the juggler's hand.*

19. _____ On the way up, the work done on the ball by gravity is *–mgh.*

20. _____ On the way down, the work done on the ball by gravity *decreases* the ball's kinetic energy.

21. _____ When the ball returns to the height of the juggler's hand, its kinetic energy is *more than* the kinetic energy it had when it left the juggler's hand.

22. _____ If you choose a system consisting of the juggler's ball and Earth, energy is stored in the system as *kinetic energy.*

23. _____ In a system consisting of the juggler's ball and Earth, the sum of the kinetic and potential energies *changes* because no work is done on the system.

24. _____ If the height of the juggler's hand is the reference point, when the ball returns to that height, its gravitational potential energy is *less than* 0 J.

25. _____ When a running pole-vaulter plants the end of a pole into a socket in the ground, the vaulter's kinetic energy is stored as *gravitational potential energy* in the bent pole.

11 Study Guide

Section 11.2: **Conservation of Energy**

In your textbook, read about the conservation of mechanical energy.

The diagram below shows the position of two identical balls initially at rest. Complete the following table, assuming there is neither air resistance nor frictional forces on either ball. Using the table as a guide, construct graphs of E, U_g, and K versus d for ball A on the grid. Then answer the following question.

Table 1						
	Ball A			**Ball B**		
Location (*d*)	*E*	U_g	*K*	*E*	U_g	*K*
1.00 m						
0.50 m						
0.00 m						

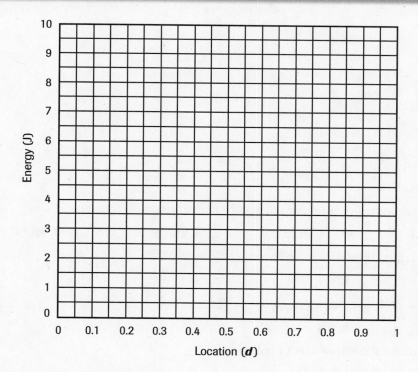

1. How would the graphs of E, U_g, and K versus d for ball B compare with the graphs you constructed for ball A?

_____

11 Study Guide

In your textbook, read about analyzing collisions.

The diagrams below show the motion of two identical 2.0 kg boxes before and after they collide. Sketch bar graphs of the energy of each system before and after the collision. Circle the letter of the choice that best completes each statement.

Before   **After**

A $v = 1.0$ m/s $v = 0$ m/s $v = 0$ m/s $v = 1.0$ m/s

B $v = 1.0$ m/s $v = 0$ m/s $v = -1.3$ m/s $v = 0.3$ m/s

C $v = 1.0$ m/s $v = 0$ m/s $v = 0.5$ m/s

2. The conservation of momentum occurs in collisions _____.

   a. A and B   **b.** A and C   **c.** B and C   **d.** A, B, and C

3. An elastic collision occurs in collision _____.

   a. A   **b.** B   **c.** C

4. An inelastic collision occurs in collision _____.

   a. A   **b.** B   **c.** C

5. A superelastic collision occurs in collision _____.

   a. A   **b.** B   **c.** C

6. The conservation of energy occurs in collisions _____.

   a. A and B   **b.** A and C   **c.** B and C   **d.** A, B, and C

12 Study Guide

Use with Chapter 12.

Thermal Energy
Vocabulary Review

Write the term that correctly completes each statement. Use each term once.

absolute zero	heat of fusion	second law of thermodynamics
calorimeter	heat of vaporization	specific heat
conduction	kelvin melting point	thermal energy
entropy	kinetic-molecular theory	thermodynamics
first law of thermodynamics	melting point	thermometer
heat engine	radiation	

1. _____ A device that measures temperature is a(n) _____.

2. _____ The transfer of kinetic energy when particles collide is _____.

3. _____ The _____ states that natural processes go in a direction that maintains or increases the universe's total entropy.

4. _____ The _____ states that matter is made up of particles that are always in motion.

5. _____ A device that continuously converts thermal energy to mechanical energy is a(n) _____.

6. _____ The temperature at which a substance changes from solid to liquid is called the _____.

7. _____ The lowest possible temperature is _____.

8. _____ A device that measures changes in thermal energy is a(n) _____.

9. _____ The transfer of energy by electromagnetic waves is _____.

10. _____ The amount of energy that must be added to raise the temperature of a unit mass one unit is the _____ of a material.

11. _____ The unit of temperature on the Kelvin scale is the _____.

12. _____ The amount of energy needed to melt 1 kg of a substance is the _____ of the substance.

13. _____ The _____ states that the total increase in thermal energy of a system is the sum of the work done on it and the heat added to it.

14. _____ The disorder in a system is _____.

15. _____ The study of heat is _____.

16. _____ The overall energy of motion of the particles that make up the object is the _____ of the object.

17. _____ The amount of thermal energy needed to change 1 kg of liquid to a gas is the _____.

12 Study Guide

• • • • • • • • • • • •

Section 12.1: Temperature and Thermal Energy

In your textbook, read about the theory and measurement of thermal energy.

For each of the statements below, write true *or rewrite the italicized part to make the statement true.*

1. _____ In a hot body, particles tend to move *faster* than in a cooler body.

2. _____ At a given temperature, all the particles in a body have *the same energy.*

3. _____ The thermal energy in an object *doesn't* depend on the number of particles in it.

4. _____ Two bodies are in *thermal* equilibrium if they are at the same temperature.

5. _____ A kelvin is equal in size to a *Celsius* degree.

6. _____ Absolute zero is equal to *0°C.*

7. _____ The equation that allows conversion of a Celsius temperature to a Kelvin temperature is $T_k + 273.15 = T_c$.

8. _____ The *caloric* theory could successfully explain why objects become warm when they are rubbed together.

In your textbook, read about temperature measurement.

Express each temperature in the scale indicated.

9. The freezing point of water, in degrees Celsius _____

10. The freezing point of water, in kelvins _____

11. The boiling point of water, in degrees Celsius _____

12. The boiling point of water, in kelvins _____

13. The lowest possible temperature, in degrees Celsius _____

14. The lowest possible temperature, in kelvins _____

In your textbook, read about thermal-energy transfer.

For each term on the left, write the corresponding symbol.

_____	15. heat	C
_____	16. degree Celsius	ΔT
_____	17. kelvin	$°C$
_____	18. specific heat	Q
_____	19. energy change	K
_____	20. temperature change	ΔE

12 Study Guide

In your textbook, read about thermal-energy transfer and specific heat.
Answer the following questions.

21. Describe the typical direction of heat transfer when a cooler body is in contact with a warmer one.

_____

22. Write the equation for calculating the amount of heat transferred, given the mass, specific heat, and temperature change.

_____

23. Name the three means of thermal transfer.

_____

_____

24. How does the specific heat of liquid water compare in general with that of most other substances?

_____

_____

In your textbook, read about calorimetry.
The diagram below shows a calorimeter just after addition of an object and after thermal equilibrium is reached.
Refer to the diagram to answer the following questions.

25. What is the approximate value of T_f?

_____

26. What is the approximate value of T_i?

_____

27. Is the value of ΔT for the water positive or negative?

_____

28. Has heat flowed from the object to the water, or to the object from the water?

_____

29. Is Q for the object positive or negative?

_____

30. Is Q for the water positive or negative?

_____

31. Assuming no heat loss to the surroundings, how do the ΔE values for the water and the object compare?

_____

12 Study Guide

• • • • • • • • • • • • • •

Section 12.2: Change of State and Laws of Thermodynamics

In your textbook, read about changes of state.

Circle the letter of the choice that best completes the statement or answers the question.

1. The energy needed to melt 1 kg of a substance is called the _____.

   a. heat of vaporization

   b. entropy

   c. heat of fusion

   d. melting point

2. The temperature at which all added thermal energy converts a material from liquid to gas is the _____.

   a. melting point

   b. boiling point

   c. heat of fusion

   d. heat of vaporization

3. How do the specific heats of ice, liquid water, and steam compare?

   a. They are equal.

   b. That of ice is highest.

   c. That of steam is highest.

   d. That of liquid water is highest.

4. Which equation correctly relates heat, mass, and heat of vaporization?

   a. $Q = m/H_v$

   b. $Q = H_v/m$

   c. $Q = m + H_v$

   d. $Q = mH_v$

5. Is Q positive or negative for a melting solid and for a freezing liquid?

   a. negative in both cases

   b. positive in both cases

   c. positive for the melting solid, negative for the freezing liquid

   d. negative for the melting solid, positive for the freezing liquid

12 Study Guide

In your textbook, read about changes of state.

For each of the statements below, write true *or rewrite the italicized part to make it true.*

6. _____ When a liquid changes to a gas, it *releases* thermal energy.

7. _____ During melting, the kinetic energy of the particles *does not* change.

8. _____ An increase in the range of particle speeds in an object represents an *increase* in entropy.

9. _____ The heat required to melt a solid *does not* depend on the mass of the sample.

10. _____ In a plot of temperature versus heat added, the portion of the graph representing the boiling process is *horizontal*.

In your textbook, read about the first and second laws of thermodynamics.

Decide whether each statement relates more closely to the first law of thermodynamics or to the second law.
Write first law *or* second law.

11. Total entropy tends to increase.

_____

12. Energy is neither created nor destroyed.

_____

13. Thermal-energy increases depend on the work done and the heat added.

_____

14. Heat does not flow from a cold body to a hot body.

_____

15. Waste heat is generated whenever thermal energy is converted into mechanical energy.

_____

16. Energy can be converted from one form to another.

_____

17. The total amount of useful energy tends to decrease.

_____

12 Study Guide

In your textbook, read about devices that convert energy.

For each of the statements below, write true *or rewrite the italicized part to make it true.*

18. A *heat engine* converts thermal energy to mechanical energy.

_____

19. A heat engine requires a low-temperature receptacle into which *mechanical* energy can be delivered.

_____

20. An automobile internal combustion engine is an example of a *heat pump*.

_____

21. Using mechanical energy, a refrigerator removes thermal energy from a warmer body.

_____

22. A heat pump is a refrigerator that can run in *one direction*.

_____

In your textbook, read about entropy.

Decide whether the process is likely to occur spontaneously. Write yes *or* no.

23. A hot body absorbs thermal energy from a cooler one. _____

24. A set of particles becomes more orderly. _____

25. An engine generates waste heat. _____

26. Gas particles collect in one corner of a container. _____

27. Total entropy increases. _____

28. Usable energy increases. _____

13 Study Guide

Use with Chapter 13.

States of Matter
Vocabulary Review

Write the term that correctly completes each statement. Use each term once.

adhesion	capillary action	evaporation	pressure
amorphous solid	cohesive force	fluid	surface tension
Archimedes' principle	condensation	pascal	thermal expansion
Bernoulli's principle	crystal lattice	Pascal's principle	volatile
buoyant force	elasticity	plasma	

1. _____ The SI unit of pressure is the _____.

2. _____ An upward force on an object in a liquid is a(n) _____.

3. _____ A _____ contains electrons and positively charged ions.

4. _____ A fixed pattern of particles within a solid is a(n) _____.

5. _____ An increase in temperature may cause _____.

6. _____ "The magnitude of the buoyant force on an object equals the weight of fluid displaced by the object" is a statement of _____.

7. _____ "A change in pressure at any point on a confined fluid is transmitted undiminished throughout the fluid" is a statement of _____.

8. _____ The tendency of the surface of a liquid to contract to the smallest possible area is _____.

9. _____ A liquid that evaporates quickly is _____.

10. _____ The ability of an object to return to its original form when external forces are removed is _____.

11. _____ "As the velocity of a fluid increases, the pressure exerted by the fluid decreases" is a statement of _____.

12. _____ The escape of particles from a liquid's surface is _____.

13. _____ Force divided by area equals _____.

14. _____ The attractive force between particles of different substances is _____.

15. _____ A substance that has definite volume and shape but no regular crystal structure is a(n) _____.

16. _____ The rise of a liquid up a narrow tube is due to _____.

17. _____ The change of a gas to a liquid is _____.

18. _____ An attractive force between particles of the same substance, caused by electromagnetic attraction, is a(n) _____.

19. _____ A _____ flows and has no definite shape of its own.

13 Study Guide

• • • • • • • • • • • • • •

Section 13.1: The Fluid States

In your textbook, read about measures and equivalents for pressure.
For each term on the left, write the corresponding symbol.

_____ **1.** symbol for pressure   1 N/m^2

_____ **2.** symbol for weight   101 kPa

_____ **3.** symbol for surface area   *A*

_____ **4.** unit of pressure   *F/A*

_____ **5.** unit of weight   *F*$_g$

_____ **6.** definition of pressure   N

_____ **7.** equivalent to 1 Pa   *P*

_____ **8.** atmospheric pressure at sea level   Pa

In your textbook, read about pressure and fluids.
For each of the statements below, write true *or rewrite the italicized part to make the statement true.*

9. The shape of a container *does not affect* the pressure at any given depth of the fluid it contains.

_____

10. The buoyant force on an object depends on the weight of the *object.*

_____

11. The *apparent weight* of an object in water is equal to its actual weight minus the upward buoyant force.

_____

12. Fluids flow and have no definite *volume.*

_____

13. The pressure of the water on a body beneath its surface equals *ρhg.*

_____

14. Bernoulli's principle applies to *turbulent* flow only.

_____

13 Study Guide

In your textbook, read about Bernoulli's principle, Archimedes' principle, and Pascal's principle.

Complete the table below by writing the name of the principle that is most clearly illustrated in each situation. Choose among Bernoulli's principle, Archimedes' principle, and Pascal's principle.

Situation	Principle Illustrated
15. A man uses the hydraulic brake to stop his truck.	_____
16. An airplane rises into the air.	_____
17. An ice cube floats in water.	_____
18. A piece of paper rises when wind blows across it.	_____
19. A fish uses its air bladder to move downward in water.	_____
20. Ketchup rises up in a squeezed plastic bottle.	_____
21. A person feels lighter in water than on land.	_____
22. Curved airfoils help hold down the rear wheels of race cars.	_____

Write the term that correctly completes each statement.

The relationship between the **(23)** _____ of a moving fluid and the

(24) _____ exerted by the fluid is described by Bernoulli's principle.

Airfoils are devices that use this principle to produce **(25)** _____,

a net force in a(n) **(26)** _____ direction, when moving through a(n)

(27) _____. An airplane wing is curved so that the

(28) _____ surface has a greater curve than the **(29)** _____

surface. Air moving over the top of the wing moves a(n) **(30)** _____

distance, and therefore travels at a greater speed. The air pressure over the wing is

(31) _____ than the pressure under the wing. The flow of a fluid can

be represented by a set of lines called **(32)** _____. The closer the

lines are to each other, the greater is the **(33)** _____ and the lower is

the **(34)** _____ of the fluid. Swirling of such lines indicates that the fluid

flow is **(35)** _____, and Bernoulli's principle does not apply to the situation.

13 Study Guide

• • • • • • • • • • • • • • •

In your textbook, read about cohesive and adhesive forces.

The diagram on the left shows water molecules in a glass tube. The diagram on the right shows mercury atoms in a glass tube. The longer the vector arrows are, the greater is the force between the particles. Refer to the diagrams to answer the following questions. Use complete sentences.

36. Which arrows represent cohesive forces?

Molecules near a glass tube wall

Water molecules — Glass molecules of tube's inner wall — Mercury atoms — Glass molecules of tube's inner wall

_____

_____

_____

_____

37. Which arrows represent adhesive forces?

_____

_____

_____

38. For the water molecules, how do the cohesive forces compare to the adhesive forces?

_____

39. For the mercury atoms, how do the cohesive forces compare to the adhesive forces?

_____

40. Explain how the behavior of mercury would compare to that of water if a thin glass tube were placed in each liquid.

_____

_____

_____

_____

41. Would the top surface of mercury in a glass container be the same shape as the top surface of water in a similar container? Give the reason for your answer.

_____

_____

_____

_____

_____

13 Study Guide

• • • • • • • • • • • • • •

Section 13.2: The Solid State

In your textbook, read about solids and thermal expansion of solids.
For each of the statements below, write true *or* false.

_____ **1.** The particles in a crystalline solid do not move at all.

_____ **2.** Butter and glass are examples of amorphous solids.

_____ **3.** Elasticity is the ability of an object to return to its original form when external forces are removed.

_____ **4.** Malleability and ductility depend upon elasticity.

_____ **5.** Copper is a nonductile metal.

_____ **6.** Gold is a malleable metal.

_____ **7.** The symbol for the coefficient of linear expansion is α.

_____ **8.** Water is most dense at $0°C$.

_____ **9.** Metals used in a bimetallic strip have different rates of thermal expansion.

In your textbook, read about solids and thermal expansion.
Circle the letter of the choice that best completes the statement or answers the question.

10. For what substances is the solid state less dense than the liquid state?

   a. no liquids   **c.** water

   b. most liquids other than water   **d.** all liquids

11. A substance that can be flattened and shaped into thin sheets by hammering is _____.

   a. inelastic   **c.** ductile

   b. adhesive   **d.** malleable

12. A substance that can be pulled into thin strands of wire is said to be _____.

   a. inelastic   **c.** adhesive

   b. ductile   **d.** malleable

13. The change in volume of a material due to thermal expansion equals _____.

   a. $\beta V\Delta T$ **c.** $\alpha V\Delta T$

   b. $\beta V/\Delta T$ **d.** $\alpha V/\Delta T$

14. The coefficient of linear expansion equals _____.

   a. $\Delta T\Delta L$ **c.** $\Delta T/\Delta L$

   b. $L_1/\Delta L\Delta T$ **d.** $\Delta L/L_1\Delta T$

13 Study Guide

In your textbook, read about thermal expansion of solids.
For each term on the left, write the corresponding symbol.

_____ **15.** change of length $\qquad$ ΔT

_____ **16.** coefficient of volume expansion $\qquad$ α

_____ **17.** coefficient of linear expansion $\qquad$ ΔV

_____ **18.** change of temperature $\qquad$ $(^\circ C)^{-1}$

_____ **19.** change of volume $\qquad$ ΔL

_____ **20.** unit for coefficient of linear expansion $\qquad$ β

In your textbook, read about plasma and thermal expansion of liquids.
Use the terms below to complete the passage. You may need to use terms more than once.

electrons	**gas**	**liquid**	**temperature**
fluid	**ions**	**plasma**	

Heating a solid substance eventually turns it to a **(21)** _____ and then

to a **(22)** _____. Further increases in **(23)** _____

eventually cause collisions between particles to become violent enough that

(24) _____ are pulled off the atoms. The resulting state of matter is called

(25) _____. Along with liquids and gases, matter in this state is a

(26) _____. It contains positively charged **(27)** _____ and

negatively charged **(28)** _____. The main difference between a gas and a plasma

is that only the **(29)** _____ can conduct electricity.

Physics: Principles and Problems

14 Study Guide

Use with Chapter 14.

Waves and Energy Transfer

Vocabulary Review

Write the term that correctly completes each statement. Use each term once.

antinode	destructive interference	node	transverse wave
constructive interference	interference	normal	trough
crest	longitudinal wave	standing wave	wave
	mechanical wave	surface wave	wave pulse

1. _____ Any of the low points of a wave is a(n) _____.

2. _____ Superposition of waves with opposite amplitudes causes _____.

3. _____ Any rhythmic disturbance that carries energy through matter or space is a(n) _____.

4. _____ A wave that appears to be standing still is a(n) _____.

5. _____ A wave that requires a physical medium is a(n) _____.

6. _____ A single bump or disturbance that travels through a medium is a(n) _____.

7. _____ Superposition of waves with displacements in the same direction causes _____.

8. _____ An unmoving point at which destructively interfering pulses meet is a(n) _____.

9. _____ In a(n) _____, the disturbance moves parallel to the direction of motion of the wave.

10. _____ A point of largest displacement caused by the constructive interference of waves is a(n) _____.

11. _____ Any of the high points of a wave is a(n) _____.

12. _____ The result of any superposition of two or more waves is _____.

13. _____ In a(n) _____, the particles move in a direction that is both parallel and perpendicular to the direction of wave motion.

14. _____ In a(n) _____, the particles vibrate in a direction perpendicular to the direction of motion of the wave.

15. _____ A line that is at a right angle to a barrier is a(n) _____.

14 Study Guide

● ● ● ● ● ● ● ● ● ● ● ● ●

Section 14.1: Wave Properties

In your textbook, read about different kinds of waves.
Circle the letter of the choice that best completes each statement.

1. Waves typically transmit _____.

   a. matter only   **c.** energy only

   b. both matter and energy   **d.** neither matter nor energy

2. Water waves, sound waves, and waves that travel down a spring are all examples of _____.

   a. mechanical waves   **c.** electromagnetic waves

   b. transverse waves   **d.** longitudinal waves

3. If a wave moves in a leftward direction but the particles of the medium move up and down, the wave must be a _____.

   a. mechanical wave   **c.** surface wave

   b. transverse wave   **d.** longitudinal wave

4. A surface wave has characteristics of _____.

   a. longitudinal waves only   **c.** both longitudinal and transverse waves

   b. transverse waves only   **d.** neither longitudinal nor transverse waves

For each of the statements below, write true *or rewrite the italicized part to make the statement true.*

5. Sound is an example of a *transverse* wave.

   _____

6. Fluids usually transmit only *longitudinal* waves.

   _____

7. Waves at the top of a lake or an ocean are examples of *surface* waves.

   _____

8. Energy from the sun reaches Earth by means of *longitudinal* electromagnetic waves.

   _____

9. Waves that travel down a rope are examples of *surface* waves.

   _____

14 Study Guide

Name _____

In your textbook, read about amplitude and frequency.

For each of the statements below, write true *or rewrite the italicized part to make it true.*

10. *One hertz* is equal to one oscillation per second.

_____

11. The speed of a wave generally depends only on the *source*.

_____

12. Waves with larger amplitudes tend to transmit *less* energy than do waves with smaller amplitudes.

_____

13. The frequency of a wave does not depend on the *medium*.

_____

14. A wave of *high* frequency also has a long period.

_____

15. The higher the frequency of a wave is, the *longer* the period is.

_____

In your textbook, read about measuring waves.

For each term on the left, write the matching symbol from the list on the right.

_____ **16.** wavelength		Δd
_____ **17.** period		v
_____ **18.** speed		T
_____ **19.** frequency		Δt
_____ **20.** displacement of wave peak		f
_____ **21.** time interval		λ

In your textbook, read about the relationship of speed to wave attributes.

Use symbols to write the equation that combines the attributes on the left.

22. frequency and period $f =$ _____

23. speed, displacement, and time interval $v =$ _____

24. speed, wavelength, and frequency $v =$ _____

25. speed, wavelength, and period $v =$ _____

Physics: Principles and Problems

14 Study Guide

In your textbook, read about measuring waves.
Write the terms that correctly completes the passage.

The **(26)** _____ of a wave is its maximum displacement from its

position of rest. Doubling the amplitude of a wave increases the rate of energy transfer by a factor of

(27) _____. The time it takes for the motion of an oscillator to repeat itself in

generating a wave is the **(28)** _____ of the wave. Because the motion keeps

repeating, such a wave is a(n) **(29)** _____ wave. The number of complete

oscillations per second is the **(30)** _____ and is measured in units called

(31) _____. Both period and frequency of a wave depend only on its

(32) _____. A material that carries the energy of a mechanical wave

is a(n) **(33)** _____.

In your textbook, read about the attributes of a wave.
Refer to the drawing below to answer the following questions.

34. Which of the lettered distances represents the wavelength of wave 1?

_____

35. Which of the distances represents the amplitude of wave 1?

_____

36. Which of the two waves has the greater wavelength?

_____

37. Which of the two waves has the smaller amplitude?

_____

38. Assuming that the two waves move at equal speed, which has the higher frequency?

_____

39. Assuming that the two waves move at equal speed, which has the greater period?

_____

14 Study Guide

Section 14.2: Wave Behavior

In your textbook, read about wave reactions to boundaries.

For each of the statements below, write true *or rewrite the italicized part to make it true.*

1. _____ When a wave encounters the boundary of the medium in which it is traveling, the wave *always* reflects completely back into the medium.

2. _____ A wave that strikes a boundary is called the *incident* wave.

3. _____ If a wave passes from a lighter, more flexible spring to a heavier, stiffer one, the resulting reflected wave will be *inverted*.

4. _____ If a wave pulse is sent down a spring connected to a rigid wall, *almost none* of the wave's energy is reflected back.

Answer the following questions, using complete sentences.

5. What happens to the wavelength of water waves as they move from deep to shallow water?

_____

6. What happens to the frequency of water waves as they move from deep to shallow water?

_____

7. What happens to the speed of water waves as they move from deep to shallow water? Describe an equation that would show this change.

_____

_____

In your textbook, read about wave interference.

For each of the statements below, write true *or rewrite the italicized part to make it true.*

8. _____ According to the principle of superposition, the medium's displacement caused by two or more waves is the algebraic *difference between* the displacements caused by the individual waves.

9. _____ In constructive interference, the resulting wave has an amplitude *smaller* than that of any of the individual waves.

10. _____ Two waves *cannot* exist in the same medium at the same time.

11. _____ A *continuous* wave appears to be standing still.

12. _____ If the trough of one wave occurs at the same point as the *crest* of another wave, the two may cancel out, producing zero amplitude at that point.

13. _____ When a continuous wave crosses a boundary and moves more *slowly,* the amplitude increases.

14 Study Guide

In your textbook, read about two-dimensional waves.
Answer the following questions, using complete sentences.

14. What is a ray?

_____

15. What is a ripple tank?

_____

_____

16. State the law of reflection, and explain how each of the two kinds of angles involved are measured.

_____

_____

_____

_____

17. What is meant by refraction?

_____

18. In how many dimensions do the waves travel in the following three cases: a wave moving along a rope, a wave on the surface of water, and a sound wave.

_____

_____

_____

In your textbook, read about diffraction and interference of waves.
Write the terms that correctly complete the passage.

When waves reach a small opening in a barrier, they form waves that have a(n)

(19) _____ shape. This effect is an example of **(20)** _____.

The smaller the **(21)** _____ is, compared to the size of the barrier, the

(22) _____ pronounced this effect is. When there are two closely spaced

openings in a barrier, two sets of **(23)** _____ waves are produced. Nodes lie

along lines between lines of **(24)** _____. Nodes form where there is

(25) _____ interference.

15 Study Guide

Sound

Vocabulary Review

Write the term that correctly completes each statement. Use each term once.

beat	dissonance	harmonic	sound level
consonance	Doppler shift	octave	timbre
decibel	fundamental	pitch	

1. _____ The amplitude of sound, as measured on a logarithmic scale, is called _____.

2. _____ Any higher frequency that is a multiple of the fundamental frequency is a(n) _____.

3. _____ An oscillation of wave amplitude caused by the sounding of two nearly identical frequencies is called a(n) _____.

4. _____ A unit used to measure sound level is the _____.

5. _____ A jarring combination of pitches is called _____.

6. _____ Two frequencies in a 1:2 ratio differ by a(n) _____.

7. _____ The lowest frequency that will resonate in a pipe is the _____.

8. _____ The apparent change in pitch caused by the motion of a sound source is called the _____.

9. _____ The apparent highness or lowness of a note, associated with frequency of vibration is called _____.

10. _____ Tone color or tone quality is called _____.

11. _____ A pleasant combination of pitches is called _____.

15 Study Guide

Section 15.1: Properties of Sound

In your textbook, read about sound waves.
Write the term that correctly completes each statement.

Sound waves move in the same direction as the particles of the medium and are therefore

(1) _____ waves. The waves are caused by variations in

(2) _____ relating to the different **(3)** _____ of

molecules. Therefore, sound cannot travel through a(n) **(4)** _____. The

(5) _____ of a sound wave is the number of pressure oscillations per second.

The **(6)** _____ is the distance between successive regions of high or low

pressure. The speed of a sound wave in air depends on the **(7)** _____ of the

air. At 20°C, sound moves through air at sea level at a speed of **(8)** _____ m/s.

In general, the speed of sound is **(9)** _____ in liquids and solids than in gases.

Reflected sound waves are **(10)** _____. The reflection of sound waves can be

used to find the **(11)** _____ between a source and a reflecting surface.

Sound waves can **(12)** _____, producing nodes, where little sound is heard.

Sound waves can also be **(13)** _____; they spread outward after passing

through a narrow opening. The equation that relates velocity, frequency, and wavelength is

(14) _____.

In your textbook, read about loudness.
For each of the statements below, write true *or rewrite the italicized part to make the statement true.*

15. Sound level is measured on a *logarithmic* scale. _____

16. The ear detects *pressure* variations as sound. _____

17. Hearing loss can result from long exposure to *dissonant* sound levels. _____

18. Sound level is measured in *hertz*. _____

19. Loudness, as perceived by the human ear, is directly proportional to *length* of a pressure wave.

_____

20. A *40-dB* increase is perceived as roughly a doubling of the loudness of a sound. _____

Physics: Principles and Problems

15 Study Guide

In your textbook, read about sound waves and loudness.

For each term on the left, write the corresponding symbol from those on the right. Some symbols may be used more than once.

_____ **21.** period   dB

_____ **22.** amplitude   Hz

_____ **23.** speed   m

_____ **24.** frequency   m/s

_____ **25.** loudness   s

_____ **26.** pitch

_____ **27.** wavelength

In your textbook, read about pitch and the Doppler effect.

State whether the process would make the apparent pitch of a sound higher, lower, or have no effect on it.

28. moving the listener away from the sound source _____

29. decreasing the frequency _____

30. increasing the number of decibels _____

31. decreasing the wavelength, at constant wave speed _____

32. increasing the wavelength, at constant wave speed _____

33. moving the sound source toward the listener _____

34. decreasing the wave amplitude _____

35. increasing the wavelength, at constant frequency _____

36. decreasing the period _____

In your textbook, read about the Doppler shift.

The drawing below shows the crests of sound waves produced by a point source, S, that is moving. The two ears represent two listeners at different positions. Refer to the drawing to answer the following questions.

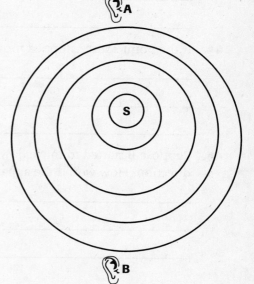

37. Which direction is the point source moving? Give a reason for your answer.

_____

_____

_____

38. How do the apparent wavelengths at A and B compare?

_____

_____

39. How does the speed of the sound waves compare at A and B?

_____

_____

40. How does the apparent frequency at point A compare to that at point B? Give a reason for your answer, in terms of the meaning of the word *frequency* and of the equation relating frequency to speed and wavelength.

_____

_____

_____

41. How loud is the sound heard at A compared to that heard at B when A and B are equally far from the source? Give a reason for your answer.

_____

_____

_____

42. Is the sound heard at A higher or lower pitch than that heard at B? Give a reason for your answer.

_____

_____

_____

43. If the point source began to move faster in the same direction, would the apparent sound at A and B change? If yes, how would it change?

_____

_____

44. If the point source stopped moving, how would the apparent sound at A and B change, if at all?

_____

_____

_____

45. Suppose B started to move downward while the point source continued to move in its original direction. How would the apparent sound at B change, if at all?

_____

_____

_____

15 Study Guide

Section 15.2: The Physics of Music

In your textbook, read about pipe resonators and other sources of sound.

Circle the letter of the choice that best completes the statement or answers the question.

1. Sound is produced when there are _____.

   a. increases in pressure   **c.** increases in temperature

   b. oscillations in pressure   **d.** electromagnetic waves

2. The frequencies of vibrating air that will be set into resonance are determined by an air column's _____.

   a. radius   **b.** length   **c.** mass   **d.** width

3. Resonance occurs when _____.

   a. any constructive interference occurs   **c.** a standing wave is created.

   b. any destructive interference occurs   **d.** no nodes are formed

4. In which kind of resonator is the pressure of the reflected wave inverted?

   a. closed-pipe only   **c.** both open- and closed-pipe

   b. open-pipe only   **d.** neither open- nor closed-pipe

5. In a standing sound wave in a pipe, nodes are regions of _____.

   a. maximum or minimum pressure and low displacement

   b. maximum or minimum pressure and high displacement

   c. mean atmospheric pressure and low displacement

   d. mean atmospheric pressure and high displacement

6. In a standing sound wave in a pipe, two antinodes are separated by _____.

   a. one-quarter wavelength   **c.** one-half wavelength

   b. one wavelength   **d.** two wavelengths

In your textbook, read about resonance frequencies in pipes.

For each of the statements below, write true *or* false.

_____ 7. A closed pipe can't have resonance unless it has antinodes at both ends.

_____ 8. In a closed pipe, a column of length $\lambda/4$ will be in resonance with a tuning fork.

_____ 9. An open pipe can't have resonance unless it has nodes at both ends.

_____ 10. In an open pipe, a column of length $3\lambda/4$ will be in resonance with a tuning fork.

_____ 11. For both open and closed pipes, resonance lengths are spaced at half-wavelength intervals.

15 Study Guide

In your textbook, read about sound detectors.

Answer the following questions, using complete sentences.

12. Briefly describe energy conversion by a microphone.

_____

_____

_____

13. Describe the pathway that sound waves follow as they enter the ear and eventually lead to the sensation of sound.

_____

_____

_____

_____

In your textbook, read about sound qualities and beat.

For each of the statements below, write true *or rewrite the italicized part to make the statement true.*

14. _____ The *highest* frequency that will resonate in a musical instrument is called the fundamental.

15. _____ In a *closed-pipe* instrument, such as a clarinet, the harmonics are odd-number multiples of the fundamental frequency.

16. _____ A sound spectrum of an instrument is a graph of wave amplitude versus *speed*.

17. _____ Sounds perceived as *consonant* in most Western cultures tend to have frequencies that are in small, whole-number ratios.

18. _____ Interference between two nearly identical frequencies causes a *consonance*.

19. _____ A beat is an oscillation of wave amplitude.

20. _____ The frequency of the beat equals the magnitude of *difference* between the frequencies of the two waves.

In your textbook, read about musical intervals.

Write the frequency ratio for the pitches in each musical interval.

21. octave _____

22. fifth _____

23. major third _____

24. fourth _____

16 Study Guide

Light

Vocabulary Review

Write the term that correctly completes each statement. Use each term once.

complementary color	luminous	polarized	secondary pigment
dye	luminous flux	primary pigment	spectrum
illuminance	luminous intensity	ray model	translucent
illuminated	opaque	secondary color	transparent
light	pigment		

1. _____ The illumination of a surface is _____.

2. _____ The _____ of a given color forms white light when it combines with that color.

3. _____ The _____ of a point source is the luminous flux that falls on 1 m² of a sphere with a 1-m radius.

4. _____ A measure of the total rate at which light is emitted from a source is _____.

5. _____ Light that vibrates in a particular plane is _____.

6. _____ A color formed from two primary colors of light is a(n) _____.

7. _____ The range of frequencies of electromagnetic waves that stimulates the retina of the eye is _____.

8. _____ The _____ uses straight lines to describe how light behaves.

9. _____ A material that transmits light without distorting it is _____.

10. _____ The ordered arrangement of colors from red through violet is the _____.

11. _____ A colored material that is made up of particles larger than molecules is a(n) _____.

12. _____ A molecule that absorbs certain wavelengths and transmits others is a(n) _____.

13. _____ A(n) _____ absorbs only one primary color from white light.

14. _____ A(n) _____ absorbs two primary colors of light.

15. _____ A material that transmits light, but objects cannot be seen clearly through it is a(n) _____ material.

16. _____ A material that transmits no incident light is a(n) _____ material.

17. _____ A(n) _____ body does not emit light but simply reflects light produced by a source.

18. _____ A(n) _____ body emits light waves.

16 Study Guide

• • • • • • • • • • • • • •

Section 16.1: Light Fundamentals

In your textbook, read about characteristics of light.

For each of the statements below, write true *or rewrite the italicized part to make the statement true.*

_____ **1.** Light waves have wavelengths from about *400* nm to about 700 nm.

_____ **2.** The shortest wavelengths of light are seen as *red* light.

_____ **3.** Light travels in a *straight* line in a vacuum.

_____ **4.** The speed of light in a vacuum is approximately *3.00×10^{10} m/s.*

In your textbook, read about characteristics of light.

Circle the letter of the choice that best completes the statement or answers the question.

5. Light behaves like _____.

    a. particles only

    b. waves only

    c. both particles and waves

    d. neither particles nor waves

6. Geometric optics studies light by means of _____.

    a. ray diagrams

    b. the wave model

    c. ripple tanks

    d. a particle-wave model

7. The fact that sharp shadows are cast by the sun is an indication that light _____.

    a. is a wave.

    b. travels in straight lines

    c. is made up of colors

    d. travels in a curved path

8. A straight line that represents the path of a very narrow beam of light is

    a. normal

    b. a complement

    c. a ray

    d. a wave

9. The orbital period of which of the following was studied in the seventeenth century to determine the speed of light?

    a. Io

    b. Saturn

    c. Jupiter

    d. Earth's moon

10. How long does light take to cross Earth's orbit?

    a. 2 s

    b. 8 min

    c. 16 min

    d. 22 min

11. Light of which of the following colors has the longest wavelength?

    a. red

    b. yellow

    c. blue

    d. violet

16 Study Guide

• • • • • • • • • • • • •

In your textbook, read about measures of light.
Complete the table below.

Table 1		
Quantity	**Name of Unit**	**Symbol for Unit**
illuminance		
luminous flux		
luminous intensity		

In your textbook, read about sources of light.
Write the term that correctly completes each statement.

A body that **(12)** _____ light waves is luminous, and a body that

simply **(13)** _____ light waves given off by a source is illuminated. A(n)

(14) _____ object emits light as a result of its high temperature. The official

SI unit from which all light intensity units are calculated is the **(15)** _____.

Luminous flux expresses the **(16)** _____ at which light is given

off. Illuminance is the **(17)** _____ of a surface. If the distance from

a surface to a point source of light is doubled, the illumination reaching the surface is only

(18) _____ as great. The relationship between illuminance and luminous

flux is given by the equation **(19)** _____, where the distance to the surface is

represented by the symbol **(20)** _____. This equation is valid only if the light

from the source is traveling **(21)** _____ to the surface. It is also valid only for

sources small enough or far away enough to be **(22)** _____ sources.

In your textbook, read about light sources and quantities.
For each situation below, write the letter of the matching item.

_____ **23.** symbol for the speed of light		**a.** 1 lm/m^2
_____ **24.** area of the surface of a sphere		**b.** $1/r^2$
_____ **25.** symbol for luminous flux		**c.** $4\pi r^2$
_____ **26.** symbol for illuminance		**d.** c
_____ **27.** equivalent to the speed of light		**e.** E
_____ **28.** equivalent to 1 lx		**f.** λf
_____ **29.** proportional to illumination		**g.** P
_____ **30.** equivalent to luminous intensity		**h.** $P/4\pi$

16 Study Guide

. . . .

Section 16.2: Light and Matter

In your textbook, read about the additive color process.

The diagram below represents three overlapping circles of equally intense light of different pure colors. Assume that the circles are projected onto a white screen in an otherwise completely dark room.

1. What color (if any) would region A be?

_____

2. What color would region B be?

_____

3. What color would region C be?

_____

4. What color would region D be?

_____

5. What color would region E be?

_____

6. What color types of light—primary or secondary—are red, blue, and green light?

_____

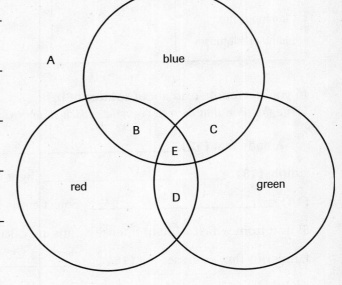

7. What color type of light would be in region B? Give a reason for your answer.

_____

8. What color type of light would be in region C?

_____

9. What color type of light would be in region D?

_____

10. The color in region B is the complementary color to which color?

_____

11. What happens if two complementary colors are projected together at the correct intensities onto a white screen?

_____

12. The color in region C is complementary to which color?

_____

13. The color in region D is complementary to which color?

_____

16 Study Guide

In your textbook, read about pigments.
Answer the following questions, using complete sentences.

14. What does a primary pigment absorb from white light?

_____

15. What does a secondary pigment absorb from white light?

_____

16. Is the absorption of light to form pigment colors an additive or a subtractive process?

_____

17. What color are the three primary pigments?

_____

18. What color are the three secondary pigments?

_____

19. What color(s) does yellow pigment absorb from light?

_____

20. What color(s) does yellow pigment reflect?

_____

21. What colors does red pigment absorb from light?

_____

22. What is the complementary pigment to cyan pigment?

_____

23. What color would result from the mixing of two complementary pigments?

_____

In your textbook, read about thin films.
For each of the statements below, write true *or rewrite the italicized part to make the statement true.*

24. _____ The colors produced by an oil film on water result from thin-film *interference.*

25. _____ When a soap film is held vertically, it is *thicker* at the top than at the bottom.

26. _____ When a light wave traveling through the air reaches the top surface of a soap film, the wave that is reflected there is *inverted.*

27. _____ When a light wave that has traveled into a soap film reaches the back surface, the wave that is reflected there is *inverted.*

28. _____ When a soap film has a thickness of $\lambda/4$, the wave reflected from the back surface *destructively interferes with* the wave reflected from the top surface.

16 Study Guide

• • • • • • • • • • • • • •

29. _____ When a soap film has a thickness of $5\lambda/4$, the wave reflected from the back surface *reinforces* the wave reflected from the top surface.

30. _____ In a soap film, the $\lambda/4$ requirement is met at the same locations for *all colors* of light.

31. _____ The explanation of thin-film interference does not require a *wave* model of light.

In your textbook, read about polarization.
For each of the statements below, write true *or rewrite the italicized part to make the statement true.*

32. Light that has been polarized vibrates in *all planes.*

_____

33. Polaroid material allows electromagnetic waves vibrating in one direction to pass through, while absorbing waves vibrating in the *perpendicular* direction.

_____

34. Light can be polarized by *refraction.*

_____

35. Photographers use polarizing filters to block *reflected* light.

_____

17 Study Guide

Use with Chapter 17.

Reflection and Refraction

Vocabulary Review

Write the term that correctly completes each statement. Use each term once.

angle of incidence   dispersion   refraction

angle of reflection   index of refraction   regular reflection

angle of refraction   normal   Snell's law

critical angle   optically dense   total internal reflection

diffuse reflection

1. _____ When light bounces off surfaces that are not very smooth, _____ occurs.

2. _____ A line perpendicular to a surface is a(n) _____.

3. _____ When light passes from one medium to a less optically dense medium at an angle so great that there is no refracted ray, _____ occurs.

4. _____ The separation of light into its spectrum is _____.

5. _____ When light bounces off surfaces that are extremely smooth, so that the light returns to the observer in parallel beams, _____ occurs.

6. _____ The angle that an incoming beam makes with the normal is the _____.

7. _____ The relationship of the angle of incidence to the angle of refraction is stated in _____.

8. _____ If the angle of refraction is smaller than the angle of incidence, the medium in which the angle is smaller is more _____.

9. _____ The angle that a refracted ray makes with the normal is the _____.

10. _____ For light going from a vacuum into another medium, the constant *n* is the _____.

11. _____ The angle made with the normal by a beam of light that has bounced off a surface is the _____.

12. _____ The bending of light at the boundary between two media is _____.

13. _____ The _____ describes a refracted ray that lies along the boundary of a substance.

17 Study Guide

• • • • • • • • • • •

Section 17.1: How Light Behaves at a Boundary

In your textbook, read about reflection and refraction.
For each of the statements below, write true *or rewrite the italicized part to make it true.*

1. _____ The angle of incidence is the angle between the incoming light beam and the *surface.*

2. _____ The velocity of light *does not* depend on the medium through which the light is traveling.

3. _____ The angle of incidence equals the angle of *reflection.*

4. _____ A mirror causes *diffuse reflection.*

5. _____ *Reflection* involves a bending of light.

6. _____ The angle of incidence *differs* from the angle of refraction.

Write the term that correctly completes each statement.

When a beam of light strikes a rough surface, it reflects at **(7)** _____ angles,

producing **(8)** _____ reflection. When a beam of light strikes a very smooth

surface, the reflected rays are **(9)** _____ to each other, producing

(10) _____ reflection. If a light beam is not reflected, but is bent instead,

the light is **(11)** _____. The angle of incidence is measured between the

(12) _____ ray and the **(13)** _____. The angle of refraction

is measured between the **(14)** _____ ray and the **(15)** _____.

Refraction does not occur if the angle of incidence is **(16)** _____ degrees. When a

light ray enters a medium that is more **(17)** _____ dense, its speed

(18) _____, and the refracted ray bends **(19)** _____ the

normal. If a light ray passes into a medium in which it travels faster, the refracted ray bends

(20) _____ the normal.

17 Study Guide

Name _____

In your textbook, read about Snell's law and the effect of different media on light.

The diagram below represents a light ray passing through two media. Refer to the diagram to answer the following questions. Use complete sentences.

21. Which labeled line represents the incident ray? How can you tell?

_____

_____

22. Which line represents the refracted ray? How can you tell?

_____

_____

23. Which line represents the boundary between the two media?

_____

_____

24. Which line represents the normal? How can you tell?

_____

25. Which labeled angle represents the angle of incidence? How can you tell?

_____

26. Which labeled angle represents the angle of refraction? How can you tell?

_____

27. Which is greater: the angle of incidence or the angle of refraction?

_____

28. Which medium is more optically dense? How can you tell?

_____

_____

29. Which medium has the lower refractive index? How can you tell?

_____

30. Write an equation for Snell's law.

_____

Medium 1   **Medium 2**

Physics: Principles and Problems

Study Guide **99**

17 Study Guide

31. Using Snell's law, complete the following equation, showing the ratio of the indices of refraction for medium 1 and medium 2: $n_2/n_1 =$ _____.

_____

32. In which medium does the light travel faster? How can you tell?

_____

In your textbook, read about the index of refraction and speed of light.
Match each quantity on the left with the correct symbol.

_____ **33.** angle of refraction c

_____ **34.** angle of incidence θ_r

_____ **35.** speed of light in a vacuum n

_____ **36.** speed of light in a medium   sin

_____ **37.** frequency of light f

_____ **38.** wavelength of light θ_i

_____ **39.** index of refraction v

_____ **40.** sine λ

Circle the letter of the choice that best completes each statement.

41. Compared to its speed in air, the speed of light in glass is _____.

  a. the same   **b.** faster.   **c.** slower   **d.** not measurable

42. Which of the following has the highest index of refraction? _____

  a. a vacuum   **b.** air   **c.** diamond   **d.** crown glass

43. For most practical purposes, the index of refraction of air can be considered _____.

  a. 0   **c.** infinite

  b. 1.00   **d.** equal to that of the other medium involved

44. The wavelength of light in a given material equals _____.

  a. the speed of light in the material times frequency

  b. frequency times the speed of light in the material

  c. the speed of light in the material divided by frequency

  d. frequency divided by the speed of light in the material

45. Which expression equals the index of refraction of a given medium?

  a. c/v_{medium} **b.** v_{medium}/c **c.** $c - v_{medium}$ **d.** $v_{medium} - c$

17 Study Guide

•••••••••••••••

Section 17.2: Applications of Reflected and Refracted Light

In your textbook, read about total internal reflection.
For each of the statements below, write true *or* false.

_____ **1.** The critical angle is the incident angle that causes the refracted ray to lie along the boundary.

_____ **2.** The sine of the critical angle for a substance from which light is passing into air is equal to $1.00/n_i$.

_____ **3.** Total internal reflection cannot be achieved for light that is passing from water to air.

_____ **4.** All substances have the same critical angle.

_____ **5.** Plants can use total internal reflection for light transport.

_____ **6.** A single bundle of optical fibers can carry thousands of telephone conversations at once.

_____ **7.** Total internal reflection occurs whenever light passes from one medium to a less optically dense medium.

_____ **8.** When incident light is at the critical angle, θ_r equals $0°$.

_____ **9.** The core of an optical fiber is metal.

_____ **10.** Each time light moving through an optical fiber strikes the surface, the angle of incidence is larger than the critical angle.

_____ **11.** Cladding covers the outside of an optical fiber.

_____ **12.** Optical fibers are flexible.

In your textbook, read about the effects of refraction.
Circle the letter of the choice that best completes the statement or answers the question.

13. As temperature increases, the index of refraction of air _____.

   a. increases   **c.** remains constant

   b. decreases   **d.** becomes negligible

14. The mirage effect is caused by _____.

   a. total internal reflection

   b. polarization

   c. temperature differences in index of refraction

   d. differences in the speeds of different colors of light

15. Which of the following is correct regarding sunlight? _____

   a. It reaches us only after the sun has actually risen.

   b. It continues to reach us after the sun has actually set.

   c. It stops reaching us before the sun has actually set.

   d. It corresponds exactly to sunrise and sunset.

17 Study Guide

• • • • • • • • • • • • •

16. When all the colors of light are combined, _____.

   a. black results

   b. the frequencies add together, producing light of higher frequency

   c. the colors completely cancel out because of destructive interference

   d. white light is produced

17. Which color of light is bent most as it goes through a prism?

   a. red   **b.** yellow   **c.** green   **d.** violet

18. The color of light that has the lowest index of refraction is _____.

   a. red   **b.** yellow   **c.** green   **d.** violet

19. Diamond has _____.

   a. a low refractive index and little color variation in the index

   b. a low refractive index and lots of color variation in the index

   c. a high refractive index and little color variation in the index

   d. a high refractive index and lots of color variation in the index

20. Which description fits the spectrum of light from an incandescent lamp?

   a. a continuous band only

   b. bright lines only

   c. both a continuous band and bright lines

   d. neither a continuous band nor bright lines

21. Which description fits the spectrum of light from a fluorescent lamp?

   a. a continuous band only

   b. bright lines only

   c. both a continuous band and bright lines

   d. neither a continuous band nor bright lines

22. Production of a rainbow by water droplets depends on _____.

   a. differences of angles of incidence for lights of different colors

   b. differences of angles of refraction for lights of different colors

   c. differences of speed for lights of different colors

   d. equality of index of refraction for lights of all colors

23. A puddle mirage seen by a motorist is actually light from _____.

   a. the ground underneath the puddle

   b. the ground surrounding the puddle

   c. the sky.

   d. passing vehicles.

18 Study Guide

Use with Chapter 18.

Mirrors and Lenses

Vocabulary Review

Write the term that correctly completes each statement. Use each term once.

achromatic lens	convex lens	focal point	principal axis
chromatic aberration	convex mirror	lens/mirror equation	real image
concave lens	erect image	magnification	spherical aberration
concave mirror	focal length	object	virtual image

1. _____ An image at which light rays actually converge is a(n) _____.

2. _____ A(n) _____ reflects light from its inwardly curving surface.

3. _____ The straight line perpendicular to the surface of a mirror at its center is the _____.

4. _____ The mathematical relationship between focal length, distance of object, and distance of image is expressed by the _____.

5. _____ A transparent refracting device that is thinner in the middle than at the edges is a(n) _____.

6. _____ A transparent refracting device that is thicker in the middle than at the edges is a(n) _____.

7. _____ The distance between the focal point and the mirror or lens is the _____.

8. _____ Any source of diverging light rays is a(n) _____.

9. _____ An image at which light rays do not actually converge is a(n) _____.

10. _____ The place at which light rays parallel to the principal axis of a concave mirror converge is the _____.

11. _____ An undesirable effect in which an object viewed through a lens appears to be ringed with color is _____.

12. _____ An image that is not inverted is a(n) _____.

13. _____ An undesirable effect in which the parallel rays reflected in a concave mirror fail to meet at a point is _____.

14. _____ A spherical mirror that reflects light from its outwardly curving surface is a(n) _____.

15. _____ A lens constructed so as to avoid undesirable color effects is a(n) _____.

16. _____ The ratio of the size of an image to the size of the object that produces it is the _____.

18 Study Guide

Section 18.1: Mirrors

In your textbook, read about concave mirrors.
For each of the statements below, write true *or rewrite the italicized part to make the statement true.*

1. _____ Rays *perpendicular* to the principal axis of a concave mirror converge at or near the focal point.

2. _____ The focal length of a concave mirror is *half* the radius of curvature.

3. _____ If the object is *farther out* than the center of curvature of a concave mirror, its image appears between the focus and the center of curvature.

4. _____ Concave mirrors can produce *only virtual* images.

5. _____ Concave mirrors *cannot* act as magnifiers.

In your textbook, read about real images formed by concave mirrors.
Circle the letter of the choice that best answers each question.

6. Which of the following correctly states the lens/mirror equation?

   a. $f = d_i + d_o$

   b. $1/f = d_i + d_o$

   c. $f = 1/d_i + 1/d_o$

   d. $1/f = 1/d_i + 1/d_o$

7. Which of the following is a correct relationship?

   a. $m = h_i + h_o$

   b. $m = h_i - h_o$

   c. $m = h_i/h_o$

   d. $m = h_o/h_i$

8. Which of the following indicates that an image produced by a concave mirror is upright?

   a. a positive value for h_i

   b. a negative value for h_i

   c. a positive value for d_i

   d. a negative value for d_i

9. To which of the following is m equal?

   a. d_o/d_i

   b. $-d_o/d_i$

   c. d_i/d_o

   d. $-d_i/d_o$

In your textbook, read about virtual images and image defects in concave mirrors.
Circle the letter of the choice that best answers each question.

10. Which of the following indicates that an image produced by a concave mirror is virtual?

   a. a positive value for h_i

   b. a negative value for h_i

   c. a positive value for d_i

   d. a negative value for d_i

11. If an object is placed at the focal point of a concave mirror, where will the image be?

   a. also at the focal point

   b. at the center of curvature

   c. at infinity

   d. at the surface of the mirror

18 Study Guide

12. Which of the following posed a problem for the Hubble Space Telescope?

a. improperly ground lenses

b. chromatic aberration

c. spherical aberration

d. cracked spherical mirrors

13. Why don't parabolic mirrors have trouble with spherical aberration?

a. All parallel rays are reflected to a single spot.

b. All parallel rays focus on infinity.

c. They use a secondary mirror for correction.

d. They have a virtual focus point.

In your textbook, read about real images formed by concave mirrors.

The diagram below shows a concave mirror and an object. Refer to the diagram to answer the following questions.

Bottle
C   F

Concave mirror

14. What does the letter *F* stand for?

_____

15. What does the dashed line represent?

_____

16. Under what condition will rays be reflected through point F?

_____

17. Relative to points C and F, roughly where will the image be?

_____

18. Will the value of d_i be positive or negative? Why?

_____

19. Will the image be real or virtual? Why?

_____

20. Will the image be reduced or enlarged?

_____

21. Will the value of h_i be greater or less than that of h_o?

_____

22. Will the image be erect or inverted?

_____

23. Will the value of h_i be positive or negative? Why?

_____

24. If the object was moved closer to C but still remained to the left of it, what would happen to the image?

_____

25. What would happen to the image if the object was moved to C?

_____

_____

In your textbook, read about convex mirrors.
For each of the statements below, write true *or rewrite the italicized part to make the statement true.*

26. _____ The focal length of a convex mirror is *negative*.

27. _____ Rays reflected from a convex mirror always *converge*.

28. _____ Convex mirrors reflect an *enlarged* field of view.

29. _____ The images produced by convex mirrors are *real* images.

30. _____ When the magnification is negative, an image will be *erect*.

31. _____ Compared to the size of the corresponding objects, the images produced by convex mirrors are always *the same size*.

Section 18.2: Lenses

In your textbook, read about real images formed by convex lenses.
Circle the letter of the choice that best completes the statement or answers the question.

1. Convex lenses typically have _____ .

    a. one focal point   **c.** a virtual focal point

    b. two focal points   **d.** no focal point

2. For a convex lens, if an object is between f and $2f$, the image will be _____ .

    a. smaller than the object   **c.** the same size as the object

    b. larger than the object   **d.** at infinity

3. For a lens, which of the following relationships is correct?

    a. $m = h_o/h_i$ **c.** $m = -h_o/h_i$

    b. $m = d_i/d_o$ **d.** $m = -d_i/d_o$

18 Study Guide

4. The relationship $1/f = 1/d_i + 1/d_o$ is _____.

   a. valid for any lens

   b. not valid for lenses

   c. valid for convex lenses only

   d. valid for concave lenses only

5. What kinds of images can convex lenses produce?

   a. real only

   b. virtual only

   c. both real and virtual

   d. neither real nor virtual

6. What is the principal advantage of using a large convex lens rather than a small one?

   a. elimination of spherical aberration

   b. elimination of chromatic aberration

   c. increasing the size of the focal point

   d. collection of more light rays

7. If an object is placed at the focal point of a convex lens, the refracted rays will _____.

   a. emerge in a parallel beam

   b. converge at the other focal point

   c. converge at the lens surface

   d. diverge

In your textbook, read about virtual images formed by convex lenses.
Answer the following questions, using complete sentences.

8. What type of lens can be used as a magnifying glass?

   _____

9. When a lens is used as a magnifying glass, where is the object placed?

   _____

10. When a lens is used as a magnifying glass, what sign(s) do d_i and h_i have?

   _____

In your textbook, read about concave lenses and lens defects.
For each of the statements below, write true *or rewrite the italicized part to make the statement true.*

11. _____ The images produced by concave lenses are always *inverted*.

12. _____ A concave lens is *thinner* in the center than at the edges.

13. _____ Concave lenses refract light rays so that the rays *converge*.

14. _____ The images produced by concave lenses are *virtual and enlarged*.

15. _____ Lenses suffer from spherical aberration because the rays that pass through *do not* all pass through the focus.

16. _____ The edges of a lens act like a *prism*, scattering light in a ring of color.

17. _____ You can reduce *spherical aberration* by joining a concave lens with a convex lens.

18 Study Guide

In your textbook, read about microscopes and telescopes.
Circle the letter of the choice that best completes the statement or answers the question.

18. The objective lens of a microscope is used to produce an image located _____.

   a. at the ocular lens

   b. between the ocular lens and its focal point

   c. at the focal point of the ocular lens

   d. beyond the ocular lens and its focal point

19. What kind of image is a telescope designed to produce for the viewer?

   a. real and inverted

   b. real and erect

   c. virtual and inverted

   d. virtual and erect

20. An astronomical refracting telescope uses _____.

   a. two concave lenses

   b. a combination of concave and convex lenses

   c. two convex lenses

   d. a variety of lenses and mirrors

19 Study Guide

Use with Chapter 19.

Diffraction and Interference of Light

Vocabulary Review

Write the term that correctly completes each statement. Use each term once.

coherent waves   diffraction grating   monochromatic light

constructive interference   first-order line   Rayleigh criterion

corpuscular model   grating spectrometer   resolving power

destructive interference   interference fringes   wavelet

diffraction

1. _____ A(n) _____ has parallel slits that diffract light and form an interference pattern.

2. _____ Light of only one wavelength is _____.

3. _____ The slight spreading of light around barriers is _____.

4. _____ Waves that are in phase are _____.

5. _____ The patterns of bright and dark bands produced when light passes through a double slit are _____.

6. _____ The _____ indicates whether two closely spaced star images will be resolved.

7. _____ The ability of an instrument, such as a telescope, to reveal the separateness of closely spaced images is its _____.

8. _____ When crests of waves overlap, _____ occurs.

9. _____ A bright band directly on either side of the central band is a(n) _____.

10. _____ A repeating disturbance produced when the crest of a wave is replaced by a wave source is a(n) _____.

11. _____ When crests of one wave overlap troughs of another wave, _____ occurs.

12. _____ An instrument used to measure light wavelengths produced by a diffraction grating is a(n) _____.

13. _____ The theory that light is made up of tiny particles is called the _____.

19 Study Guide

• • • • • • • • • • • • •

Section 19.1: When Light Waves Interfere

In your textbook, read about diffraction and the properties of light.

Circle the letter of the choice that best completes the statement or answers the question.

1. One sign that the corpuscular model of light isn't entirely correct is that light _____.

    a. travels in absolutely straight lines
    b. produces fuzzy shadow edges
    c. produces sharp shadow edges
    d. adds energy to matter

2. The crest of any wave can be replaced by a series of _____.

    a. equally spaced wave sources that are in step with each other
    b. equally spaced wave sources that interfere with each other
    c. unequally spaced wave sources that are in step with each other
    d. unequally spaced wave sources that interfere with each other

3. Interference fringes result from _____.

    a. constructive and destructive interference
    b. particle interactions
    c. wavelet creation
    d. refraction

4. A monochromatic light source emits light of _____.

    a. all frequencies
    b. one wavelength
    c. different wavelengths that interfere constructively
    d. one refractive index

5. How many slits were present in the barrier Young used to observe interference fringes?

    a. none   b. one   c. two   d. three

6. Wave crests that reach the same points at the same times are said to be _____.

    a. out of phase
    b. in phase
    c. noncoherent
    d. diffractive

7. Where two wave crests overlap, _____.

    a. a bright band is created
    b. a dark band is created
    c. diffraction occurs
    d. a colored band is created

8. Where a wave crest and a wave trough overlap, _____.

    a. a bright band is created
    b. a dark band is created
    c. diffraction occurs
    d. a colored band is created

9. In a two-slit experiment that uses monochromatic light, what appears at the center of the screen?

    a. bands of two different colors
    b. a dark band
    c. a complete spectrum
    d. a bright band

19 Study Guide

• • • • • • • • • • • • • •

10. In a two-slit experiment that uses white light, what appears at the center of the screen?

    a. bands of two different colors   **c.** a complete spectrum

    b. a dark band   **d.** a bright band

11. In a two-slit experiment that uses white light, what types of bands appear away from the center of the screen?

    a. bright bands only   **c.** colored spectra

    b. dark bands only   **d.** monochromatic bands

In your textbook, read about measuring wavelength with two-slit diffraction.
For each term on the left, write the matching item.

_____	**12.** width of a single slit	d
_____	**13.** wavelength	L
_____	**14.** separation of two slits	λ
_____	**15.** distance between the screen and slits	P
_____	**16.** location of the central bright band	P_0
_____	**17.** location of the first-order line	w
_____	**18.** distance between the central bright line and first-order line	x

The diagram below shows a two-slit experimental setup. Refer to the diagram to answer the following questions. Use complete sentences.

19. Describe the band that appears on the screen at point A. What kind of interference is occurring there?

_____

_____

20. What kind of band appears at point B? What kind of interference is occurring there?

_____

_____

21. Describe the band that appears on the screen at point C. What kind of interference is occurring there?

_____

_____

19 Study Guide

• • • • • • • • • • • • • •

22. What does the length E represent?

_____

23. Explain how the wavelength of the light can be calculated from the two-slit setup.

_____

_____

24. Write an equation calculating wavelength, first using the labels from the diagram, and then using the standard symbols.

_____

In your textbook, read about single-slit diffraction.

Circle the letter of the choice that best completes the statement or answers the question.

25. Which of the following is true of the diffraction of light compared to that of sound?

   a. Light is diffracted more because it has smaller wavelengths.

   b. Light is diffracted more because it has larger wavelengths.

   c. Sound is diffracted more because it has smaller wavelengths.

   d. Sound is diffracted more because it has larger wavelengths.

26. If light is passed through a single slit, _____.

   a. it is not diffracted

   b. a pattern of equally spaced bright bands results

   c. a wide, bright central band with dimmer bands on either side is produced

   d. a narrow, dim central band with brighter bands on either side is produced

27. In a single-slit situation, the distance between the central band and the first dark band is equal to _____.

   a. $\lambda L/w$

   b. wL/λ

   c. $\lambda w/L$

   d. $w/\lambda L$

19 Study Guide

Section 19.2: Applications of Diffraction

In your textbook, read about diffraction gratings.

For each of the statements below, write true *or rewrite the italicized part to make the statement true.*

1. _____ When white light falls on a diffraction grating, *white bands* are produced.

2. _____ Diffraction gratings are made by using a diamond to scratch fine lines *on glass.*

3. _____ The spacing between the lines on diffraction gratings is typically about *1 mm.*

4. _____ Wavelength *cannot* be measured as precisely with diffraction gratings as with double slits.

Write the term that correctly completes each statement. Use each term once.

θ	colors	interference
λ/d	diffract	narrower
angle	distance	wavelengths
broader	grating spectrometer	

A diffraction grating has many parallel slits that **(5)** _____ light

and form a(n) **(6)** _____ pattern. This pattern has bright bands that are

(7) _____ than those produced by a double slit, and the dark regions

are **(8)** _____. The pattern makes it easier to distinguish individual

(9) _____ and to measure **(10)** _____ more precisely.

The equation used in the calculation states that x/L is equal to **(11)** _____,

where the variable in the denominator is the **(12)** _____ between the grating's

lines. Instead of measuring the distance from the central band to the first bright band, most laboratory

instruments measure the **(13)** _____ between them. The symbol for that

quantity is **(14)** _____. The instrument used for the measurement is called a

(15) _____.

19 Study Guide

• • • • • • • • • • • • • •

In your textbook, read about determining wavelength with diffraction gratings.
Circle the letter of the choice that best completes the statement or answers the question.

16. For a diffraction grating, the wavelength equals _____.

    a. $\sin d$ **b.** $\sin d\theta$ **c.** $d/\sin \theta$ **d.** $d \sin \theta$

17. When monochromatic light is used with a diffraction grating, what is produced?

    a. no diffraction pattern

    b. no central band, but bright bands to the left and right

    c. a bright central band with bright bands to the left and right

    d. a dark central band with white bands to the left and right

18. How do the screen locations of the red lines produced by red light shone on a diffraction grating compare with the locations of the red lines produced by white light?

    a. Those produced by the red light are above.

    b. Those produced by the red light are to the left.

    c. Those produced by the white light are closer together.

    d. They are in the same places.

19. The sine of the angle between bright bands is approximately equal to _____.

    a. d/L **b.** L/x **c.** x/L **d.** d/x

20. Which quantity is read directly from the calibrated base of a grating spectrometer?

    a. θ **b.** λ **c.** f **d.** c

In your textbook, read about telescope and microscope resolution.
For each of the statements below, write true *or rewrite the italicized part to make the statement true.*

21. _____ Decreasing the width of a lens used in a telescope causes the diffraction pattern to become *narrower.*

22. _____ Two stars will be just resolved if the central bright band of one star falls on the *first dark band* of the second star.

23. _____ The diffraction pattern formed by blue light in a microscope is *wider* than that formed by red light.

24. _____ Using a larger lens is practical in reducing effects of diffraction on the resolving power of *both microscopes and telescopes.*

25. _____ *White* light would be more useful than green light in reducing diffraction patterns formed in a microscope.

26. _____ Telescope diffraction causes light from a star to appear *brighter.*

    Physics: Principles and Problems

20 Study Guide

Static Electricity

Vocabulary Review

Write the term that correctly completes each statement. Use each term once.

charged	coulomb	elementary charge
charging by conduction	Coulomb's law	insulators
charging by induction	electroscope	neutral
conductors	electrostatics	plasma

1. _____ Materials through which charges will not move easily are electrical _____.

2. _____ The study of electrical charges that can be collected and held in one place is _____.

3. _____ A(n) _____ is a device used to determine charge.

4. _____ The magnitude of the charge of an electron is the _____.

5. _____ Separating the charges in an object without touching the object is _____.

6. _____ Materials such as metals are electrical _____. They allow charges to move about easily.

7. _____ The positive charge in _____ objects exactly balances the negative charge.

8. _____ Giving a neutral body a charge by touching it with a charged body is _____.

9. _____ The magnitude of the force between charge q_A and charge q_B, separated by a distance d, is proportional to the magnitude of the charges and inversely proportional to the square of the distance; this is a statement of _____.

10. _____ The _____ is the SI standard unit of charge.

11. _____ A(n) _____ is a gaslike state of negatively charged electrons and positively or negatively charged ions.

12. _____ An object that exhibits electrical interaction after rubbing is said to be _____.

Name _____

20 Study Guide

• • • • • • • • • • • • • •

Section 20.1: Electrical Charge

In your textbook, read about charged objects.

Circle the letter of the choice that best completes each statement.

1. Electricity caused by rubbing is _____.

   a. static electricity

   b. lightning

   c. current electricity

   d. charge

2. An object that exhibits electrical interaction after rubbing is said to be _____.

   a. positive

   b. electrical

   c. charged

   d. negative

3. Two objects with the same type of charge _____.

   a. have no affect on each other

   b. repel each other

   c. attract each other

   d. have to be positive

4. Two objects with opposite charges _____.

   a. have no affect on each other

   b. repel each other

   c. attract each other

   d. have to be negative

5. Two types of charges are _____.

   a. yellow and green

   b. top and bottom

   c. attractive and repulsive

   d. positive and negative

In your textbook, read about charged objects.

Complete the chart below by marking the appropriate column for the charge on each material after it is rubbed.

Table 1		
Material	**Positively charged**	**Negatively charged**
6. plastic		
7. wool		
8. hard rubber		
9. fur		
10. glass		

In your textbook, read about the microscopic reasons for charge.

Answer the following questions.

11. What are the negative and positive parts of an atom?

_____

20 Study Guide

• • • • • • • • • • • • • •

12. How can an atom become charged?

_____

13. What happens when two neutral objects, such as rubber and fur, are rubbed together?

_____

In your textbook, read about conductors and insulators.
Decide whether the examples below are insulators or conductors. Mark the correct column.

Table 2		
Example	**Insulator**	**Conductor**
14. a material through which a charge will not move easily		
15. glass		
16. air as a plasma		
17. aluminum		
18. an object, held at the midpoint and rubbed only one end, becomes charged only at the rubbed end		
19. copper		
20. dry wood		
21. a material through which charges move about easily		
22. graphite		
23. charges removed from one area are not replaced by charges from another area		
24. most plastics		
25. dry air		
26. charges applied to one area spread quickly over the entire object		

Section 20.2: Electrical Force

In your textbook, read about forces on charged bodies and lightning.
For each of the statements below, write true *or rewrite the italicized part to make the statement true.*

1. There are *two* kinds of electrical charges, positive and negative.

_____

2. Charges *cannot* exert force on other charges over a distance.

_____

20 Study Guide

• • • • • • • • • • • • • • • •

3. The force between two charged objects is *weaker* when the objects are closer together.

_____

4. *Opposite* charges repel.

_____

5. If an electroscope is given a *positive* charge, the leaves will spread.

_____

6. Neutral objects can attract charged objects because of separation of charge in the *charged* object.

_____

7. Lightning bolts *discharge* clouds.

_____

In your textbook, read about electroscopes.
Refer to the drawings to answer the following questions.

8. What is the net charge on the electroscope?

_____

_____

9. By what method is the electroscope being charged?

_____

_____

_____

_____

10. The electroscope has a net negative charge. What will happen if the electroscope is touched with an object that has a negative charge?

_____

_____

11. What will happen if the electroscope is touched with an object that has a positive charge?

_____

_____

_____

20 Study Guide

••••••••••••••

12. What is the charge on the metal sphere A?

_____

13. By what method are these metal spheres being charged?

_____

In your textbook, read about Coulomb's law.
Circle the letter of the choice that best completes each statement.

According to Coulomb's law, the magnitude of the force on a charge q_A caused by charge q_B a distance d away can be written $F = K(q_A q_B / d^2)$.

14. The force, F, _____ with the square of the distance between the centers of two charged objects.

   a. varies directly

   b. varies inversely

   c. varies negatively

   d. doesn't vary

15. The force, F, _____ with the charge of two charged objects.

   a. varies directly

   b. varies inversely

   c. varies negatively

   d. doesn't vary

16. When the charges are measured in coulombs, the distance is measured in meters, and the force is measured in newtons, the constant, K, is _____

   a. 1

   b. 1.60×10^{-19} C

   c. 9.0×10^9 N·m^2/C^2

   d. unknown

20 Study Guide

· · · · · · · · · · · · · · · · ·

17. Coulomb's law can be used to determine _____ of an electrical force.

   a. the direction

   b. the magnitude

   c. the charge

   d. both the magnitude and the direction

In your textbook, read about the application of electrical forces on neutral bodies.
Answer the following questions.

18. According to Newton's third law of motion, how is a neutral object affected by a charged object?

_____

_____

_____

_____

_____

19. Give two examples of applications of electrical forces on neutral particles.

_____

_____

_____

_____

_____

21 Study Guide

Use with Chapter 21.

Electric Fields
Vocabulary Review

Circle the letter of the choice that best completes each statement.

1. The unit used to measure the electric potential difference is the _____.

   a. volt

   b. voltmeter

   c. coulomb

   d. joule

2. The _____ of a charged object exerts force on other charged objects.

   a. charge

   b. capacitance

   c. electric field

   d. voltage

3. The ratio of charge to potential difference of an object is its _____.

   a. capacitance

   b. capacity

   c. voltage

   d. electric potential difference

4. The instrument that measures potential difference is the _____.

   a. voltmeter

   b. ammeter

   c. potential difference meter

   d. capacitor

5. The direction and strength of an electric field are depicted by _____ .

   a. tangents

   b. electric field lines

   c. spokes

   d. magnetic field lines

6. The change in potential energy per unit charge is _____.

   a. volt

   b. work

   c. electric potential difference

   d. capacitance

7. Touching an object to Earth to eliminate excess charge is _____.

   a. connecting

   b. equalizing

   c. recharging

   d. grounding

8. A device that stores charge by having a specific capacitance is a(n) _____.

   a. charge holder

   b. battery

   c. capacitor

   d. electric field

9. Capacitance is measured in _____.

   a. coulombs

   b. volts

   c. ohms

   d. farads

10. Electric charge may be visible as a(n) _____ on a power line.

    a. corona

    b. electric field line

    c. electric vector

    d. plasma

21 Study Guide

Section 21.1: Creating and Measuring Electric Fields

In your textbook, read about electric fields.
Answer the following questions, using complete sentences.

11. What produces an electric field?

_____

12. Why must you use a test charge to observe an electric field?

_____

13. How does Coulomb's law relate to test charges?

_____

_____

14. If arrows represent electric field vectors in a picture of an electric field, how are the magnitude and direction of the field shown?

_____

_____

15. How do you find the electric field from two charges?

_____

_____

16. Why should an electric field be measured only by a small test charge?

_____

_____

_____

In your textbook, read about models for electric fields.
Answer the following questions.

17. Explain what a Van de Graaff machine is and one way it can be used to show field lines.

_____

_____

_____

18. Do field lines and electric fields really exist? How are field lines and electric fields useful?

_____

_____

_____

21 Study Guide

In your textbook, read about electric field vectors.
Refer to the illustration to answer the following questions.

19. At what point is the magnitude of the electric field the greatest? Explain how you can tell from the drawing that this is true.

   _____

   _____

   _____

20. Points B and C are the same distance from the field charge. What could cause the force measured on a test charge at point B to be twice as large as the force measured on a test charge at point C?

   _____

   _____

   _____

21. If an arrow representing the electric field were drawn at point D, how long would it be relative to the other arrows in the drawing? Why?

   _____

   _____

In your textbook, read about electric field lines.
Answer the following questions.

22. Draw two electric charges, one positive and one negative. Assume they are so far apart that there is no interaction between the charges.

23. Draw electric field lines around each charge. Show that the field around the negative charge is twice as strong as the field around the positive charge.

21 Study Guide

Name _____

Section 21.2: Applications of Electric Fields

In your textbook, read about electric potential.

Circle the letter of the choice that best completes the statement or answers the question.

1. Which equation defines the electric potential difference?

    a. $E = F/q'$

    b. $\Delta V = \Delta V_e/q'$

    c. $V = J/C$

    d. $q = mg/E$

2. When you do positive work on a two-charge system, the electric potential energy _____.

    a. increases

    b. decreases

    c. does not change

    d. always disappears

3. Only _____ electric potential can be measured.

    a. points of

    b. absolute values of

    c. differences in

    d. attractions between

4. The electric potential _____ when a positive charge is moved toward a negative charge.

    a. increases

    b. stays the same

    c. decreases

    d. becomes positive

5. A positive test charge is located at point A. If the test charge is moved to some point B and then back to point A, what is the change in the electric potential?

    a. The electric potential increases.

    b. The electric potential decreases.

    c. The electric potential becomes zero.

    d. The electric potential does not change.

In your textbook, read about electric potential and uniform fields.

For each of the statements below, write true *or rewrite the italicized part to make the statement true.*

6. Two large, flat conducting plates parallel to each other can create a constant electric force and field. *Both are charged negatively.*

    _____

7. The direction of an electric field between two parallel conducting plates is *from the positive plate to the negative plate.*

    _____

8. The *electrical* difference between two points a distance d apart in a uniform field is represented by the equation $\Delta V = Ed$.

    _____

9. The potential increases in the direction *opposite* the electric field direction.

    _____

10. The potential is *lower* near the positively charged plate.

    _____

Physics: Principles and Problems

21 Study Guide

• • • • • • • • • • • • • •

In your textbook, read about Millikan's oil-drop experiment.

Write the term that correctly completes each statement. Use each term once.

charged	gravitational field	multiple	suspended
electric field	ionized	potential difference	uniform
electron	magnitude		

Millikan used a(n) **(11)** _____ electric field between two parallel plates to

measure the charge on an electron. **(12)** _____ oil drops between the plates fell

from the air unless the **(13)** _____ between the two plates was adjusted. When

the top plate was positive enough, an oil drop was **(14)** _____ between the

plates. At this adjustment, the force of Earth's **(15)** _____ and the force of the

(16) _____ were the same magnitude. From the **(17)** _____

of the electric field, the charge on the drop was calculated. When Millikan **(18)** _____

the air to add or remove electrons from the drops, the change in the charge of a drop was always a

(19) _____ of 1.6×10^{-19} C. Therefore, Millikan proposed that each

(20) _____ always carried that charge.

In your textbook, read about objects sharing a charge.

Refer to the illustration. For each of the statements below, write true *or rewrite the italicized part to make the statement true.*

21. In drawing A, the electric potential of *sphere 1* is high.

_____

22. When the spheres touch, negative charges flow from *sphere 2 to sphere 1.*

_____

23. When the spheres touch, the potential of sphere *2 decreases* and the potential of sphere 1 decreases.

_____

24. In drawing B, the potential of sphere 1 now *equals* the potential of sphere 2.

_____

25. If sphere 2 were smaller than sphere 1, the two spheres *would not* have reached the same potential by touching.

_____

Metal spheres of equal size

21 Study Guide

In your textbook, read about grounding and conductors.

Answer the following questions.

26. Why can an object be touched to Earth to eliminate excess charge on a body?

_____

_____

27. Give one example of an object that requires grounding to prevent damage or injury.

_____

_____

_____

28. Explain why people inside a car are protected from electric fields generated by lightning.

_____

29. Explain how a lightning rod works.

_____

_____

_____

_____

In your textbook, read about capacitance and capacitors.

Circle the letter of the answer that best completes each statement.

30. A small device invented by Pieter Van Musschenbroek that can store a large electric charge is the
_____ .

    a. capacitor   **c.** resistor

    b. Leyden jar   **d.** electric field

31. For a given shape and size of an object, the ratio of charge stored to _____ is a constant.

    a. resistance   **c.** current

    b. potential difference   **d.** size

32. All capacitors are made up of two _____, separated by an insulator.

    a. insulators   **b.** plates   **c.** conductors   **d.** wires

33. Capacitors are used in electric circuits to store _____ .

    a. charge   **b.** current   **c.** resistance   **d.** capacitance

34. The capacitance of a capacitor is _____ the charge on it.

    a. dependent on   **b.** linked to   **c.** changed by   **d.** independent from

22 Study Guide

Use with Chapter 22.

Current Electricity

Vocabulary Review

For each description on the left, write the letter of the matching item.

_____ **1.** a closed loop though which charges can flow

_____ **2.** the flow of positive charge

_____ **3.** a variable resistor or rheostat

_____ **4.** a flow of charged particles

_____ **5.** the property that determines how much current is present

_____ **6.** a flow of 1 C/s

_____ **7.** a circuit diagram

_____ **8.** a device that measures current

_____ **9.** several voltaic cells connected together

_____ **10.** device designed to have a specific resistance

_____ **11.** a connection that provides only one path for a current

_____ **12.** a device that measures the potential difference of a circuit

_____ **13.** a connection of two or more electric devices that provides more than one current path

_____ **14.** a device that converts light energy to electric energy

_____ **15.** 100 watts of electric energy delivered continuously and used for 1 h

a. ammeter

b. ampere

c. battery

d. conventional current

e. electric circuit

f. electric current

g. kilowatt-hour

h. parallel connection

i. photovoltaic cell

j. potentiometer

k. resistance

l. resistor

m. schematic

n. series connection

o. voltmeter

22 Study Guide

• • • • • • • • • • • • • •

Section 22.1: Current and Circuits

In your textbook, read about electric circuits.

Circle the letter of the choice that best completes the statement or answers the question.

1. If two conductors at different potential differences are connected by another conductor, charges flow from the conductor with the _____ potential difference to the conductor with the _____ potential difference.

   a. higher, lower   **b.** lower, higher   **c.** negative, positive.   **d.** medium, higher

2. If two conductors, A and B, are connected by another conductor, when does the flow of charge stop?

   a. when the potential difference of A is lower than the potential difference of B

   b. when the potential difference of A is higher than the potential difference of B

   c. when the potential difference of all conductors is equal

   d. never

3. Batteries and generators are both sources of _____.

   a. light   **c.** photovoltaic cells

   b. electric energy   **d.** kinetic energy

4. A(n) _____ is a closed loop that consists of a charge pump connected to a device that reduces the potential energy of the flowing charges.

   a. electric circuit   **c.** resistor

   b. generator   **d.** potentiometer

5. The potential energy lost by the charges moving through a device in a circuit is represented by _____.

   a. ΔV **c.** PE

   b. E **d.** qV

6. A general term that could refer to a battery, photovoltaic cell, or generator in a circuit is _____.

   a. ammeter   **c.** charge pump

   b. resistor   **d.** current

7. No generator is 100 percent efficient, and the kinetic energy that is not converted to electric energy usually _____.

   a. stays electric energy   **c.** becomes light energy

   b. becomes thermal energy   **d.** disappears

8. Because q is conserved, the net change in potential energy of the charges going completely around the circuit _____.

   a. must be zero

   b. is higher at the beginning than at the end

   c. is lower at the beginning than at the end

   d. is a negative number

22 Study Guide

• • • • • • • • • • • • • •

In your textbook, read about electric power.

Write the term that correctly completes each statement. Use each term once.

ammeter	coulomb	energy	power
ampere	electric current	potential difference	watts
charge			

Power measures the rate at which **(9)** _____ is transferred. The energy

carried by an electric current depends on the **(10)** _____ transferred and the

potential difference across which it moves. The unit used for quantity of electric charge is the

(11) _____. Thus, the rate of flow of electric charge, or

(12) _____, is measured in coulombs per second. One coulomb per second is

a(n) **(13)** _____. A(n) **(14)** _____ is used to measure cur-

rent. The **(15)** _____ of an electric device is found by multiplying the

(16) _____ by the current. The power, or energy delivered to the electric device

per second, is measured in joules per second, or **(17)** _____.

In your textbook, read about resistance.

For each of the statements below, write true *or rewrite the italicized part to make the statement true.*

18. _____ If you put a glass rod between two conductors that have a potential
difference between them, you will have *a very large current.*

19. _____ *Resistance* is measured by placing a potential difference across two
points on a conductor and measuring the current.

20. _____ Resistance is the ratio of the potential difference to the *charge.*

21. _____ The resistance of a conductor is measured in *ohms.*

22. _____ One ohm, 1Ω, is the resistance that permits a current of 1 A when
a *potential difference of 1 V* is applied across the resistance.

23. _____ A device that has a *changing resistance* and appears to be independent of the potential difference is said to obey Ohm's law.

24. _____ To reduce current, you need a large resistance in a *large volume.*

25. _____ Superconductors are materials that have *high* resistance.

22 Study Guide

Name _____

In your textbook, read about control of current.
Answer the following questions.

26. How does voltage affect the current that passes through a resistor?

_____

_____

27. How can the current be reduced if the voltage is kept constant?

_____

_____

28. Explain how a variable resistor, or potentiometer, works.

_____

_____

_____

_____

In your textbook, read about symbols used in schematic diagrams.
Complete the table below by writing the correct symbols or the names of components.

Component	Symbol	Component	Symbol
capacitor			
conductor		no electric connection	
fuse			
lamp			

22 Study Guide

• • • • • • • • • • • • •

In your textbook, read about schematic diagrams of circuits.

Complete the schematic diagrams below.

29. Label the components of the schematic diagram below.

30. Draw a schematic diagram for the circuit in the drawing below.

10 Ω

Current flow

3A

$$I = \frac{V}{R}$$

$$= \frac{30\ V}{10\ \Omega}$$

$$= 3\ A$$

30 V

31. Draw a schematic diagram for a circuit that has a battery, a lamp, a motor, a switch, and an ammeter, with a voltmeter across the motor.

22 Study Guide

Name _____

Section 22.2: Using Electrical Energy

In your textbook, read about resistors used to turn electric energy into thermal energy.
Circle the letter of the choice that best completes each statement.

1. A space heater, a hot plate, and the heating element in a hair dryer are designed to convert almost all the electric energy into _____.

   a. kinetic energy
   b. potential energy
   c. thermal energy
   d. solar energy

2. Household appliances that convert electric energy into thermal energy act as _____ when they are in a circuit.

   a. resistors   **b.** motors   **c.** ammeters   **d.** voltage dividers

3. When a charge moves through a resistor, its _____ is reduced.

   a. current
   b. potential difference
   c. resistance
   d. charge

4. The _____ dissipated in a resistor is proportional to the square of the current that passes through it and to the resistance.

   a. voltage   **b.** power   **c.** current   **d.** kinetic energy

5. A resistor gets hot because the power that cannot pass through it is changed _____.

   a. from thermal energy to electric energy
   b. from kinetic energy to thermal energy
   c. from electric energy to kinetic energy
   d. from electric energy to thermal energy

In your textbook, read about transmission of electric energy and power companies.
For each of the statements below, write true *or rewrite the italicized part to make the statement true.*

6. _____ When power is transmitted over long distances, energy is lost as *thermal* energy.

7. _____ To reduce the loss of energy during transmittal of power over long distances, either the current or the *voltage* must be reduced.

8. _____ All *wires* have some resistance, even though the resistance is small.

9. _____ Cables of high conductivity and *small* diameter are used to transmit power long distances to reduce the resistance and reduce loss of energy as thermal energy.

10. _____ Current can be reduced without reducing power, by increasing the *voltage*.

11. _____ Electric companies measure their energy sales in *joules per second times seconds*.

23 Study Guide

Use with Chapter 23.

Series and Parallel Circuits

Vocabulary Review

For each description on the left, write the letter of the matching item.

_____ **1.** circuit in which all current travels though each device

_____ **2.** short piece of metal that melts if too large a current passes through it

_____ **3.** occurs when a circuit forms that has a very low resistance

_____ **4.** circuit in which there are several different paths for a current

_____ **5.** automatic switch that opens a circuit when the current reaches some set value

_____ **6.** circuit that has some resistors in parallel and some in series

_____ **7.** value of a single resistor that could replace all resistors in a circuit without changing the current

_____ **8.** device used to measure the current in part of a circuit

_____ **9.** device used to measure the potential drop across some part of a circuit

_____ **10.** detects small differences in current caused by an extra current path and opens the circuit

_____ **11.** series circuit used to produce a voltage source from a higher-voltage battery

a. ammeter

b. circuit breaker

c. combination series-parallel circuit

d. equivalent resistance

e. fuse

f. ground-fault interrupter

g. parallel circuit

h. series circuit

i. short circuit

j. voltage divider

k. voltmeter

23 Study Guide

Section 23.1: Simple Circuits

In your textbook, read about current in series circuits.

Circle the letter of the choice that best completes the statement or answers the question.

1. The current is _____ a series circuit.

    a. higher at the beginning of   **c.** lower at the beginning of

    b. the same everywhere in   **d.** variable in

2. In an electric circuit, the increase in voltage provided by the generator or other energy source, ΔV_{source}, is equal to the _____ of voltage drops across the resistors.

    a. subtraction   **b.** multiplication   **c.** sum   **d.** average

3. Which of the following equations is not correct?

    a. $I = \dfrac{\Delta V_{source}}{(R_1 + R_2)}$ **c.** $I = \dfrac{\Delta V_{source}}{(R_1 + R_2 + R_3)}$

    b. $I = \dfrac{\Delta V_{source}}{R}$ **d.** $I = R_3 + \dfrac{\Delta V_{source}}{(R_1 + R_2)}$

4. Which of the following equations correctly computes the equivalent resistance for a series circuit with four resistors?

    a. $R = R_1 + R_2 + R_3 + R_4$ **c.** $\dfrac{1}{R} = \dfrac{1}{R_1} + \dfrac{1}{R_2} + \dfrac{1}{R_3} + \dfrac{1}{R_4}$

    b. $R = R_1 \times R_2 \times R_3 \times R_4$ **d.** $R = \dfrac{(R_1 \times R_2)}{(R_3 \times R_4)}$

5. In a series circuit, the equivalent resistance is _____ any single resistance.

    a. larger than   **c.** equal to

    b. determined by   **d.** smaller than

6. If the battery voltage does not change, adding more devices in series _____ the current.

    a. sometimes decreases   **c.** sometimes increases

    b. always decreases   **d.** always increases

7. Given the voltage of a series circuit, you first calculate _____ to find the current through the circuit.

    a. the voltage   **c.** the power

    b. the equivalent resistance   **d.** the equivalent voltage

23 Study Guide

In your textbook, read about voltage drops in series circuits.
Answer the following questions, using complete sentences.

8. Why must the net change in potential be zero as current moves through a circuit?

_____

_____

_____

_____

_____

9. How do you find the potential drop across an individual resistor?

_____

_____

_____

10. What type of circuit is used in a voltage divider?

_____

_____

11. What is the purpose of a voltage divider?

_____

_____

_____

12. What determines the resistance of a photoresistor?

_____

_____

_____

13. Why are photoresistors often used in voltage dividers? In what special devices can they be used?

_____

_____

_____

_____

23 Study Guide

• • • • • • • • • • • • • •

In your textbook, read about parallel circuits.
Refer to the circuit diagram below. Circle the letter of the best answer for each question.

14. What type of circuit does this diagram represent?

   a. series circuit

   b. parallel circuit

   c. combination series-parallel circuit

   d. tandem circuit

15. How many current paths are in this circuit?

   a. one

   b. four

   c. three

   d. five

16. How would you calculate the total current of this circuit?

   a. Total current is found by computing the average of the currents through each path.

   b. Total current is found by adding the currents through each path.

   c. Total current is found by subtracting the currents through each path.

   d. Total current cannot be calculated for this circuit.

17. If the 10-Ω resistor were removed from the circuit, which of the following would *not* be true?

   a. The current through the 20-Ω resistor would be unchanged.

   b. The sum of the current in the branches of the circuit would change.

   c. The total current through the generator would change.

   d. The current through the 50-Ω resistor would change.

18. Which of the following is true for this circuit?

   a. The equivalent resistance of this circuit is smaller than 10 Ω.

   b. $R = R_1 + R_2 + R_3$

   c. $R = \dfrac{1}{R_1} + \dfrac{1}{R_2} + \dfrac{1}{R_3}$

   d. $R = R_1 \times R_2 \times R_3$

23 Study Guide

Name _____

Section 23.2: Applications of Circuits

In your textbook, read about safety devices.

For each of the statements below, write true *or rewrite the italicized part to make it true.*

1. When appliances are connected in *parallel,* each additional appliance placed in operation reduces the equivalent resistance in the circuit and causes more current to flow through the wires.

_____

2. The *length* of the metal in a fuse determines the amount of current that will melt the fuse and break the circuit.

_____

3. When a circuit breaker *opens,* it allows current to flow.

_____

4. Ground-fault interrupters can be used as safety devices on circuits in which the current flows along *a single path* from the power source into the electric outlet and back to the source.

_____

5. Electric wiring in homes uses only *series* circuits.

_____

6. Low resistance causes the current to be very *small* and may result in a short circuit.

_____

In your textbook, read about combined series-parallel circuits.

Circle the letter of the choice that best answers the question.

7. Which diagram represents a combined series-parallel circuit in which a 30-Ω resistor and a 75-Ω resistor are connected in parallel to a 125-V source through a 2-Ω resistor in series?

a.

c.

b.

d.

23 Study Guide

• • • • • • • • • • • • • • •

In your textbook, read about ammeters and voltmeters.
Redraw the circuit diagram below according to the following directions.

8. Insert an ammeter in the circuit that would measure the current of the entire circuit.

9. Insert an ammeter in the circuit that would measure the current that flows through the 60-Ω resistor.

10. Insert a voltmeter that would measure the voltage drop across the 10-Ω resistor.

Write the term that correctly completes each statement. Use each term once.

ammeter	low	series
high	parallel	voltmeter

A(n) **(11)** _____ measures current. It is placed in

(12) _____ with the resistor if you want to measure the current through

a resistor. So that it will change the current as little as possible, its resistance should be as

(13) _____ as possible. A(n) **(14)** _____ measures the

voltage drop across a resistor. It should be connected in **(15)** _____ with a

resistor to measure the potential drop across that resistor. So that it will change the current as little as

possible, its resistance should be as **(16)** _____ as possible.

Physics: Principles and Problems

24 Study Guide

Magnetic Fields

Vocabulary Review

For each description on the left, write the letter of the matching item.

_____ **1.** a current-carrying coil of wire that has a north pole and a south pole

_____ **2.** the strength of a magnetic field

_____ **3.** used to find the direction of the magnetic field around a current-carrying wire

_____ **4.** the combined magnetic fields of electrons in a group of atoms

_____ **5.** used to find the direction of the magnetic field around an electromagnet

_____ **6.** used to find the direction of the force on a current-carrying wire in a magnetic field

_____ **7.** a device used to measure very small currents

_____ **8.** the number of magnetic field lines passing through a surface

_____ **9.** having a north pole and a south pole

_____ **10.** the magnetic forces that exist around magnets

_____ **11.** imaginary lines used to help visualize a magnetic field

_____ **12.** a long coil of wire consisting of many loops

_____ **13.** a device that converts electrical energy to kinetic energy

_____ **14.** several rotating loops of wire in an electric motor

a. armature

b. domain

c. electric motor

d. electromagnet

e. first right-hand rule

f. galvanometer

g. magnetic field

h. magnetic field lines

i. magnetic flux

j. magnetic induction

k. polarized

l. second right-hand rule

m. solenoid

n. third right-hand rule

24 Study Guide

Section 24.1 Magnets: Permanent and Temporary

In your textbook, read about magnets.

For each of the statements below, write true *or rewrite the italicized part to make it true.*

1. _____ When a magnet is allowed to swing freely, it comes to rest lined up in *an east-west* direction.

2. _____ A *compass* is a small magnet mounted so that it is free to turn.

3. _____ Like poles *attract* each other.

4. _____ Magnets *do not always* have two opposite poles.

5. _____ If Earth is considered a giant magnet, the south pole of the Earth-magnet is near Earth's *geographic north pole.*

6. _____ Many permanent magnets are made of *pure iron.*

In your textbook, read about magnetic fields.

Answer the following questions, using complete sentences.

7. Describe one method for showing the magnetic field around a magnet.

   _____

   _____

   _____

8. What does *magnetic flux* mean in terms of both magnetic field lines and magnetic field strength? Where is it greatest on a magnet?

   _____

   _____

   _____

9. Describe the direction and shape of magnetic field lines of a bar magnet.

   _____

   _____

   _____

   _____

10. Describe three things that happen when a sample made of iron, cobalt, or nickel is placed in the magnetic field of a permanent magnet.

    _____

    _____

    _____

    _____

24 Study Guide

In your textbook, read about magnetic fields around current-carrying wires and electromagnets.
Answer the following questions, using complete sentences.

11. In the drawing at the right, what is the direction of the conventional current?

_____

12. Is the strength of the magnetic field greater at point A or point B?

_____

_____

13. Describe the direction of the magnetic field inside and outside of the loop, shown at the right.

_____

_____

14. In the drawing of an electromagnet shown below, which end is the magnetic north pole?

_____

_____

15. Describe two ways to increase the strength of the magnetic field around an electromagnet, besides placing an iron rod inside the coil.

_____

_____

_____

In your textbook, read about domains in magnetic materials.
For each of the statements below, write true *or* false.

_____ **16.** The magnetic fields of the electrons in a group of neighboring atoms cannot combine together.

_____ **17.** When a piece of iron is not in a magnetic field, the domains point in random directions.

_____ **18.** In permanent magnets, the domains point in random directions.

_____ **19.** The material on the tape for a recorder is chosen so that the alignment of the domains is only temporary.

_____ **20.** The direction of the magnetization in different rocks on the seafloor varies, indicating that the north and south poles of Earth have exchanged places many times.

24 Study Guide

Name _____

Section 24.2: Forces Caused by Magnetic Fields

In your textbook, read about forces on current-carrying wires in magnetic fields.
Circle the letter of the choice that best completes each statement.

1. The force on a current-carrying wire in a magnetic field is _____ both the direction of the magnetic field and the direction of current.

   a. parallel to   **b.** at right angles to   **c.** opposite   **d.** independent of

2. The magnitude of the force on a current-carrying wire in a magnetic field is proportional to _____.

   a. the strength of the field, the current in the wire, and the length of the wire in the magnetic field

   b. only the strength of the field

   c. only the strength of the field and the current in the wire

   d. the strength of the field, the current in the wire, and the voltage in the wire

3. Magnetic induction is measured in _____.

   a. newtons   **b.** teslas   **c.** amperes   **d.** volts

4. The direction of Earth's magnetic field is toward the _____.

   a. equator   **c.** south magnetic pole

   b. north magnetic pole   **d.** surface

In your textbook, read how to find the direction of force on a current-carrying wire in a magnetic field.
Answer the following questions, using complete sentences.

5. In the drawing at the right, what is the direction of the force on the current-carrying wire?

   _____

6. In the drawing at the right, what is the direction of the force on the current-carrying wire?

   _____

7. Are the current-carrying wires in the drawing at the right attracted or repelled?

   _____

142 *Study Guide*   *Physics: Principles and Problems*

24 Study Guide

Name _____

In your textbook, read about uses of the force on a current-carrying wire in a magnetic field.
For each of the following statements, write true *or* false.

_____ **8.** A loudspeaker changes sound energy into electrical energy.

_____ **9.** The amplifier driving the loudspeaker sends a current through a coil of wire mounted on a paper cone and placed in a magnetic field.

_____ **10.** The force exerted on the coil of wire in a magnetic field in a loudspeaker pushes the coil into or out of the field, depending on the magnitude of the current.

_____ **11.** The forces exerted on a current-carrying loop of wire in a magnetic field cannot be used to measure current.

_____ **12.** In an electric motor, the loop of current-carrying wire must rotate 180°.

In your textbook, read about galvanometers.
Write the term that correctly completes each statement. Use each term once.

current	loop	proportional	torque
direction	magnetic fields	series	voltmeter
down	multiplier	spring	wire
galvanometers	parallel		

(13) _____ that exert forces on a loop of wire carrying a current can be used to measure very small currents. A small loop of **(14)** _____ that is carrying a current is placed in the strong magnetic field of a permanent magnet. The current passing through the

(15) _____ goes in one end and out the other. The **(16)** _____ of the force on the wire resulting from the magnetic field can be determined by using the third right-hand rule. One side of the loop is forced **(17)** _____; the other side of the loop is forced up. The resulting **(18)** _____ rotates the loop. The magnitude of the torque acting on the loop is proportional to the magnitude of the **(19)** _____. This principle is used in **(20)** _____ to measure small currents. A small spring in a galvanometer exerts a torque that opposes the torque resulting from the current; thus the amount of torque is

(21) _____ to the current. A galvanometer can be used as a(n)

(22) _____ or an ammeter. A galvanometer can be converted to an ammeter by connecting it in **(23)** _____ with a resistor having a resistance smaller than that of the galvanometer. To convert the galvanometer to a voltmeter, the galvanometer is connected in

(24) _____ with a resistor called a **(25)** _____.

Physics: Principles and Problems

24 Study Guide

In your textbook, read about force exerted on charged particles by magnetic fields.
Answer the following questions, using complete sentences.

26. Explain how pictures form on the screen of a cathode-ray tube in a computer monitor or television set.

_____

_____

_____

_____

_____

27. On what does the force produced by a magnetic field on a single electron depend?

_____

_____

_____

28. Why is the direction of the force on an electron in a magnetic field opposite to the direction given by the third right-hand rule?

_____

_____

29. Why does a charged particle in a uniform magnetic field have a circular path?

_____

_____

_____

30. What do high-energy nuclear-particle accelerators use magnets for, and how does this process work?

_____

_____

31. Explain what causes the aurora borealis.

_____

_____

_____

_____

_____

25 Study Guide

Electromagnetic Induction

Vocabulary Review

Circle the letter of the choice that best completes each statement.

1. The induction of *EMF* in a wire carrying changing current is _____.
   a. mutual inductance
   b. magnetic induction
   c. electromotive force
   d. self-inductance

2. The part of a transformer that is connected to a source of AC voltage is the _____.
   a. armature   b. primary coil   c. secondary coil   d. core

3. The potential difference given to charges by a charge pump is the _____.
   a. electromotive force   b. current   c. electronic force   d. eddy current

4. The law that states that the direction of the induced current is such that the magnetic field resulting from the induced current opposes the change in the field that caused the induced current is _____.
   a. Ohm's law   b. Newton's law   c. Faraday's law   d. Lenz's law

5. Generating a current in a circuit by relative motion between a wire and a magnetic field is _____.
   a. electromagnetic induction
   b. magnetism
   c. electric induction
   d. current induction

6. A device that increases the voltage is a _____.
   a. step-down transformer
   b. step-up transformer
   c. capacitor
   d. generator

7. A varying *EMF* is induced in the _____ of a transformer.
   a. primary coil   b. secondary coil   c. tertiary coil   d. armature

8. A(n) _____ increases or decreases AC voltages.
   a. generator   b. armature   c. transformer   d. electric motor

9. The induction of an *EMF* in one coil as a result of a varying magnetic field in another coil is _____.
   a. self-inductance
   b. electric induction
   c. mutual inductance
   d. magnetic induction

10. A(n) _____ converts mechanical energy to electric energy.
    a. electric generator   b. electric motor   c. transformer   d. capacitor

11. A(n) _____ is used to decrease voltage.
    a. step-up transformer
    b. step-down transformer
    c. electric generator
    d. electric motor

12. When a piece of metal moves through a magnetic field, _____ are produced. They produce a magnetic field that opposes the motion that caused them.
    a. resistances   b. electromagnets   c. permanent magnets   d. eddy currents

25 Study Guide

Section 25.1: Creating Electric Current from Changing Magnetic Fields

In your textbook, read about production of an electric current with a magnetic field.

Circle the letter of the choice that best completes each statement.

1. Michael Faraday found that _____ could be produced by moving a wire through a magnetic field.

   a. a resistance   **b.** a current   **c.** charge   **d.** magnetism

2. When a wire is held stationary or moved _____ to a magnetic field, no current flows.

   a. parallel   **b.** perpendicular   **c.** tangent

3. An electric current is generated in a wire in a magnetic field only when _____.

   a. the wire is stationary in the field

   b. the wire cuts magnetic field lines

   c. the wire is moved parallel to the field

   d. a small current exists in the wire before it is placed in the magnetic field

4. To generate a current in a wire in a magnetic field, _____.

   a. the conductor must move through the magnetic field while the magnetic field remains stationary

   b. the magnetic field must move past the conductor while the conductor remains stationary

   c. there must be relative movement between the wire and the magnetic field

   d. there must be a battery connected to the wire

5. Electromotive force is not a force; it is a _____.

   a. current   **b.** resistance   **c.** charge   **d.** potential difference

6. *EMF* is measured in _____.

   a. volts   **b.** amperes   **c.** ohms   **d.** newtons

7. The *EMF* produced in a wire moving in a magnetic field depends only on the _____.

   a. field strength

   b. current in the wire

   c. magnetic field strength, the length of the wire in the field, and the velocity of the wire in the field

   d. magnetic field strength, the length of the wire in the field, and the current in the wire

8. If a wire moves through a magnetic field at an angle to the field, only the component of the wire's velocity that is _____ generates *EMF.*

   a. positive

   b. parallel to the direction of the magnetic field

   c. negative

   d. perpendicular to the direction of the magnetic field

25 Study Guide

• • • • • • • • • • • •

In your textbook, read about microphones and generators.
Answer the following questions, using complete sentences.

9. Explain how *EMF* is produced in a microphone.

_____

_____

_____

10. Explain how a sound wave is converted to an electric signal in a microphone.

_____

11. What is the purpose of an electric generator?

_____

12. Describe how an electric generator works.

_____

_____

13. What is one way to increase the induced *EMF* produced by a generator?

_____

14. Explain why the strength of the electric current changes as the armature of an electric generator turns.

_____

_____

_____

_____

15. Explain why the direction of the electric current changes as the armature of an electric generator turns.

_____

_____

_____

16. Compare and contrast electric generators and electric motors.

_____

_____

_____

_____

_____

25 Study Guide

• • • • • • • • • • • • •

In your textbook, read how to find the direction of a current induced in a wire by a changing magnetic field. *Answer the following questions.*

17. In the drawing on the right, in which direction does the current move?

_____

18. Which right-hand rule is used to find the direction of the current in the drawing on the right?

_____

19. The drawing above represents five positions of one side of a wire loop as it turns in a magnetic field. The current produced when the wire loop is in position A is indicated on the graph below. Mark the approximate points on the graph that correspond to positions B through E.

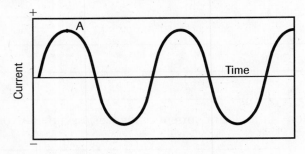

In your textbook, read about alternating-current generators.
For each of the statements below, write true *or rewrite the italicized part to make the statement true.*

20. _____ In the United States, electric utilities use generators with a *60-Hz* frequency.

21. _____ As the armature in a generator turns, the current *remains constant.*

22. _____ The power associated with an alternating current is *constant.*

23. _____ The power of an alternating current is always *positive.*

24. _____ Alternating current and voltage are often described in terms of their *effective* current and voltage.

25 Study Guide

Section 25.2: Changing Magnetic Fields Induce *EMF*

In your textbook, read about Lenz's law.

For each of the statements below, write true *or rewrite the italicized part to make the statement true.*

1. _____ When a current is produced in a wire by electromagnetic induction, the direction of the current is such that the magnetic field produces a force on the wire that *opposes* the original motion of the wire.

2. _____ The direction of an induced current is such that the magnetic field resulting from the induced current opposes *the field* that caused the induced current.

3. _____ If the N-pole of a magnet is moved toward the right end of the coil, the right end of the coil *attracts* the magnet and becomes an N-pole.

4. _____ If a generator produces a larger current, then the armature will be *more difficult* to turn.

5. _____ The opposing force on an armature means that mechanical energy must be supplied to the generator to produce electric energy; this fact is consistent with *the law of conservation of energy.*

In your textbook, read about applications of Lenz's law.

Answer the following questions, using complete sentences.

6. Explain why a large current flows when an electric motor is first turned on but is reduced as the motor begins to turn.

_____

_____

_____

_____

7. What can cause a spark when a motor's plug is pulled from an outlet?

_____

_____

8. How does a sensitive balance use Lenz's law to stop its oscillation?

_____

_____

_____

_____

25 Study Guide

Name _____

In your textbook, read about self-inductance.
Write the term that correctly completes each statement. Use each term once.

constant	*EMF*	magnetic field lines
current	increases	self-inductance
decreases	larger	zero

(9) _____ through a coil of wire generates a magnetic field. If the current

increases, the magnetic field **(10)** _____. This can be pictured as creation of new

(11) _____. As they expand, they cut through the coil of wires, generating a(n)

(12) _____ to oppose the current increase. This generating process is called

(13) _____. The faster the current changes, the **(14)** _____

the opposing *EMF* and the slower the current change. If the current reaches a steady value, the magnetic

field is **(15)** _____, and the *EMF* is **(16)** _____. When the

current **(17)** _____, the *EMF* generated helps prevent the reduction in magnetic

field and current.

In your textbook, read about transformers.
Circle the letter of the choice that best completes each statement.

18. Transformers can change _____ with relatively little loss of energy.

    a. power   **b.** resistances   **c.** voltages   **d.** magnetic fields

19. A transformer has _____ coils, electrically insulated from each other, but wound around the same
iron core.

    a. two   **b.** three   **c.** four   **d.** five

20. When the primary coil is connected to a source of AC voltage, the changing current creates a _____.

    a. steady magnetic field   **c.** varying magnetic field

    b. potential difference   **d.** resistance

21. In the secondary coil, the varying magnetic field induces a _____.

    a. varying *EMF*   **b.** steady *EMF*   **c.** resistance   **d.** charge

22. In a step-up transformer, the number of coils of wire in the primary coil is _____ the number of
coils in the secondary coil.

    a. equal to   **b.** less than   **c.** double   **d.** greater than

23. In an ideal transformer, the electric power delivered to the secondary circuit is _____ the power
supplied to the primary circuit.

    a. equal to   **b.** less than   **c.** double   **d.** greater than

        Physics: Principles and Problems

26 Study Guide

Use with Chapter 26.

Electromagnetism

Vocabulary Review

Write the letter of the choice that best completes each statement.

1. A wire that is connected to an alternating current source that forms or receives electromagnetic waves is a(n) _____.

   a. receiver   **b.** dish   **c.** antenna   **d.** cable

2. The combination of an antenna, coil and capacitor circuit, and amplifier is a _____.

   a. receiver   **c.** mass spectrometer

   b. radio   **d.** secondary antenna

3. Atoms that have the same chemical properties but different masses are _____.

   a. nuclides   **b.** isotopes   **c.** isomers   **d.** elements

4. Energy that is carried through space in the form of electromagnetic waves is _____.

   a. electromagnetic radiation   **c.** magnetic fields

   b. electric fields   **d.** electricity

5. Crystals that bend or deform when a voltage is applied across them show the property of _____.

   a. conductance   **c.** magnetism

   b. electromagnetic waves   **d.** piezoelectricity

6. An instrument that is used to find the masses of positive ions is a(n) _____.

   a. mass spectrometer   **c.** analytical scale

   b. precise balance   **d.** scintillation counter

7. Electromagnetic waves of relatively high frequency that are generated by accelerating electrons to high speeds using 20 000 or more volts and then crashing the electrons into matter are _____.

   a. gamma rays   **c.** X rays

   b. infrared rays   **d.** visible light rays

8. Electric and magnetic fields that move through space make up a(n) _____.

   a. electric current   **c.** static charge

   b. electromagnetic wave   **d.** electric wave

9. The type(s) of radiation with the longest wavelengths is(are) _____.

   a. microwaves   **c.** radio waves

   b. light   **d.** X rays and gamma rays

10. The type(s) of radiation with the highest frequency is(are) _____.

   a. ultraviolet   **c.** radio waves

   b. light   **d.** X rays and gamma rays

26 Study Guide

Section 26.1: Interaction Between Electric and Magnetic Fields and Matter

In your textbook, read about Thomson's experiment to measure the mass of an electron.

Refer to the diagram below. Write the term or letter that correctly completes each statement. Use each item once.

cathode-ray tube   electric field   magnitude

charge-to-mass ratio   electrons   straight path

circular path   forces   velocity

direction   magnetic field

Fluorescent coating

The **(1)** _____ of

an electron was first measured in 1897 by

J. J. Thomson. For his experiment, Thomson used

a(n) **(2)** _____ with all

of the air removed. An electric field accelerated

(3) _____ off the negatively

charged cathode, labeled **(4)** _____ in the diagram, toward the positively charged

anode, labeled **(5)** _____. Electrons that passed through a hole in the anode fol-

lowed a(n) **(6)** _____ toward a fluorescent screen, which glowed where the

electrons hit.

Electric and magnetic fields in the center of the tube exerted **(7)** _____

on the electrons. The **(8)** _____ was perpendicular to the beam of electrons.

The **(9)** _____ was at right angles to both the beam and the electric field. When the

electric field was stronger, the electrons struck the fluorescent screen at the point labeled

(10) _____. When the magnetic field was stronger, the electrons struck the

fluorescent screen at point **(11)** _____. When the electric and magnetic fields were

adjusted until the forces of the two fields were equal in **(12)** _____ and

opposite in **(13)** _____, the electrons struck the screen at point

(14) _____. The magnetic and electric field forces were balanced only for electrons

that had a specific **(15)** _____ If the electric field was turned off, only the force due

to the magnetic field remained, and the electrons followed a(n) **(16)** _____.

26 Study Guide

• • • • • • • • • • • • • •

In your textbook, read about Thomson's experiment to measure the mass of a proton.
For each of the statements below, write true *or* false.

_____ **17.** Positively charged particles, when they are in an electric field, bend the same direction as electrons.

_____ **18.** Positively charged particles, when they are in an magnetic field, bend the opposite way from electrons.

_____ **19.** When electrons are pulled off hydrogen atoms, the hydrogen has a net negative charge.

_____ **20.** The mass of the proton was determined from the charge-to-mass ratio.

_____ **21.** The mass of the proton was determined to be 9.107×10^{-31} kg.

In your textbook, read about mass spectrometers.
Circle the letter of the choice that best completes each statement.

22. When Thomson put neon gas into the tube, he found two dots on the screen instead of one, because neon has two _____.

    a. atoms   **b.** isomers   **c.** isotopes   **d.** masses

23. The masses of positive ions can be measured precisely using a(n) _____, an adaptation of a cathode-ray tube.

    a. ordinary balance   **c.** mass spectrometer

    b. analytic scale   **d.** ion accelerator

24. Accelerated _____ strike the ion source of a mass spectrometer, knocking off electrons and thus forming positive gas ions.

    a. electrons   **b.** protons   **c.** ions   **d.** atoms

25. In a mass spectrometer, a(n) _____ produces an electric field to accelerate the ions.

    a. magnetic field   **c.** antenna

    b. potential difference   **d.** magnet

26. The ions that are undeflected move into a region with a uniform magnetic field where they follow a(n) _____.

    a. narrow path   **b.** straight path   **c.** circular path   **d.** elliptical path

27. The charge-to-mass ratio of the ion is determined by the equation _____.

    a. $q/m = 2V/B^2r^2$ **b.** $r = mv/qB$ **c.** $KE = mv^2/2$ **d.** $q/m = 2V/Br$

28. In the mass spectrometer, the ions leave a mark when they hit a _____.

    a. fluorescent screen   **c.** glass screen

    b. cathode-ray tube   **d.** photographic film

29. Besides being used to measure the mass of positive ions, mass spectrometers can also _____.

    a. make negative ions from atoms   **c.** separate isotopes of atoms

    b. combine atoms   **d.** create isotopes of atoms

26 Study Guide

Section 26.2: Electric and Magnetic Fields in Space

In your textbook, read about electromagnetic waves.

For each of the statements below, write true *or rewrite the italicized part to make the statement true.*

1. _____ A changing magnetic field can produce a changing electric field *without* a wire.

2. _____ Maxwell postulated that a changing electric field produces a *constant* magnetic field.

3. _____ Either accelerating charges or changing magnetic fields can produce *combined electric and magnetic fields* that move through space, known as electromagnetic waves.

4. _____ Electromagnetic waves move at the speed of *sound.*

5. _____ In order of *increasing* wavelength, the types of radiation are radio waves, microwaves, infrared, light, ultraviolet, and X rays and gamma rays.

In your textbook, read about production of electromagnetic waves.

Circle the letter of the choice that best completes each statement.

6. The alternating current source connected to an antenna produces a _____.

   a. constant current that produces a constant electric field

   b. constant current that produces a changing electric field

   c. changing current that produces a constant electric field

   d. changing current that produces a changing electric field

7. The changing electric field produced by an antenna generates a _____.

   a. wind

   b. constant magnetic field

   c. changing magnetic field

   d. charge

8. The magnetic field of an electromagnetic wave oscillates _____ the electric field.

   a. parallel to

   b. at lower frequency than

   c. at higher frequency than

   d. at right angles to

9. The electric field and magnetic field of an electromagnetic wave are _____ the direction of the motion of the wave.

   a. at right angles to

   b. opposite to

   c. parallel to

   d. independent of

10. An electromagnetic wave produced by an antenna is _____.

   a. energetic

   b. out of phase

   c. faster than the speed of light

   d. polarized

26 Study Guide

• • • • • • • • • • • • •

In your textbook, read about using a coil and a capacitor to generate high-frequency electromagnetic waves.

For each of the statements below, write true *or rewrite the italicized part to make the statement true.*

11. _____ When the battery is removed from a circuit containing a coil and capacitor, the *coil* discharges and the stored electrons flow through the coil, creating a magnetic field.

12. _____ When the magnetic field of the coil collapses, a *back-EMF* recharges the capacitor in the opposite direction.

13. _____ To increase the oscillation frequency, the size of the coil and the capacitor must be made *larger*.

14. _____ Microwaves and infrared waves *cannot* be generated using a coil and capacitor and an antenna.

In your textbook, read about the pendulum analogy for the coil and capacitor circuit.
For each pendulum analogy, write the letter of the matching coil and capacitor property.

_____ 15. the pendulum bob

_____ 16. The pendulum bob moves fastest when its displacement from vertical is zero.

_____ 17. When the bob is at its greatest angle, it has zero velocity.

_____ 18. The potential energy of the pendulum is largest when its displacement is greatest. The kinetic energy is largest when the velocity is greatest.

_____ 19. The sum of the potential and kinetic energies and thermal energy losses of the pendulum is constant.

_____ 20. The pendulum will eventually stop swinging if it is left alone.

_____ 21. Gentle pushes applied at the correct times will keep a pendulum moving.

a. The largest current flows through the coil when the charge on the capacitor is zero.

b. When the current is largest, the energy stored in the magnetic field is greatest. When the current is zero, the electric field of the capacitor is largest.

c. Voltage pulses applied to the coil and capacitor circuit at the right frequency will keep the oscillations going.

d. the electrons in the coil and capacitor

e. When the capacitor holds the largest charge, the current through the coil is zero.

f. Oscillations of the coil and capacitor will die out if energy is not added to the circuit.

g. The sum of the magnetic field energy, the electric field energy, the thermal losses, and the energy carried away by electromagnetic fields is constant.

26 Study Guide

• • • • • • • • • • • • •

In your textbook, read about detection of electromagnetic waves.
Answer the following questions, using complete sentences.

22. Explain how electromagnetic waves are detected by an antenna.

_____

_____

23. An antenna designed to receive radio waves is much longer than one designed to receive microwaves. Why is there a size difference?

_____

_____

_____

24. Describe two ways in which the detected *EMF* can be increased.

_____

_____

_____

25. Explain how radio and television waves of a certain frequency can be selected. Describe briefly how selection works.

_____

_____

_____

In your textbook, read about X rays.
Circle the letter of the choice that best completes each statement.

26. If electrons have _____ kinetic energy with a very _____ voltage, X rays are produced when the electrons are stopped suddenly by matter.

    a. low, high   **c.** low, low

    b. high, high   **d.** high, low

27. X rays can penetrate _____, but are blocked by _____.

    a. lead, bone   **c.** bone, lead

    b. bone, soft body tissue   **d.** soft body tissue, bone

28. When electrons crash into matter, _____ are converted into X rays.

    a. the electrons   **c.** their potential energies

    b. their kinetic energies   **d.** the atoms in the matter

27 Study Guide

Use with Chapter 27.

Quantum Theory

Vocabulary Review

Circle the letter of the choice that best completes each statement.

1. For light to cause the emission of an electron of a specific metal, its frequency must be at least the _____.

   a. threshold frequency.

   b. work function

   c. de Broglie frequency

   d. emission frequency

2. Discrete bundles of energy of light and other forms of radiation are _____.

   a. quarks

   b. photons

   c. electromagnetic waves

   d. isotopes

3. The emission of electrons when electromagnetic radiation falls on an object is the _____.

   a. threshold frequency

   b. Heisenberg principle

   c. Compton effect

   d. photoelectric effect

4. _____ states that the position and momentum of a particle cannot be precisely known at the same time.

   a. The Heisenberg uncertainty principle

   b. The third law of motion

   c. The position uncertainty law

   d. Compton's law

5. The energy needed to free the most weakly bound electron from a metal is the _____ of the metal.

   a. threshold frequency

   b. minimum energy

   c. work function

   d. weak electron energy

6. The wavelength of a particle is referred to as its _____.

   a. photon

   b. de Broglie wavelength

   c. threshold wavelength

   d. Compton effect

7. The increase in wavelength of X-ray photons when they are scattered off electrons is the _____.

   a. Compton effect

   b. Heisenberg uncertainty principle

   c. X scatter effect

   d. photon principle

8. Energy that exists only in packages of specific amounts is _____.

   a. specified.   **b.** pulsing.   **c.** quantized.   **d.** discontinuous.

9. A body that is so hot that it glows is _____.

   a. incandescent   **b.** fluorescent   **c.** phosphorescent   **d.** radioactive

27 Study Guide

• • • • • • • • • • • • • •

Section 27.1: Waves Behave Like Particles

In your textbook, read about radiation from incandescent bodies.
For each of the following statements, write true *or rewrite the italicized part to make the statement true.*

1. _____ Hot bodies contain *charges*, which radiate electromagnetic waves.

2. _____ Light and infrared radiation are produced by the vibration of particles within *an incandescent body*.

3. _____ Energy is emitted from incandescent bodies at *one specific frequency* that depends on the temperature.

4. _____ As the temperature of a hot body increases, the frequency at which the maximum energy is emitted *decreases*.

5. _____ The total power emitted by an incandescent body *increases* with increasing temperature.

In your textbook, read about Planck's theory that energy is quantized.
Circle the letter of the choice that best completes the statement or answers the question.

6. Max Planck calculated the spectrum of radiation emitted from incandescent bodies based on his assumption that _____.

   a. energy is a wave   **c.** matter is a wave

   b. energy is not continuous   **d.** matter is a particle

7. In the equation $E = nhf$, which of the following is *not* a possible value of n?

   a. 0   **b.** 3   **c.** 5/4   **d.** 6

8. Planck's theory depends on the fact that _____.

   a. atoms always radiate electromagnetic waves

   b. atoms always radiate electromagnetic waves when they are vibrating

   c. atoms emit radiation only when their vibration energy changes

   d. atoms emit radiation only if they have a source of electricity

9. If the energy of an atom changes from an initial energy to a final energy, the energy radiated is equal to _____.

   a. the initial energy

   b. the final energy

   c. the product of the initial energy and the final energy

   d. the change in energy

10. Because the constant h is extremely _____, the energy-changing steps are too _____ to be noticeable in ordinary bodies.

   a. small, small   **c.** large, large

   b. large, small   **d.** small, large

27 Study Guide

Name _____

In your textbook, read about the photoelectric effect.

For each of the statements below, write true *or rewrite the italicized part to make the statement true.*

11. _____ The *absorption of energy* when electromagnetic radiation hits an object is called the photoelectric effect.

12. _____ Electromagnetic radiation of *any* frequency will eject electrons from a metal.

13. _____ If the frequency of the incident light shone on a metal is below the threshold frequency, no level of *intensity* will cause ejection of electrons.

14. _____ The *electromagnetic wave theory* cannot explain why electrons are ejected immediately even in dim light if the frequency of the radiation is at or above the threshold level.

In your textbook, read about Einstein's theories on the photoelectric effect.

Answer the following questions, using complete sentences.

15. How does Einstein's photoelectric-effect theory explain the existence of a threshold frequency?

_____

_____

_____

16. What does Einstein's theory say about conservation of energy?

_____

_____

_____

17. Why will all of the photoelectrons ejected from the same metal not have the maximum kinetic energy?

_____

_____

_____

18. Briefly describe an experiment that supports Einstein's theory for the photoelectric effect.

_____

_____

_____

_____

_____

Physics: Principles and Problems

27 Study Guide

Name _____

• • • • • • • • • • • • • •

In your textbook, read about the kinetic energy of photoelectrons.

Refer to the graphs below that show the maximum kinetic energy of photoelectrons versus frequency for two different metals. Then answer the questions.

19. What is the numerical value of the slope of the line in graph A? In graph B?

_____

20. To what constant are the slopes equal?

_____

21. How can you tell that these are graphs for two different metals?

_____

22. What is the approximate threshold frequency in graph A?

_____

23. What is the minimum frequency required to produce photoelectrons from the metal in graph B?

_____

24. At what frequency do the photoelectrons produced from the metal in graph A have no kinetic energy?

_____

25. Will a frequency of 1.0×10^{15} Hz eject electrons from the metal in graph B? Why or why not?

_____

26. What is the relationship between the frequency of the radiation and the kinetic energy of the photoelectrons?

_____

_____

27. How would you use the graphs to find the work function of these metals?

_____

_____

Physics: Principles and Problems

27 Study Guide

In your textbook, read about the Compton effect.
Answer the following questions, using complete sentences.

28. Which of Einstein's theories did Compton's experiment test?

_____

_____

29. Briefly describe Compton's experiment.

_____

_____

_____

30. What were the results of Compton's experiment?

_____

_____

_____

31. How is wavelength related to the energy of a photon?

_____

32. What did Compton's results mean?

_____

_____

33. In later experiments, Compton observed that electrons were ejected from the graphite block. What hypothesis did Compton suggest to explain this?

_____

_____

34. How did Compton test his hypothesis and what did he find?

_____

_____

_____

35. How is a photon like matter?

_____

36. How is a photon not like matter?

_____

27 Study Guide

. . . .

Section 27.2: Particles Behave Like Waves

In your textbook, read about the wave nature of matter.
Write the term that correctly completes each statement. Use each term once.

de Broglie wavelength	electrons	waves	$\lambda = h/p$
diffracted	objects	X rays	$p = h/\lambda$
diffraction grating	particles		

Louis-Victor de Broglie was first to suggest that particles could behave like

(1) _____. He proposed that the momentum of a particle is represented

by the equation **(2)** _____. Therefore, the wavelength of a particle is

(3) _____. The wavelength of a particle is known as the

(4) _____. One of the problems with de Broglie's theory was that effects such as

diffraction and interference had never been observed for **(5)** _____. Thomson

performed an experiment that showed that electrons are **(6)** _____ just as light

is. In his experiment, he aimed a beam of **(7)** _____ at a very thin crystal. The

crystal acted as a **(8)** _____. Electrons diffracted from the crystal formed the same

pattern that **(9)** _____ of a similar wavelength formed. The wave nature of most

(10) _____ is not observable because the wavelengths are extremely short.

In your textbook, read about the dual wave and particle description of light and matter.
Circle the letter of the choice that best completes each statement.

11. The spreading of light used to locate a particle can be reduced by _____ of the light.

   a. decreasing the wavelength   **c.** increasing the wavelength

   b. decreasing the frequency   **d.** increasing the intensity

12. The Compton effect means that, when light of short wavelengths strikes a particle, the _____ of
the particle is changed.

   a. size   **b.** momentum   **c.** charge   **d.** identity

13. According to the Heisenberg uncertainty principle, it is impossible to measure precisely both the
_____ and the _____ of a particle at the same time.

   a. charge, position   **c.** charge, mass

   b. position, momentum   **d.** wavelength, momentum

28 Study Guide

Use with Chapter 28.

The Atom

Vocabulary Review

Write the term that correctly completes each statement. Use each term once.

absorption spectrum   excited state   quantum number

α particle   ground state   scintillation

coherent light   incoherent light   spectroscope

electron cloud   laser   spectroscopy

emission spectrum   quantum mechanics   stimulated emission

energy level   quantum model

1. _____ A(n) _____ is a relatively massive, positively charged, fast-moving particle released by an atom.

2. _____ The lowest energy level for an electron is the _____.

3. _____ In _____, the light waves are in step.

4. _____ A small flash of light emitted by a detection screen is a(n) _____.

5. _____ A(n) _____ has dark lines in an otherwise continuous spectrum.

6. _____ A device that produces light by stimulated emission is a(n) _____.

7. _____ A(n) _____ is a quantized energy state of an electron in an atom.

8. _____ The _____ of an atom is the region in which there is a high probability of finding an electron.

9. _____ A field of physics that uses the quantum model of the atom to make predictions about atomic structure and behavior is _____.

10. _____ In _____, the light waves are not in step.

11. _____ A(n) _____ is the set of light wavelengths given off by an atom.

12. _____ The study of the light given off by atoms is _____.

13. _____ When atoms in an excited state are struck by other photons, they release photons in _____.

14. _____ The _____ predicts the probability that an electron is at a specific location.

15. _____ A device used to study the light given off by an atom is a(n) _____.

16. _____ The principal _____ determines the values of r and E.

17. _____ An electron that has absorbed energy is in a(n) _____.

28 Study Guide

• • • • • • • • • • • • • •

Section 28.1: **The Bohr Model of the Atom**

In your textbook, read about the nuclear model of the atom.

The diagram below shows an experiment, with a close-up of the atoms in area C. Refer to the diagram to answer the following questions.

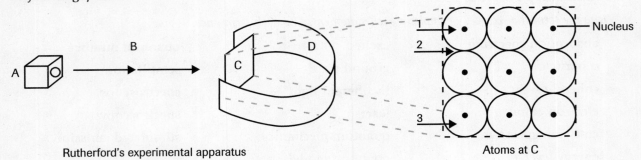

Rutherford's experimental apparatus

Atoms at C

1. What kind of material does container A hold?

_____

2. What makes up ray B? What characteristics does the ray have?

_____

_____

3. What type of material is C?

_____

4. What is D, and what role does it play?

_____

_____

5. What will happen to the particle labeled 1? Why?

_____

_____

6. What will happen to the particle labeled 2? Why?

_____

_____

7. What will happen to the particle labeled 3? Why?

_____

_____

8. Will most of the particles that pass into object C behave like particle 1, 2, or 3? What does that tell us about atoms?

_____

_____

9. From his experiment, what did Rutherford conclude about the atom and its component parts, including electrons?

_____

_____

In your textbook, read about spectra.
Circle the letter of the choice that best completes the statement or answers the question.

10. The spectrum of an incandescent solid is typically _____.

   a. a set of colored lines   **c.** a band of colors with dark lines

   b. a single colored line   **d.** a continuous band of colors

11. What information can an emission spectrum reveal about the elements present in a sample?

   a. their identities only

   b. their relative concentrations only

   c. both their identities and their relative concentrations

   d. neither their identities nor their relative concentrations

12. The Fraunhofer lines appear in the spectrum of _____.

   a. sodium   **b.** all flames   **c.** the moon   **d.** the sun

13. Which element was discovered through study of the Fraunhofer lines?

   a. hydrogen   **b.** helium   **c.** lithium   **d.** sodium

14. If the planetary theory of electrons were correct, at what wavelengths would light be released by an atom?

   a. at all wavelengths   **c.** at certain specific values

   b. in a band at the red end only   **d.** in a band at the violet end only

15. The visible spectrum of hydrogen consists of _____.

   a. two lines   **c.** a single narrow band

   b. four lines   **d.** a continuous wide band

16. The energy of a photon of light released by an atom is equal to _____.

   a. hc/λ **c.** λ/f

   b. $hc\lambda$ **d.** $h\lambda/f$

28 Study Guide

• • • • • • • • • • • • • •

17. What does the fact that an emission spectrum contains only certain wavelengths show about electrons?

a. Their energy is continuous.   **c.** They are present in the nucleus.

b. Their energy is quantized.   **d.** They have a negative charge.

In your textbook, read about the Bohr model of atoms.
For each of the statements below, write true *or rewrite the italicized part to make the statement true.*

18. _____ Bohr hypothesized that the laws of electromagnetism *do not* operate inside atoms.

19. _____ An electron *releases* energy when it moves from the ground state to an excited state.

20. _____ The orbits of electrons in excited states tend to be *smaller* than those of electrons in the ground state.

21. _____ According to the Bohr model, the energy of an *electron* in an atom is quantized.

22. _____ The electromagnetic radiation emitted by hydrogen when the electron drops into its ground state is *infrared waves*.

23. _____ The electromagnetic radiation emitted by hydrogen when the electron drops into the second energy level from higher levels is *visible light*.

In your textbook, read about the symbols used in Bohr's calculations.
For each term on the left, write the matching item.

_____	**24.** charge	λ
_____	**25.** Coulomb's constant	E
_____	**26.** angular momentum	h
_____	**27.** radius of orbit	K
_____	**28.** principal quantum number	mvr
_____	**29.** Planck's constant	n
_____	**30.** wavelength	q
_____	**31.** total energy	r

Section 28.2: The Quantum Model of the Atom

In your textbook, read about the shortcomings of the Bohr model of the atom and about the quantum model.
Circle the letter of the choice that best completes the statement or answers the question.

1. Which quantity equals a whole-number multiple of the wavelength of an electron?

a. r **c.** $2\pi r$

b. πr **d.** πr^2

28 Study Guide

2. The modern quantum model of the atoms precisely predicts _____ for an electron at a given moment.

  a. the probability of being at a specific location   **c.** position and velocity

  b. position and momentum   **d.** direction and position

3. The probability of finding an electron in the electron cloud of an atom is _____.

  a. zero   **b.** low   **c.** high   **d.** infinite

4. A shortcoming of the Bohr model of the atom is its inability to _____.

  a. provide correct values for the lines in the hydrogen spectrum

  b. explain why angular momentum is quantized

  c. explain chemical properties of the elements

  d. predict the ionization energy for hydrogen

5. Application of the theories of electromagnetism to Bohr's model predicted _____.

  a. a positive charge for electrons   **c.** great stability for the atom

  b. collapse of the atom   **d.** a highly diffuse nucleus

6. Wavelength of a particle is equal to _____.

  a. h/c **b.** mv/h **c.** h/mv **d.** mvr

7. Which of the following is *not* true of quantum theory?

  a. It is based on the wave model.

  b. It predicts the probability that the electron is at a given radius.

  c. It proposes a planetary picture of the atom.

  d. It can be used to give details of the structure of molecules.

8. The circumference of the Bohr orbit equals _____.

  a. $2\pi r$ **b.** πr^2 **c.** λ **d.** $\lambda/2\pi r$

9. Which of the following is true of n?

  a. It is always a negative number.   **c.** It may take on any value.

  b. It cannot be expressed as a number.   **d.** It is always a whole number.

In your textbook, read about the structure and operation of lasers.
Write the term that correctly completes each statement.

Light emitted by a(n) **(10)** _____ source has many wavelengths and moves in all

directions. Because the waves are out of step with each other, this light is **(11)** _____.

When an atom in an excited state is struck by a(n) **(12)** _____ with the correct

amount of energy, the atom will emit another **(13)** _____ of identical

(14) _____, which will be in step with the first one. In a laser, a flash of light

28 Study Guide

• • • • • • • • • • • • • •

that has a(n) **(15)** _____ wavelength than that of the laser is used to excite the

atoms. As the atoms decay to a(n) **(16)** _____ energy state, they lase, or give off

light by **(17)** _____ emission. As photons are produced, they strike other

(18) _____, which give off more photons. The photons are trapped inside a glass

(19) _____ capped at each end with parallel **(20)** _____,

one of which is 100% **(21)** _____. The other is only partially

(22) _____ and allows some of the photons through. Because all the photons

produced by the laser are in step, the light is **(23)** _____. The beam produced

is very narrow and thus very **(24)** _____. It also is all one wavelength, so it is

(25) _____.

In your textbook, read about applications of laser technology.
For each of the statements below, write true *or* false.

_____ **26.** A hologram is a photographic recording of the phase and intensity of light.

_____ **27.** Lasers are used in spectroscopy to remove atoms.

_____ **28.** Fiber optics transmits lasers, using total internal reflection.

_____ **29.** Laser beams spread out greatly over long distances.

_____ **30.** Lasers can cut a wide variety of materials.

29 Study Guide

Use with Chapter 29.

Solid State Electronics
Vocabulary Review

Write the term that correctly completes each statement. Use each term once.

band theory	extrinsic semiconductor	junction transistor
conduction band	forbidden gap	*n*-type semiconductor
depletion layer	forward-biased diode	*p*-type semiconductor
diode	hole	transistor
dopant	intrinsic semiconductor	valence band

1. _____ The lowest band that is not filled to capacity with electrons is the _____.

2. _____ A semiconductor that conducts by means of holes is a(n) _____.

3. _____ A(n) _____ conducts as a result of thermally freed electrons and holes.

4. _____ The highest band that contains electrons is the _____.

5. _____ A(n) _____ has a region of one type of doped semiconductor sandwiched between layers of the opposite type.

6. _____ A(n) _____ is produced by adding impurity atoms to a semiconductor.

7. _____ An impurity added to a semiconductor is a(n) _____.

8. _____ An empty energy level in the valence band is a(n) _____.

9. _____ A(n) _____ consists of a *p*-type semiconductor joined with an *n*-type semiconductor.

10. _____ The region around a diode junction that has neither holes nor free electrons is the _____.

11. _____ Any simple switch made of doped semiconducting material is a(n) _____.

12. _____ A semiconductor that conducts by means of electrons is a(n) _____.

13. _____ A range of energy values that no atom can possess is a(n) _____.

14. _____ The _____ of solids explains electric conduction in terms of energy bands and forbidden gaps.

29 Study Guide

Name _____

Section 29.1: Conduction in Solids

In your textbook, read about the band theory of solids.

For each of the statements below, write true *or rewrite the italicized part to make the statement true.*

1. _____ Electric charges are easy to displace in *conductors.*

2. _____ When two atoms are brought close together, their electric fields *don't affect* one another.

3. _____ When a large number of atoms is brought close together, their energy levels spread into *narrow* bands.

4. _____ There are forbidden gaps of energy for atoms that are *far apart* in large numbers.

5. _____ The band theory explains electric conduction in *gases.*

6. _____ The *inner bands* of atoms in a solid are full.

7. _____ The lowest band that is not filled to capacity with electrons is the *valence* band.

8. _____ The highest band that contains electrons is the *conduction* band.

9. _____ In conductors, the valence band and the conduction band are the *same.*

10. _____ The size of the forbidden gap between a full valence band and the conduction band determines whether a solid is an *insulator.*

In your textbook, read about conductors and insulators.

Circle the letter of the choice that best completes the statement or answers the question.

11. _____ is a very good conductor of electricity.

    a. Silicon   **c.** Sulfur

    b. Aluminum   **d.** Iodine

12. A material that conducts electricity well tends to have _____.

    a. no valence electrons

    b. partially filled bands

    c. completely filled bands

    d. conduction and valence bands that are far apart

29 Study Guide

• • • • • • • • • • • • •

13. When an electric field is applied on a length of wire, _____.

   a. there is random motion but no overall drifting in one direction

   b. there is overall drifting in one direction, but no random motion

   c. there are both random motion and overall drifting in one direction

   d. there is neither random motion nor overall drifting in one direction

14. How is conductivity related to resistivity?

   a. The two are directly related.

   b. The two are equal.

   c. Conductivity is the reciprocal of resistivity.

   d. Their relationship can't be described in general terms.

15. What happens to the conductivity of metals as temperature increases?

   a. It remains the same.   **c.** It decreases.

   b. It increases.   **d.** It follows no general rule.

16. _____ is an insulator.

   a. Copper   **b.** Silicon   **c.** Gold   **d.** Table salt

17. In an insulating material, _____.

   a. the valence band is filled and the conduction band is empty

   b. the valence band is empty and the conduction band is filled

   c. both the valence band and the conduction band are empty

   d. both the valence band and the conduction band are filled

18. What is the effect if a relatively small electric field is placed across an insulator?

   a. No current flows.

   b. A small current flows.

   c. A large current flows.

   d. The insulator acts like a conductor.

In your textbook, read about semiconductors.
For each item on the left, write the letter of the matching item.

_____ **19.** a pure semiconductor   **a.** dopant

_____ **20.** an atom with four valence electrons   **b.** extrinsic semiconductor

_____ **21.** any impurity added to a semiconductor   **c.** hole

_____ **22.** an empty energy level in the valence band   **d.** intrinsic semiconductor

_____ **23.** any semiconductor that conducts because   **e.** silicon
        of added impurities

29 Study Guide

• • • • • • • • • • • • • •

In your textbook, read about doped semiconductors.
Write the term that correctly completes each statement.

Dopants provide extra **(24)** _____ or extra negatively charged

(25) _____ to a semiconductor. If an atom with five valence electrons replaces

an atom with four valence electrons, one electron is unneeded for **(26)** _____.

The extra electron serves as a **(27)** _____ electron. Adding a small amount of

(28) _____ to the electron will move it into the **(29)** _____

band. The resulting conductor is a(n) **(30)** _____ semiconductor; it carries

electricity by means of particles that have a(n) **(31)** _____ charge. If an atom

with three valence electrons replaces an atom with four valence electrons, an extra

(32) _____ forms. The atoms can accept electrons and can be used as a(n)

(33) _____ semiconductor. In either type of semiconductor, the net charge

on the semiconductor is **(34)** _____. As temperature increases, the electric

conductivity of semiconductors **(35)** _____ and their resistivity

(36) _____. This also happens to the electric conductivity of certain semicon-

ductors when **(37)** _____ intensity upon them increases.

Section 29.2: Electronic Devices

In your textbook, read about diodes.
The diagrams below show a diode used with two kinds of biasing. Refer to the diagrams to answer the following questions.

1. What function does the battery serve?

_____

_____

29 Study Guide

• • • • • • • • • • • • • •

2. Which way is conventional current flowing in each diagram, clockwise or counterclockwise?

_____

3. Which way are electrons flowing in each diagram?

_____

4. What differs in the *p*-type and *n*-type semiconductors?

_____

_____

5. What kind of biasing does each diode have? How you can tell?

_____

_____

_____

6. Compare the depletion layer in the two diodes.

_____

7. Compare the quantity of current flow through the two diodes. Which is a conductor, and which is a large resistor?

_____

_____

In your textbook, read about transistors.
Circle the letter of the choice that best completes the statement or answers the question.

8. Transistors are used mainly as .

   a. resistors

   b. voltage amplifiers

   c. rectifiers

   d. insulators

9. How many layers of semiconductor are in a simple junction transistor?

   a. one   **c.** three

   b. two   **d.** four

10. What type of transistor has a center that is an *n*-type semiconductor?

   a. *n* transistor

   b. *p* transistor

   c. *npn* transistor

   d. *pnp* transistor

29 Study Guide

11. In an *npn* transistor, conventional current flows from the _____.

    a. base to the emitter

    b. emitter to the base

    c. diode to the collector

    d. rectifier to the collector

12. In an *npn* transistor, electrons flow from the _____.

    a. emitter to the base to the collector

    b. collector to the base to the emitter

    c. base to the collector to the emitter

    d. base to the emitter to the collector

13. What carries current in a *pnp* transistor?

    a. electrons

    b. holes

    c. protons

    d. nothing

14. Current through the collector is _____ than current through the base.

    a. a little smaller

    b. a little larger

    c. much smaller

    d. much larger

30 Study Guide

The Nucleus

Vocabulary Review

Write the term that correctly completes each statement. Use each term once.

activity	gamma decay	nuclear reaction
alpha decay	gluon	nuclide
antiparticle	grand unification theory	pair production
atomic mass unit	graviton	positron
atomic number	half-life	quark
beta decay	lepton	strong nuclear force
elementary particle	mass number	transmute
force carrier	neutrino	weak boson

1. _____ The nucleus of an isotope is a(n) _____.

2. _____ The number of decays per second is the _____ of a radioactive substance.

3. _____ During some types of radioactive decay, the radioactive element will _____, or change into another element.

4. _____ A member of the family of fundamental particles that carry forces between matter is a _____.

5. _____ The _____ family of fundamental particles includes protons, neutrons, and mesons.

6. _____ The electron and neutrino are examples of the _____ family of fundamental particles.

7. _____ A particle of antimatter is a(n) _____.

8. _____ Energy can be converted to matter when a gamma ray passes close by a nucleus and _____ occurs.

9. _____ Physicists are trying to create a _____ that connects the electromagnetic, weak, strong, and gravitational forces.

10. _____ The particle that carries the strong force that holds the nucleus together is the _____.

11. _____ The emission of an α particle is _____.

12. _____ The little neutral particle emitted during beta decay is the _____.

13. _____ The attractive force between protons and neutrons that are close together is the _____.

14. _____ The emission of a β particle is _____.

15. _____ The particle involved in the weak nuclear interaction is the _____.

16. _____ The particle that carries the gravitational force is the _____.

17. _____ An antielectron, or _____, has the same mass as an electron but a positive charge.

18. _____ The number of protons in a nucleus is the atom's _____.

19. _____ The time required for one-half of a radioactive sample to decay is the _____ of that element.

20. _____ The sum of the number of protons and neutrons in a nucleus is the _____.

21. _____ A nucleus emits a gamma ray during the process of _____.

22. _____ Whenever the number of protons or neutrons in a nucleus changes, a(n) _____ occurs.

23. _____ The mass of one proton, 1.66×10^{-27} kg, is equal to one _____.

24. _____ A fundamental unit of matter that does not appear to be divisible into smaller units is a(n) _____.

Section 30.1: Radioactivity

In your textbook, read about the atomic nucleus.
For each of the statements below, write true *or* false.

_____ 1. The only charged particle in the nucleus is the proton.

_____ 2. Most of the mass of an atom comes from the mass of protons.

_____ 3. The weak nuclear force overcomes the electrical force between protons to hold the nucleus together.

_____ 4. Neutrons are not affected by the strong nuclear force.

_____ 5. All nuclides of an element have the same number of protons but different numbers of neutrons.

_____ 6. The mass of an individual atom is close to a whole number of mass units, while the atomic mass of an average sample of that type of atom is not, because it contains a mixture of isotopes.

_____ 7. One mass unit is now defined on the basis of the mass of a proton.

_____ 8. In the notation $^{A}_{Z}X$, A is the mass number, Z is the atomic number, and X is any element.

30 Study Guide

In your textbook, read about radioactive decay.

Circle the letter of the choice that best completes each statement.

9. Photographic plates that Becquerel had near uranium compounds were exposed because _____.

   a. their coverings had a light leak

   b. uranium reacted chemically with the photographic plates

   c. uranium emits light rays

   d. uranium undergoes radioactive decay

10. Three types of radiation produced by radioactive decay are _____.

    a. alpha, beta, and gamma   c. ultraviolet, light, and infrared

    b. gamma, X ray, and light   d. alpha, beta, and delta

11. A thick sheet of paper can stop _____.

    a. X rays   b. gamma rays   c. β particles   d. alpha radiation

12. α particles are _____.

    a. high-speed electrons   c. high-energy photons

    b. the nucleus of a helium atom   d. low-energy photons

13. β particles are emitted when _____ during radioactive decay.

    a. a proton changes to a neutron   c. an electron changes energy levels

    b. a neutron changes to a proton   d. a valence electron is ejected

14. When a nucleus emits a gamma ray during gamma decay, _____.

    a. both the mass number and the atomic number change

    b. the atomic number increases by one and the mass number stays the same

    c. neither the mass number nor the atomic number changes

    d. the mass number decreases by four and the atomic number stays the same

In your textbook, read about nuclear reactions and equations.

For each of the statements below, write true *or rewrite the italicized part to make the statement true.*

15. _____ A *chemical reaction* occurs whenever the number of neutrons or protons in a nucleus changes.

16. _____ *All* nuclear reactions occur with a release of energy.

17. _____ Nuclear reactions can release excess energy in the form of *kinetic energy* of emitted particles.

18. _____ Nuclear reactions *cannot* be written in equation form.

19. _____ The total number of nuclear particles *stays the same* during a nuclear reaction.

20. _____ In a nuclear equation, the sum of the atomic numbers on the right side must *equal* the sum of the atomic numbers on the left side.

30 Study Guide

In your textbook, read about the half-lives of radioactive elements.

Refer to the graph below to answer the following questions. Use complete sentences.

21. What fraction of the original amount of radioactive atoms remains after 24.6 years?

_____

22. How many milligrams of radioactive atoms remain after 12.3 years?

_____

23. Define half-life.

_____

_____

24. What is the half-life of the element in the graph?

_____

25. At what time will the activity of the sample be one-eighth of the original activity?

_____

26. Based on Table 30-1 in your textbook, what is the identity of the element represented in the graph?

_____

27. According to Table 30-1, what type of radiation is produced by this element?

_____

Section 30.2: The Building Blocks of Matter

In your textbook, read about nuclear bombardment and nuclear accelerators.

Answer the following questions, using complete sentences.

1. Why are neutrons often used to bombard nuclei?

_____

2. Explain how a linear accelerator accelerates protons.

_____

_____

_____

3. Why can synchrotrons be smaller than linear accelerators?

_____

30 Study Guide

In your textbook, read about particle detectors.

For each of the statements below, write true *or rewrite the italicized part to make the statement true.*

4. _____ *Exposure of photographic film* is one way to detect radiation from radioactive decay.

5. _____ The *Geiger-Mueller tube* detects radiation because high-speed particles emitted during radioactive decay ionize matter they bombard.

6. _____ In a *Wilson cloud chamber,* trails of small vapor droplets form in a liquid held just above the boiling point.

7. _____ Modern experiments use *spark chambers* in which a discharge is produced in the path of a particle passing through the chamber.

8. _____ Because *charged* particles do not produce charges and leave tracks, the laws of conservation and momentum in collisions are used to detect production of the particles in spark chambers.

In your textbook, read about elementary particles.

Complete the table by marking quark, lepton, or force carrier for each particle.

Table 1			
Particle	**Quark**	**Lepton**	**Force Carrier**
9. electron			
10. photon			
11. neutrino			
12. muon			
13. charm			
14. down			
15. gluon			
16. bottom			

In your textbook, read about particles and antiparticles.

Circle the letter of the choice that best completes each statement.

17. The wide range of energies of electrons emitted during beta decay suggested that another particle, later found to be the ———, was emitted with the β particle.

    a. photon   **b.** antineutrino   **c.** electron   **d.** muon

18. A proton within the nucleus can change into a neutron with the emission of a _____ and a neutrino.

    a. positron   **b.** antineutrino   **c.** muon   **d.** photon

19. The existence of beta decay indicates that there is a force, called the _____, acting in the nucleus.

    a. strong nuclear force   **c.** transient nuclear force

    b. beta force   **d.** weak nuclear force

20. When a particle and an antiparticle collide, the two can annihilate each other, resulting in _____.

    a. conversion of matter into energy   **c.** pair production

    b. creation of energy   **d.** creation of matter

21. Matter and antimatter particles must be produced in pairs to satisfy the law of conservation of _____.

    a. energy   **b.** matter   **c.** charge   **d.** quarks

In your textbook, read about quarks and leptons.
Answer the following questions.

22. Which quarks make up a proton? A neutron? How do they differ?

_____

_____

23. Why can't individual quarks be observed?

_____

24. Describe the steps that occur during beta decay using the quark model.

_____

_____

In your textbook, read about unification theories.
Write the term that correctly completes each statement.

The force between charged particles is carried by **(25)** _____. The electric

force acts over a long distance because a photon has **(26)** _____. The weak force

acts over short distances because a boson has **(27)** _____. In the high-energy col-

lisions produced in accelerators, the **(28)** _____ and weak interactions have the

same strength and range. Astrophysical theories indicate that, during massive stellar explosions, the two

interactions are **(29)** _____. These theories unify the electromagnetic and weak

forces into a single **(30)** _____. Physicists are trying to create a grand unification

theory that includes the **(31)** _____ as well.

31 Study Guide

Use with Chapter 31.

Nuclear Applications

Vocabulary Review

For each term on the left, write the letter of the matching item.

_____ **1.** the part of a nuclear reactor that absorbs neutrons and controls the rate of the chain reaction

_____ **2.** the difference between the energy of the assembled nucleus and the particles in it

_____ **3.** the union of small nuclei to form larger ones

_____ **4.** liquefied fuel enclosed in tiny glass spheres and imploded by laser beams

_____ **5.** a nuclear reactor that produces more fuel than it uses

_____ **6.** the difference between the mass of the nucleus and the masses of the particles in it

_____ **7.** a proton or a neutron

_____ **8.** necessity for safe use of energy from fusion

_____ **9.** the substance in a nuclear reactor that slows fast neutrons

_____ **10.** a division of a nucleus into two or more fragments

_____ **11.** reactions that take place when nuclei have large amounts of thermal energy

_____ **12.** the process in which neutrons released by one fission induce other fissions

_____ **13.** a neutron released by a fission reaction and moving at a high speed

_____ **14.** a neutron that has been slowed by a moderator

_____ **15.** a process that increases the number of fissionable nuclei

a. binding energy

b. breeder reactor

c. chain reaction

d. control rod

e. controlled fusion

f. enrichment

g. fast neutron

h. fission

i. fusion

j. inertial confinement fusion

k. mass defect

l. moderator

m. nucleon

n. slow neutron

o. thermonuclear reactions

31 Study Guide

• • • • • • • • • • • • • •

Section 31.1: **Radioactivity**

In your textbook, read about what holds the nucleus together.

For each of the statements below, write true *or rewrite the italicized part to make the statement true.*

1. _____ The force that overcomes the mutual repulsion of the charged protons is the *electromagnetic force.*

2. _____ An assembled nucleus has *more* energy than the separate protons and neutrons in it.

3. _____ The binding energy comes from the nucleus's converting some of its *mass to energy.*

4. _____ Because mass is converted to energy to hold the nucleons together, the mass of an assembled nucleus is *more* than the sum of the masses of the nucleons that compose it.

5. _____ The mass defect is the *total* of the sum of the masses of the individual nucleons and the actual mass.

6. _____ The binding energy is calculated using the equation $E = mc^2$ to compute the energy equivalent of the experimentally determined mass defect.

In your textbook, read about how the nuclear binding energy relates to nuclear reactions.

Circle the letter of the choice that best completes each statement.

7. Nuclei whose atomic masses are larger than that of iron are _____ strongly bound and are therefore _____ stable than iron.

   a. more, less

   b. less, less

   c. more, more

   d. less, more

8. A nuclear reaction will occur naturally if energy is _____ by the reaction.

   a. released

   b. absorbed

   c. used up

   d. conserved

9. When a nucleus undergoes radioactive decay, the resulting nucleus is _____ the original nucleus.

   a. less stable than

   b. more stable than

   c. as stable as

10. At atomic numbers below 26, reactions that add nucleons to the nucleus make the nucleus _____.

    a. lighter

    b. more reactive

    c. more stable

    d. less stable

31 Study Guide

Section 31.2: Using Nuclear Energy

In your textbook, read about the production of artificial radioactivity.
Write the term that correctly completes each statement.

In 1934, Irene Joliot-Curie and Frederic Joliot bombarded aluminum with

(1) _____, producing phosphorus atoms and neutrons.

(2) _____ were also produced, even after the alpha bombardment

stopped. The positrons came from the new **(3)** _____. Radioactive isotopes

arise from stable isotopes bombarded with α particles, **(4)** _____,

neutrons, electrons, or gamma rays. The resulting unstable nuclei may emit alpha radiation,

(5) _____, gamma radiation, and positrons.

In your textbook, read about artificial radioactivity used in medicine.
Answer the following questions, using complete sentences.

6. Explain how tracer isotopes are used in medicine.

_____

_____

_____

_____

7. Name an instrument that can detect the decay products of tracer isotopes.

_____

_____

8. Explain how a PET scanner works.

_____

_____

_____

_____

_____

9. How can $^{60}_{27}$Co be used in medicine?

_____

31 Study Guide

In your textbook, read about nuclear fission.
Complete each statement.

10. The division of a nucleus into two or more fragments is _____.

11. In a fission reaction, the total mass of the products is _____ than the total mass of the reactants, and energy is produced.

12. Repeated fission reactions, or a _____, takes place when neutrons produced by earlier fission reactions cause the fission of other nuclei.

In your textbook, read about nuclear reactors.
Circle the letter of the choice that best completes each statement.

13. Most of the neutrons released by the fission of $^{235}_{92}U$ atoms are _____.

    a. moving at slow speeds

    b. slow neutrons

    c. in pairs

    d. moving at high speeds

14. When a $^{238}_{92}U$ nucleus absorbs a fast neutron, it _____.

    a. becomes a new isotope

    b. fuses with another atom

    c. starts moving at a high speed

    d. undergoes fission

15. Slow neutrons are more likely to be absorbed by _____ and to make a chain reaction possible.

    a. $^{235}_{92}U$

    b. $^{239}_{94}Pu$

    c. $^{238}_{92}U$

    d. $^{92}_{36}Kr$

16. When Fermi produced the first controlled chain reaction on December 2, 1942, he used _____ as a moderator.

    a. hydrogen   **c.** heavy water

    b. water   **d.** graphite

17. Enrichment increases _____ in the fuel for nuclear reactors.

    a. the amount of gold   **c.** the number of fusionable nuclei

    b. the number of fissionable nuclei   **d.** the number of slow neutrons

31 Study Guide

• • • • • • • • • • • • • •

In your textbook, read about the nuclear reactors used in the United States.
Refer to the drawing to answer the following questions.

Write labels for the drawing.

18. _____

19. _____

20. _____

21. _____

22. _____

23. _____

24. _____

25. _____

26. _____

27. _____

28. What type of reactor is shown in the drawing?

_____

_____

29. What purposes does water serve in this reactor?

_____

30. Describe how the reactor produces electric energy.

_____

_____

_____

31. Why do fuel rods glow blue when they hit water? What is this effect called?

_____

_____

_____

In your textbook, read about the products of fission reactions.
For each of the statements below, write true *or rewrite the italicized part to make the statement true.*

32. _____ Old rods that can no longer be used in a reactor *aren't* radioactive.

33. _____ Plutonium could be removed from radioactive waste and *recycled to fuel other reactors.*

34. _____ The world's supply of uranium is *unlimited.*

31 Study Guide

35. _____ From some reactors, *more fuel* can be recovered than was originally present.

In your textbook, read about nuclear fusion.
Circle the letter of the choice that best completes each statement.

36. In nuclear fusion, nuclei with _____ combine to form a nucleus with _____.

  a. small masses, a larger mass
  c. large masses, a larger mass
  b. low velocities, a higher velocity
  d. low energy, a higher energy

37. In the sun, _____ hydrogen nuclei fuse to form one helium nucleus.

  a. two   **b.** three   **c.** four   **d.** six

38. The energy released by a fusion reaction _____.

  a. is the energy equivalent of the mass difference between the products and the reactants
  b. depends on the temperature at which the reaction takes place
  c. transfers to the potential energy of the resultant particles
  d. is very small compared to other types of reactions

39. The reaction $^1_1H + $ _____ $ \rightarrow {}^3_2He + \gamma$ is one possible step in the proton-proton chain of fusion in the sun.

  a. ^1_1H **b.** ^2_1H **c.** ^2_1He **d.** ^4_2He

40. In a thermonuclear bomb, the high temperature necessary to produce the fusion reaction is provided by _____.

  a. dynamite   **b.** an atomic bomb   **c.** a conventional bomb   **d.** electricity

In your textbook, read about controlled fusion.
Answer the following questions, using complete sentences.

41. If energy could be produced economically by the fusion of deuterium and tritium, what would be two benefits?

_____

_____

42. What are two problems that prevent fusion reactions confined with magnetic fields from being used as an energy source?

_____

_____

43. Explain what happens during inertial confinement fusion.

_____

_____

_____

1 Study Guide

Use with Chapter 1.

What is physics?

Vocabulary Review

Write the term that correctly completes each statement. Use each term once.

physics   quintessence   technology
planets   scientific method

1. **physics** The study of matter and energy is ___.
2. **scientific method** A ___ is a systematic way to observe, experiment, and analyze the world.
3. **planets** The ___ are five bright objects that move relative to the constellations.
4. **quintessence** Greek philosophers thought that celestial bodies are made of the element ___.
5. **technology** The application of science to solve a practical problem is ___.

Section 1.1: Physics: The Search for Understanding

In your textbook, read about the work that physicists do.
Write the term that correctly completes each statement. Use each term once.

experiments   observations   theories
explanation   phenomena   universe
models   predictions

Physicists make (1) **observations**, do (2) **experiments**, and create (3) **models** or (4) **theories** to answer questions. Like all scientists, their goal is to obtain a compelling (5) **explanation** that describes many different (6) **phenomena**, makes (7) **predictions**, and leads to a better understanding of the (8) **universe**.

---

1 Study Guide

In your textbook, read about early astronomy.
For each term on the left, write the letter of the matching item.

c   9. wanderer
b   10. one of the elements that the ancient Greeks thought composed matter
d   11. the element that the ancient Greeks thought composed celestial objects
a   12. the Roman name of the god of war
e   13. the result of an element traveling in a straight line toward its own natural place

a. Mars
b. water
c. planet
d. quintessence
e. motion

In your textbook, read about Galileo.
For each of the statements below, write true or rewrite the italicized part to make the statement true.

14. Galileo estimated the heights of the mountains of the moon by their *volumes*.
shadows

15. Galileo discovered that the planet *Mars* has four moons.
Jupiter

16. Galileo discovered that the planet *Venus* has phases.
true

17. Galileo argued that the planets circle the sun.
true

18. Galileo wrote most of his scientific works in his native *Latin*, so that they could be read by an educated person.
Italian

19. According to Galileo, the first step of studying a problem in an organized way is *observing*.
true

20. Galileo is considered to be the father of modern *space exploration*.
experimental science

1 Study Guide

In your textbook, read about scientific methods.

Label the following steps in the order in which scientists study problems.

2	21. Draw a conclusion.
1	22. Combine experimentation with careful measurements and analyses of results.
3	23. Subject the conclusion to additional tests to determine if it is valid.

In your textbook, read about observations of Mars.

Answer the following question.

24. List four features attributed to Mars by astronomers and the general public that made it seem like Earth.

It appeared to have ice caps that advanced and receded. Color changes were attributed to vegetation cycles. It has geographic features such as deep canyons, high mountains, and dark areas thought to be seas. Markings were thought to be channels and canals made by intelligent beings.

In your textbook, read about missions to Mars.

In the table below, enter each mission's launch date and check the appropriate accomplishment box.

Table 1

Mission	Launch Date	Result/Goal		
		Fly-by	Orbit	Land
Mariner 4 (U.S.)	1964	X		
Mariner 6 (U.S.)	1968	X		
Mariner 9 (U.S.)	1971		X	
Mars 3 (USSR)	1971			X
Mars 5 (USSR)	1973		X	
Viking 1 (U.S.)	1975			X
Viking 2 (U.S.)	1975			X
Global Surveyor (U.S.)	1996		X	
Mars Pathfinder (U.S.)	1996			X
Mars Surveyor Orbiter (U.S.)	1998		X	
Mars Surveyor Lander (U.S.)	1999			X

---

1 Study Guide

In your textbook, read about the makeup of the Mars exploration teams.

Under each heading, list four careers that are represented on a Mars exploration team.

Scientific	Engineering	Other
physicist	electrical engineer	technician
chemist	mechanical engineer	graphic designer
geologist	aeronautic engineer	manager
astronomer	computer engineer	administrator

In your textbook, read about the importance of physics.

Describe how physics is involved in each aspect of a Mars exploration mission.

25. Propulsion and guidance

Physics is involved in the design of the rocket engines, the gyroscopic directional controls, and the precision clocks that indicate the location and speed of the spacecraft.

_____

_____

26. Onboard energy systems

Solar panels and nuclear electrical sources are based on physics.

_____

_____

27. Communications

Physics is involved in the design of cameras, computers, and radio transmitters and receivers that send photos to Earth.

_____

_____

1 Study Guide

In your textbook, read about physics success stories.

For each term on the left, write the letter of the matching item.

___d___ **28.** will allow performing functions on a submicroscopic level

___f___ **29.** a result of research in heat transfer, thin films, plasma sources, vacuum technology , and new materials

___a___ **30.** once thought worthless but now used in many endeavors including data storage, medicine, and telecommunications

___b___ **31.** developed from wartime research in radar and miniature electronics

___g___ **32.** aids in quality control

___c___ **33.** developed from research into thin films, magnetic materials, and semiconductors

___e___ **34.** helps reduce automotive costs

a. laser
b. microwave oven
c. personal computer
d. nanotechnology
e. lighter weight composite materials and polymers
f. energy efficient houses
g. computerized vision system

---

2 Study Guide

A Mathematical Toolkit

Vocabulary Review

Write the term that correctly completes each statement. Use each term once.

accuracy   kilogram   precision   significant digits
base units   linear relationship   quadratic relationship   slope
derived units   meter   scientific notation   y-intercept
factor-label method   metric system   second
inverse relationship   parallax   SI

___parallax___ **1.** The apparent shift in the position of an object when it is viewed from various angles is _____.

___kilogram___ **2.** The SI base unit of mass is the _____.

___factor-label method___ **3.** A way to convert a quantity in one unit to a quantity in another unit, using a relationship between the two units, is the _____.

___meter___ **4.** The SI base unit of length is the _____.

___scientific notation___ **5.** Expressing numbers in exponential notation is _____.

___slope___ **6.** On a graph, the rise divided by the run is the _____ of the line.

___metric system___ **7.** The system of measurement established by French scientists in 1795 is the _____.

___linear relationship___ **8.** A relationship that produces a graph with a straight line is a(n) _____.

___precision___ **9.** The degree of exactness of a measurement is _____.

___base units___ **10.** The units of quantities measured against standards are the _____.

___quadratic relationship___ **11.** A relationship in which one variable varies with the square of the other variable is a(n) _____.

___y-intercept___ **12.** On a graph, the point where the line crosses the y-axis is the _____.

___SI___ **13.** The Système Internationale d'Unités, _____, is a system of measurement established by an international committee.

___inverse relationship___ **14.** A relationship in which one variable varies with the inverse of the other is a(n) _____.

___derived units___ **15.** Units that are combinations of base units are _____.

___significant digits___ **16.** In any measurement, the digits that are valid are _____.

___second___ **17.** The SI base unit of time is the _____.

___accuracy___ **18.** The extent to which a measured value agrees with the standard value of the quantity is _____.

---

2 Study Guide

Section 2.1: The Measures of Science

In your textbook, read about SI.

For each base quantity on the left, write the matching base unit and the matching symbol.

		Base Unit	Symbol
1.	length	ampere	cd
2.	**kilogram** mass	candela	**kg**
3.	**second** time	kelvin	m
4.	**kelvin** temperature	kilogram	**K**
5.	**mole** amount of a substance	meter	**mol**
6.	**ampere** electric current	mole	**A**
7.	**candela** luminous intensity	second	**cd**

(1. **meter** ... **m**)

Answer the following questions, using complete sentences.

8. What is the current definition of a meter?

A meter is the distance light travels in a vacuum during a time interval of 1/299 792 458 s.

_____

_____

9. How is a second currently defined?

A second is defined in terms of the frequency of one type of radiation emitted by a

cesium-133 atom.

_____

_____

10. What is the current definition of a kilogram?

A kilogram is the mass of a small platinum-iridium metal cylinder kept at a controlled temper-

ature and humidity.

_____

---

2 Study Guide

In your textbook, read about SI prefixes.

Complete the table.

Table 1.

Prefix	Symbol	Multiplier	Scientific Notation
11. **femto**	f	1/1 000 000 000 000 000	10^{-15}
12. pico	p	**1/1 000 000 000 000**	10^{-12}
13. **nano**	n	**1/1 000 000 000**	10^{-9}
14. micro	μ	**1/1 000 000**	10^{-6}
15. **milli**	m	1/1000	10^{-3}
16. **kilo**	k	1000	10^{3}
17. mega	M	**1 000 000**	10^{6}
18. **giga**	G	1 000 000 000	10^{9}
19. **tera**	T	**1 000 000 000 000**	10^{12}

Write the term that correctly completes each statement.

20. In scientific notation, the numerical part of a quantity is written as _____ $M \times 10^{n}$.

21. In 10^{n}, n is an _____ **integer** _____.

22. In changing the numerical part of a measurement to scientific notation, the number of places you move the decimal point to the left is expressed as a _____ **positive** _____ exponent.

23. In changing the numerical part of a measurement to scientific notation, the number of places you move the decimal point to the right is expressed as a _____ **negative** _____ exponent.

2 Study Guide

Section 2.2: Measurement Uncertainties

In your textbook, read about accuracy and precision.
Refer to the diagram below. Circle the letter of the choice that best completes each statement.

Boxes in diagram: 22.5 ± 0.2°C (A), 22.7 ± 0.2°C (B), 22.5 ± 0.1°C (C), 22.4 ± 0.3°C (D), Standard value
Vertical axis: Temperature (°C), 22.0–22.9
Horizontal axis: Student (A, B, C, D)

1. Measurements that have the same precision are those of students ___.
   (a.) A and B   b. A and C   c. A and D   d. B and D

2. Measurements that have the least precision are those of student ___.
   a. A   b. B   c. C   **(d.)** D

3. Measurements that have the greatest precision are those of student ___.
   a. A   b. B   **(c.)** C   d. D

4. Measurements that have the same accuracy are those of students ___.
   a. A and B   **(b.)** A and C   c. A and C   d. B and D

5. Measurements that have the least accuracy are those of student ___.
   a. A   **(b.)** B   c. C   d. D

6. Measurements that have the greatest accuracy are those of student ___.
   a. A and B   **(b.)** A and C   c. A and C   d. B and D

7. The most precise and accurate measurements are those of student ___.
   a. A   b. B   **(c.)** C   d. D

8. To assure the greatest precision and accuracy in reading an instrument such as a thermometer, you should read the instrument ___.
   a. below eye level   b. above eye level   **(c.)** at eye level

---

2 Study Guide

In your textbook, read about significant digits.
Write the letter of each rule that is used to determine the correct number of significant digits in each measurement below. Then write the measurement in scientific notation.

Measurement	Rules Used	Scientific Notation	Rules
9. 321 m	a	3.21×10^2 m	**a.** Nonzero digits are always significant.
10. 1201 s	a, c	1.201×10^3 s	**b.** All final zeros after the decimal point are significant.
11. 1.0 m/s	a, b	1.0 m/s	**c.** Zeros between two other significant digits are always significant.
12. 0.01 K	a, d	1×10^{-2} K	**d.** Zeros used solely as placeholders are not significant.
13. 70.010 Mg	a, b, c	7.0010×10^1 Mg	
14. 53 000 000 cm	a, d	5.3×10^7 cm	
15. 0.200 A	a, b, d	2.00×10^{-1} A	
16. 40 000 L	a, d	4×10^4 L	
17. 0.680 kg	a, b, d	6.80×10^{-1} kg	

In your textbook, read about arithmetic with significant digits.
Explain how the number of significant digits was determined for the answer to each problem.

18.
$$
\begin{array}{r}
21.65 \text{ mm} \\
14.00 \text{ mm} \\
+\ 1.2\ \ \text{ mm} \\
\hline
37.9\ \ \text{ mm}
\end{array}
$$
Perform the operation and round off the result to correspond to the least precise value involved.

19.
$$
\begin{array}{r}
0.62 \text{ m} \\
\times\ 3.57 \text{ m} \\
\hline
2.2\ \ \text{ m}^2
\end{array}
$$
Perform the operation and round off the product to the number of digits in the factor with the least number of significant digits.

20.
$$\frac{5013 \text{ m}}{2.6 \text{ s}} = 1900 \text{ m/s}$$
Perform the operation and round the quotient to the number of digits in the factor with the least number of significant digits.

2 Study Guide

Section 2.3: Visualizing Data

In your textbook, read about graphing data.

Read the paragraph below. Refer to the table to answer the questions that follow.

A student cuts an aluminum rod into four random pieces. She then measures the volume and mass of each piece. The data she records is shown. To determine how the mass of each piece varies with its volume, she constructs a graph.

Table 1	
Volume (mL)	**Mass (g)**
9.2	24.93
18.3	49.15
34.5	93.19
48.2	131.92

1. What is the range of the data of the independent variable?

   9.2–48.2 mL

2. What would be a convenient range for the *x*-axis?

   0–50 mL

3. What is the range of the data of the dependent variable?

   24.93–131.92 g

4. What would be a convenient range for the *y*-axis?

   0–140 or 150 g

In your textbook, read about linear and nonlinear relationships.

For each term on the left, write the letter of the matching item.

d   5. the equation of a linear relationship

c   6. the shape of the graph of a linear relationship

f   7. the equation of an inverse relationship

a   8. the shape of the graph of an inverse relationship

e   9. the equation of a quadratic relationship

b   10. the shape of the graph of quadratic relationship

a. hyperbola

b. parabola

c. straight line

d. $y = mx + b$

e. $y = ax^2 + bx + c$

f. $y = \dfrac{a}{x}$

---

3 Study Guide

Describing Motion

Vocabulary Review

Write the term that correctly completes each statement. Use each term once.

average acceleration	motion diagram
average speed	operational definition
average velocity	origin
coordinate system	particle model
displacement	physical model
distance	pictorial model
	position vector
	problem-solving strategy
	scalar quantity
	time interval
	vector quantity

1. **motion diagram** A series of images of an object that records the object's position after equal time intervals is a(n) _____.

2. **vector quantity** A quantity that has magnitude and direction is a(n) _____.

3. **particle model** The _____ replaces an object by a single point.

4. **coordinate system** The zero point of a variable and the direction in which the values of the variable increase is indicated in a(n) _____.

5. **position vector** An arrow that is proportional to the distance an object is from the origin and points in the direction of the object is a(n) _____.

6. **average speed** The magnitude of the average-velocity vector is _____.

7. **problem-solving strategy** A step-wise procedure for solving problems is a(n) _____.

8. **time interval** A change in time is a(n) _____.

9. **operational definition** A quantity defined in terms of the procedure used to identify it is a(n) _____.

10. **displacement** The change in position of an object is its _____.

11. **origin** The point in a coordinate system at which the variables have the value of zero is the _____.

12. **distance** The length of the displacement vector represents the _____ between the two positions.

13. **pictorial model** A model that uses symbols to represent variables is a(n) _____.

14. **average velocity** The ratio of the displacement to the time interval in which the displacement takes place is the _____.

15. **physical model** A motion diagram is an example of a(n) _____.

16. **average acceleration** The _____ is the ratio of the change in velocity to the time interval in which the change took place.

17. **scalar quantity** A quantity that has only magnitude is a(n) _____.

---

3 Study Guide

Name _____

Section 3.1: Picturing Motion

In your textbook, read about motion diagrams.

Refer to the diagrams below, showing frames from a camcorder at 2-s intervals. Circle the letter of the choice that best completes each statement.

1. In set I, the object that is moving is _____ .
   a. A   **b. B**   c. C

2. Set II shows that object B is _____ .
   a. at rest   **b.** increasing its speed   c. slowing down   d. traveling at constant speed

3. Set _____ shows object B is slowing down.
   a. I   b. II   c. III   **d. IV**

4. Set _____ shows object B at rest.
   a. I   b. II   **c.** III   d. IV

5. Set _____ shows object B traveling at a constant speed.
   a. I   b. II   c. III   d. IV

---

3 Study Guide

Name _____

Section 3.2: Where and When?

In your textbook, read about coordinate systems.

Refer to the diagrams below, showing the location of an object represented by a circle. Complete the table by writing the position vector of each object.

Table 1

Diagram	Position Vector
A	+4 m
B	−4 m
C	+5 m
D	−1 m
E	0 m

In your textbook, read about vectors, scalars, time intervals, and displacements. For each term on the left, write the letter of the matching term.

c	1. symbol that represents time interval
f	2. Greek letter delta used to mean change
i	3. definition of time interval
d	4. one way of representing the vector quantity acceleration
h	5. symbol that represents position
a	6. magnitude of the displacement vector
j	7. definition of displacement
g	8. one way of representing the vector quantity velocity
e	9. symbol that represents displacement
b	10. symbol that represents the scalar quantity mass

a. distance
b. m
c. Δt
d. $\vec{a}$
e. Δd
f. Δ
g. v
h. d
i. $t_1 - t_0$
j. $d_1 - d_0$

3 Study Guide

18. What is happening to the motion of the object in the time interval $t_{12} - t_9$?
The object is slowing down.

19. What distance does the object travel in the time interval $t_{12} - t_0$?
15 m

Section 3.3: Velocity and Acceleration

In your textbook, read about velocity.
For each of the statements below, write true or rewrite the italicized part to make the statement true.

1. **true** — The ratio $\Delta d/\Delta t$ is called the *average velocity*.
2. **average velocity** — The symbol $\overline{v}$ represents the *average acceleration*.
3. **average speed** — The magnitude of the average-velocity vector is the quantity *average distance traveled*.
4. **true** — Automobile speeds are usually measured in miles per hour (mph) or kilometers per hour (km/h).
5. **true** — The equation $d_0 + \overline{v}\,\Delta t$ represents the *position* of an object after the time interval Δt.
6. **position** — The quantity $\overline{v}\,\Delta t$ represents the *change in speed* of an object during the time interval Δt.

In your textbook, read about interpreting velocity vectors and acceleration.
Refer to the motion diagram below, showing the position at 1-s intervals of a car traveling to the right along the positive x-axis. In the space provided, draw the displacement, velocity, and acceleration vectors for each time interval. Answer the following questions.

Displacement

Velocity

Acceleration

7. What is happening to the motion of the car during the time intervals in which both the velocity and the acceleration vectors are in the positive direction?
The car is speeding up as it moves to the right.

8. What is happening to the motion of the car during the time intervals in which the velocity vectors are positive and the acceleration vectors are negative?
The car is slowing down as it moves to the right.

---

3 Study Guide

In your textbook, read about time intervals and displacements.
In the space provided, draw and label the vectors d_0 and d_1 for the given information. Then draw and label the vector Δd and determine its magnitude.

11. $d_0 = +4$ m $d_1 = +10$ m

6 m

12. $d_0 = +2$ m $d_1 = +9$ m

7 m

13. $d_0 = -4$ m $d_1 = -6$ m

-2 m

In your textbook, read about time intervals and displacements.
Refer to the motion diagram below, showing the locations of an object during a 12-s interval. Answer the following questions.

14. What is the magnitude of the position vector at $t = 0$ s?
+1 m

15. At what time does the object have a position of +8.0 m?
t = 7 s

16. What is displacement of the object in the time interval $t_6 - t_5$?
+1.5 m

17. In what time intervals does the object have a constant speed?
$t_4 - t_0$ and $t_9 - t_7$

3 Study Guide

In your textbook, read about problem-solving strategies.

Read the following problem and refer to the diagram below. Circle the letter of the choice that best completes the statement or answers the question.

A car traveling at a constant 7 m/s takes 5 s to pass through a school zone and then accelerates at 2 m/s² for 3 s. How far does the car travel in the 8 s?

School Zone

d_1 d_2 d_3
v_1 v_2 v_3

a_{12} a_{23} $+x$

1. The diagram above represents a(n) _____ of the problem.
   a. physical model
   b. operational definition
   c. pictorial model
   d. particle model

2. A likely choice for the origin of the coordinate system would be at a point _____.
   a. where the car enters the school zone
   b. halfway through the school zone
   c. at the beginning of the school zone
   d. at the end of the school zone

3. Which of the following motion diagrams represents the problem?
   a. •••• • ••••
   b. •   • •••••••
   c. •••••••••
   d. ••••• • • •

4. The problem can be thought of as a two-step problem because the car has _____.
   a. one displacement
   b. constant velocity and an acceleration
   c. equal time intervals
   d. unequal time intervals

5. If d_1 is the position of the car at the beginning of the problem and d_3 is the position of the car at the end of the problem, a good choice of d_2 is the position of the car _____.
   a. at the beginning of the school zone
   b. halfway through the school zone
   c. at the point where the car changes speeds
   d. at the point where the car stops

6. The acceleration a_{12}, between d_1 and d_2, is _____.
   a. increasing
   b. decreasing
   c. 0 m/s²
   d. +2.0 m/s²

7. The acceleration a_{23}, between d_2 and d_3, is _____.
   a. increasing
   b. decreasing
   c. 0 m/s²
   d. +2.0 m/s²

8. The vector representing acceleration a_{23} _____.
   a. points to the left
   b. points to the right
   c. is equal to zero
   d. is shorter than vector a_{12}

---

4 Study Guide

Vector Addition

Vocabulary Review

Write the term that correctly completes each statement. Use each term once.

algebraic representation
components
direction
graphical representation

magnitude
origin
Pythagorean relationship
resultant vector
scalar quantity

vector
vector decomposition
velocity

1. **graphical representation** An arrow or an arrow-tipped line segment is called a(n) _____ of a vector.

2. **algebraic representation** A(n) _____ of a vector is represented by an italicized letter in bold-face type.

3. **resultant vector** A(n) _____ is a vector that is equal to the sum of two or more vectors.

4. **Pythagorean relationship** The _____ states that the sum of the squares of the two sides of a right triangle is equal to the square of the hypotenuse.

5. **direction** The _____ of a vector is defined as the angle that the vector makes with the *x*-axis, measured counterclockwise, in a rectangular coordinate system.

6. **vector decomposition** The process of breaking a vector into its components is sometimes called _____.

7. **components** Two vectors projected on the axes of a coordinate system are called the _____ of the resultant vector.

8. **vector** A quantity that has both magnitude and direction is a(n) _____.

9. **magnitude** The _____ of a vector is always a positive quantity.

10. **displacement** Distance is the magnitude of a vector quantity called _____.

11. **scalar quantity** A quantity that has only magnitude is a(n) _____.

12. **velocity** The magnitude of an object's _____ is its speed.

13. **origin** The center of a coordinate system is called the _____.

4 Study Guide

Section 4.1: Properties of Vectors

In your textbook, read about representing vector quantities.

For the diagrams below, use the scale to determine the magnitude of each displacement vector. Determine the direction of each displacement using compass points of north, south, east, and west, or the intermediate points such as northeast and southwest. Write the value of the displacement in the space to the left.

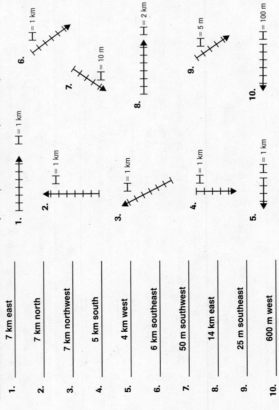

1. **7 km east**

2. **7 km north**

3. **7 km northwest**

4. **5 km south**

5. **4 km west**

6. **6 km southeast**

7. **50 m southwest**

8. **14 km east**

9. **25 m southeast**

10. **600 m west**

Read the following statement. Circle the letter of the choice that is the best response.

The displacement of a student is 2.0 km north.

11. Which is the correct algebraic representation of the displacement?

a. d = 2.0 km north   c. **d** = 2.0 km north

b. *d* = 2.0 km north   d. *d* = 2.0 km north

12. Which is the correct algebraic representation of the magnitude of the displacement?

a. d = 2.0 km   c. **d** = 2.0 km

b. *d* = 2.0 km   **d.** *d* = 2.0 km

---

4 Study Guide

In your textbook, read about representing vector quantities.

Each set of displacement vectors below is drawn to the same scale. For each situation, write its letter next to the correct number of the expression.

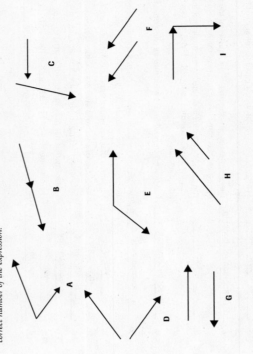

13. ____**B, F, H**____ Vectors in set have same direction.

14. __**B, D, F, G, I**__ Vectors in set have same magnitude.

15. ____**B, F**____ Vectors in set are equal.

In your textbook, read about the graphic addition of vectors.

For each of the statements below, write true or false or rewrite the italicized part to make the statement true.

16. ____**true**____ The *length* of the arrow representing a vector should be proportional to the magnitude of the quantity being represented.

17. __**protractor**__ A *ruler* is used to measure the angle that establishes the direction of the vector.

18. ____**tail**____ When adding two vectors, the first vector is drawn and the *tip* of the second vector is placed at the tip of the first vector.

19. ____**true**____ When adding vectors, the resultant vector is drawn from the *tail* of the first vector to the tip of the last vector.

20. __**independent of**__ The resultant vector is *dependent* on the order in which the vectors are added.

4 Study Guide

In your textbook, read about relative velocities.

Read the following paragraph. Write the letter of the diagram that is the best response to each question.

A boat is placed in a river, which has a current velocity, v_c, of 3.0 km/h east, relative to the shore. Relative to the river, the rower can maintain a boat speed, v_b, of 6.0 km/h.

A.

B.

C.

D.

__A__ **21.** Which diagram can be used to find the boat's velocity relative to the shore if the boat is being rowed downstream?

__C__ **22.** In which diagram is the direction of the boat's velocity relative to the shore southeastward?

__D__ **23.** In which diagram does the boat have the least speed relative to the shore?

__B, C__ **24.** In which diagrams is the speed of the boat relative to the shore equal?

Read the following paragraph. Circle the letter of the choice that is the best response to each question.

In questions 21–24, the resultant vector represents the velocity of the boat, v_s, relative to the shore. Algebraically,

$$v_s = v_b + v_c$$

If a rower wants to get to a certain point by a certain time, he or she knows what v_s is. What the rower must determine is v_b, that is, how fast and in what direction he or she must row relative to the river. Solving the above equation for v_b gives

25. The equation for v_b can be written as which of the following equations?

a. $v_b = v_c - v_s$

(b.) $v_b = v_s + (-v_c)$

c. $v_b = -(v_s + v_c)$

d. $v_b = -(v_s - v_c)$

26. Which diagram illustrates the velocity at which a boat must be rowed relative to the river if the rower wants to maintain a heading of 45.0° northeast relative to the shore? The river has a current velocity of 3.0 m/s east relative to the shore.

a.

b.

(c.)

d.

---

4 Study Guide

Section 4.2: Components of Vectors

In your textbook, read about coordinate systems.

Refer to the diagram below. Circle the letter of the choice that best completes each statement.

1. In the coordinate system shown, the positive y-axis is located _____ counterclockwise from the positive x-axis.

a. 0°

(b.) 90°

c. 180°

d. 270°

2. The y-axis crosses the x-axis at the _____.

a. angle θ

(b.) origin

c. quadrant

d. vertex

3. Vectors E and F lie in quadrant _____.

a. I

b. II

(c.) III

d. IV

4. Vector _____ has a positive horizontal component and a positive vertical component.

a. A

(b.) B

c. D

d. E

5. The sine of an angle is defined as $\sin \theta = \dfrac{\text{opposite side}}{\text{hypotenuse}}$.

The sine of the angle that vector B makes with the x-axis is _____.

a. $\sin \theta = \dfrac{B_x}{B}$

b. $\sin \theta = \dfrac{B}{B_x}$

c. $\sin \theta = \dfrac{B_x}{B_y}$

(d.) $\sin \theta = \dfrac{B_y}{B}$

6. The cosine of an angle is defined as $\cos \theta = \dfrac{\text{adjacent side}}{\text{hypotenuse}}$.

The cosine of the angle that vector D makes with the x-axis is _____.

(a.) $\cos \theta = \dfrac{D_x}{D}$

b. $\cos \theta = \dfrac{D}{D_x}$

c. $\cos \theta = \dfrac{D_x}{D_y}$

d. $\cos \theta = \dfrac{D_y}{D}$

7. Vector _____ has no horizontal component.

a. A

b. B

(c.) C

d. G

8. The horizontal component of vector F has a value of _____.

a. F

b. $F \sin \theta$

(c.) $F \cos \theta$

d. $\dfrac{F}{\cos \theta}$

9. The vertical component of vector F has a value of _____.

a. F

(b.) $F \sin θ$

c. $F \cos θ$

d. $\dfrac{F}{\cos θ}$

10. Both components of vector _____ are negative.

a. B

b. D

(c.) E

d. G

4 Study Guide

In your textbook, read about addition of vectors using components.

The diagram shows the displacement of a hiker. The data table shows the magnitudes of the vertical and horizontal components of each displacement.

Table 1

Component	Magnitude (km)
A_x	1.4
A_y	3.8
B_x	4.0
B_y	6.9
C_x	1.5
C_y	1.3

Circle the letter of the choice that is the best response.

11. What is the value of R_x, which represents the sum of the horizontal components of the displacements?

  a. $R_x = 1.4\ \text{km} + 4.0\ \text{km} + 1.5\ \text{km} = 6.9\ \text{km}$

  b. $R_x = (-1.4\ \text{km}) + (-4.0\ \text{km}) + (-1.5\ \text{km}) = -6.9\ \text{km}$

  (c.) $R_x = (-1.4\ \text{km}) + 4.0\ \text{km} + 1.5\ \text{km} = 4.1\ \text{km}$

  d. $R_x = 1.4\ \text{km} + (-4.0\ \text{km}) + (-1.5\ \text{km}) = -4.1\ \text{km}$

12. What is the value of R_y, which represents the sum of the vertical components of the displacements?

  a. $R_y = 3.8\ \text{km} + 6.9\ \text{km} + 1.3\ \text{km} = 12.0\ \text{km}$

  b. $R_y = (-3.8\ \text{km}) + (-6.9\ \text{km}) + (-1.3\ \text{km}) = -12.0\ \text{km}$

  (c.) $R_y = (-3.8\ \text{km}) + 6.9\ \text{km} + (-1.3\ \text{km}) = 1.8\ \text{km}$

  d. $R_y = 3.8\ \text{km} + (-6.9\ \text{km}) + (-1.3\ \text{km}) = -4.4\ \text{km}$

13. What is the magnitude of the resultant R?

  a. $R < 0\ \text{km}$ **b.** $R = 0\ \text{km}$ **(c.)** $R > 0\ \text{km}$

14. What is the magnitude and direction of the displacement vector Y that will return the hiker to the starting point?

  a. $Y = 0\ \text{km}$ **b.** $Y = R$ **(c.)** $Y = -R$ **d.** $Y = -2R$

---

5 Study Guide

A Mathematical Model of Motion

Vocabulary Review

Write the term that correctly completes each statement. Use each term once.

acceleration due to gravity   instantaneous velocity   slope

constant acceleration   position-time graph   uniform motion

constant velocity   rise   velocity-time graph

instantaneous acceleration   run

1. __position-time graph__ A graph that shows how position depends on time is a(n) _____.

2. __rise__ The vertical separation of any two points on a curve is the _____.

3. __instantaneous velocity__ On a position-time graph, the slope of a tangent to the curve at a specific time is the _____.

4. __uniform motion__ In _____ equal displacements occur during successive equal time intervals.

5. __constant velocity__ An object that has the same average velocity for all time intervals is moving at _____.

6. __acceleration due to gravity__ The constant acceleration that acts on falling bodies is the _____.

7. __slope__ The ratio of the rise to run is the _____ of a curve.

8. __velocity-time graph__ A graph that shows how velocity depends on time is a(n) _____.

9. __constant acceleration__ Motion that can be described by a constant slope on a velocity-time graph is _____.

10. __run__ The horizontal separation of any two points on a curve is the _____.

11. __instantaneous acceleration__ On a velocity-time graph, the slope of a tangent to the curve at a specific time is the _____.

5 Study Guide

Section 5.1: Graphing Motion in One Dimension

In your textbook, read about position-time graphs.

Answer the following questions, using complete sentences.

1. How are the position and time of a moving object related on a position-time graph?
Each position on the graph is associated with a particular time.

2. If you decide that the duration of an instant on a position-time graph is a finite period of time, where is the object during that period?
The object is in the position indicated on the graph.

3. What does your conclusion in problem 2 indicate about the motion of the object during that period?
The object is at rest.

4. If the object is moving, what can you conclude about the duration of an instant?
An instant is not a finite period of time.

5. What is the duration of an instant?
An instant lasts 0 s.

In your textbook, read about using graphs to determine position and time.

The position-time graph below shows the position of a teacher at various times as she walks across the front of the room. The position 0.0 m represents the left side of the room and movement to the right is positive. Circle the letter of the choice that best completes each statement.

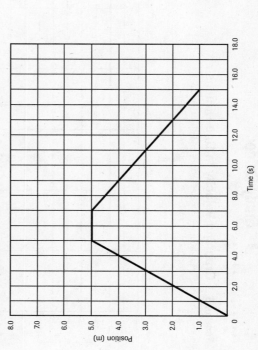

---

5 Study Guide

6. The teacher was walking to the right during the time interval ___.
a. 1.0–2.0 s *(circled)*   **b.** 6.0–7.0 s   **c.** 10.0–12.0 s   **d.** 7.0–12.0 s

7. The teacher's displacement for the time interval 0.0–3.0 s is ___.
a. –3.0 m   **b.** 0.0 m   **c.** +1.0 m *(circled)*   **d.** +3.0 m

8. The teacher's average velocity for the time interval 1.0–3.0 s is ___.
a. –1.0 m/s   **b.** +1.0 m/s *(circled)*   **c.** +2.0 m/s   **d.** +3.0 m/s

9. The teacher is standing still during the time interval ___.
a. 1.0–2.0 s   **b.** 6.0–7.0 s *(circled)*   **c.** 10.0–12.0 s   **d.** 12.0–15.0 s

10. The average velocity for the time interval 10.0–12.0 s is ___.
a. +1.0 m/s   **b.** +0.5 m/s   **c.** 0.0 m/s   **d.** –0.5 m/s *(circled)*

11. The teacher's average velocity for the time interval 0.0–15.0 s is ___.
a. –2.0 m/s   **b.** 0.0 m/s   **c.** +0.067 m/s *(circled)*   **d.** +0.75 m/s

Sketch a motion diagram for each time interval, using the teacher's position-time graph on page 26.

Time Interval	Motion Diagram
12. 0.0–5.0 s	
13. 5.0–7.0 s	
14. 7.0–15.0 s	

In your textbook, read about using position and time equations.

Refer to the equation $d = d_0 + vt$. For each of the statements below, write true or rewrite the italicized part to make the statement true.

15. **four** — The equation contains *three* quantities.

16. **true** — This equation *cannot* be used if the velocity is changing.

17. **d** — The quantity d_0 represents the position *at any time*.

18. **true** — The quantity in the equation that represents the slope of a position-time graph for this motion is *v*.

19. **true** — The displacement of the object is *vt*.

5 Study Guide
• • • • • • • • • • • • •

Section 5.2: Graphing Velocity in One Dimension

In your textbook, read about velocity-time graphs and displacement.

Refer to the velocity-time graph of a jogger to complete the two tables.

Velocity (km/min) vs Time (min)

Table 1

Segment	v	Δt	Δd
A	0.25 km/min	10.0 min	2.5 km
B	0.0 km/min	7.0 min	0.0 km
C	0.40 km/min	13.0 min	5.2 km

Table 2

Δt	Distance Ran	Displacement	Average Velocity
0.0–30.0 min	7.7 km	7.7 km	0.26 km/min

---

5 Study Guide
• • • • • • • • • • • • •

Section 5.3: Acceleration

In your textbook, read about equations of motion for uniform acceleration.

Complete each table with the values of the variables and initial conditions. Write a question mark for the unknown variable. If a variable or an initial condition is not needed to answer the problem, write an X. Then write the equation that you would use to solve the problem. It is not necessary to calculate the answer.

1. A car accelerates from 10 m/s to 15 m/s in 3.0 s. How far does the car travel in this time?

Table 1

Variables			Initial Conditions			Equation
t	d	v	a	d_0	v_0	
3.0 s	?	15 m/s	X	0 m	10 m/s	$d = d_0 + \frac{1}{2}(v_0 + v)\,t$

2. A racing car accelerates at 4.5 m/s² from rest. What is the car's velocity after it has traveled 35.0 m?

Table 2

Variables			Initial Conditions			Equation
t	d	v	a	d_0	v_0	
X	35.0 m	?	4.5 m/s²	0 m	0 m/s	$v^2 = v_0^2 + 2a(d - d_0)$

3. A car initially traveling at 15 m/s accelerates at a constant 4.5 m/s² through a distance of 45 m. How long does it take the car to cover this distance?

Table 3

Variables			Initial Conditions			Equation
t	d	v	a	d_0	v_0	
?	45 m	X	4.5 m/s²	0 m	15 m/s	$d = d_0 + v_0 t + \frac{1}{2}at^2$

4. A ball rolls past a mark on an incline at 0.40 m/s. If the ball has a constant acceleration of 0.20 m/s² what is its velocity 3.0 s after it passes the mark?

Table 4

Variables			Initial Conditions			Equation
t	d	v	a	d_0	v_0	
3.0 s	X	?	0.20 m/s²	X	0.40 m/s	$v = v_0 + at$

5 Study Guide

Section 5.4: Free-Fall

In your textbook, read about free-fall.

Refer to the diagram on the right showing the positions of a ball that was thrown upward at time t_0. Complete the tables by indicating if the direction of the velocity and the direction of the acceleration at each time is + or −, or if the value of the velocity or acceleration equals 0.

○ t_2
○ t_3
○ t_1
○ t_4
○ t_0

1. Downward direction is positive.
   Rank the magnitudes of the velocities v_0, v_1, v_2, v_3, and v_4, in decreasing order.
   v_0, v_4, v_1, v_3, and v_2

   _____

Table 1

Variable	Time				
	t_0	t_1	t_2	t_3	t_4
v	−	−	0	+	+
a	+	+	+	+	+

2. Upward direction is positive.
   Rank the magnitudes of the velocities v_0, v_1, v_2, v_3, and v_4, in decreasing order.
   v_0, v_4, v_1, v_3, and v_2

   _____

Table 2

Variable	Time				
	t_0	t_1	t_2	t_3	t_4
v	+	+	0	−	−
a	−	−	−	−	−

Refer to the velocity-time graph of the vertical velocity of a ball as it is thrown upward from the top of a building until it reaches the ground. Answer the following questions.

3. Use a red pencil to shade the area under the curve that represents the total upward displacement of the ball.

4. Use a blue pencil to shade the area under the curve that represents the total downward displacement of the ball.

5. How could you use the red and blue areas to determine the height of the building?

   Calculate the red and blue areas. Subtract the value of the red area from the value of the blue area.

   _____
   _____

---

6 Study Guide

Forces

Vocabulary Review

Write the term that correctly completes each statement. Use each term once.

agent
amplitude
apparent weight
contact force
environment
equilibrium
force
force of gravity
free-body diagram
inertia
interaction pair
kinetic friction force
long-range force
mechanical resonance
net force
Newton's first law
Newton's second law
Newton's third law
period
simple harmonic motion
static friction force
system
terminal velocity
weightlessness

1. **mechanical resonance** In _____, the amplitude of motion is increased by the repeated application of a force when the time between applications is equal to the period of oscillation.

2. **net force** The vector sum of two or more forces acting on an object is the _____.

3. **equilibrium** The net force on an object in _____ is zero.

4. **static friction force** The horizontal force exerted on one surface by another when the two surfaces are not in relative motion is the _____.

5. **Newton's second law** The acceleration of a body is directly proportional to the net force on it and inversely proportional to its mass; this is a statement of _____.

6. **apparent weight** The force exerted by a scale on an object is the _____.

7. **contact force** A force that acts on an object by touching it is a(n) _____.

8. **Newton's third law** The two forces in an interactive pair act on different objects and are equal in magnitude and opposite in direction; this is a statement of _____.

9. **environment** The world outside a system is the _____.

10. **force of gravity** An attractive force that exists between all objects is the _____.

11. **Newton's first law** An object that is at rest will remain at rest or an object that is moving will continue to move in a straight line with constant speed, if and only if the net force acting on the object is zero; this is a statement of _____.

12. **kinetic friction force** The horizontal force exerted on one surface by another when surfaces are in relative motion is the _____.

13. **system** A defined object or group of objects is a(n) _____.

6 Study Guide

•••••••••••••

14. inertia — The tendency of an object to resist changes in its motion is _____.

15. agent — The specific, identifiable cause of a force is a(n) _____.

16. period — The time to repeat one complete cycle is a(n) _____.

17. long-range force — A force that is exerted without contact is a(n) _____.

18. amplitude — In any periodic motion, the maximum displacement from equilibrium is the _____.

19. force — A push or pull is a(n) _____.

20. interaction pair — Two forces that are in opposite directions and have equal magnitudes are a(n) _____.

21. free-body diagram — In a(n) _____, a dot represents an object and arrows represent each force acting on it, with their tail on the dot and their points indicating the direction of the force.

22. simple harmonic motion — In _____, the force that restores an object to its equilibrium position is directly proportional to its displacement.

23. terminal velocity — The constant velocity that a falling object reaches when the drag force equals the force of gravity is its _____.

24. weightlessness — When an object's apparent weight is zero, the object is in a state of _____.

Section 6.1: Force and Motion

In your textbook, read about Newton's second law and combining forces.
For each of the statements below write true or false.

true ____ 1. Newton's second law can be written as the equation

$$a = \frac{F_{net}}{m}.$$

true ____ 2. The acceleration of an object and the net force acting on it are proportional.

false ____ 3. Force and acceleration are scalar quantities.

---

6 Study Guide

•••••••••••••

In your textbook, read about equilibrium and free-body diagrams.
Refer to the diagrams below. Circle the letter of the choice that best completes the statement or answers the question.

Diagram 1
A   B   C   D
F_g F_g F_g F_g

Diagram 2
A   B   C   D
F_N F_N F_N F_N
F_g F_g F_g

4. Which part of diagram 1 best represents the weight force of the bowl sitting on a shelf?
   a. A   b. B   c. C   **(d.)** D

5. F_N is a symbol that represents the _____ force.
   a. friction   b. tension   **(c.)** normal   d. weight

6. What part of diagram 2 best represents the bowl in equilibrium?
   a. A   b. B   **(c.)** C   d. D

7. The magnitude of the net force on the bowl in equilibrium is _____.
   a. F_N b. F_g **(c.)** 0   d. $2F_g$

8. The agent of F_N is _____.
   a. the bowl   b. Earth   c. friction   **(d.)** the shelf

9. The agent of F_g is _____.
   a. the bowl   **(b.)** Earth   c. friction   d. the shelf

Draw a free-body diagram of each situation.

10. A rocket immediately after vertical liftoff

11. A penny sliding at constant velocity on a desktop

12. A penny immediately after sliding off a desktop

F_{thrust}
F_g

F_N F
F_f
F_g
$F_{net} = 0$

F_g

6 Study Guide

Section 6.2: Using Newton's Laws

In your textbook, read about mass, weight, and apparent weight.

For each term on the left, write the letter of the matching item.

___c___ **1.** name of gravitational force acting on object

___d___ **2.** magnitude of acceleration caused by gravity

___a___ **3.** symbol for the acceleration caused by gravity

___g___ **4.** symbol for the weight force

___f___ **5.** expression for the weight of an object

___b___ **6.** unit of weight

___h___ **7.** property of an object that does not vary from location to location

___e___ **8.** having an apparent weight of zero

a. g
b. newton
c. weight
d. 9.8 m/s^2
e. weightlessness
f. mg
g. F_g
h. mass

In your textbook, read about scales and apparent weight.

Read the passage below and refer to the diagram next to it. Circle the letter of the choice that best completes the statement or answers the question.

A 1.0-kg mass at rest is suspended from a spring scale. The direction of positive forces that are acting or could act on the 1.0-kg mass are shown to the right.

[diagram: spring scale reading 10 N, 1.0 kg mass, arrows $+F_{scale}$, $+F_{net}$, $+F_g$]

9. The 1.0-kg mass and spring scale are being lifted at a constant speed. The net force on the mass is _____.

a. 0 N   **c.** −10 N
b. +10 N   **d.** +20 N

10. The 1.0-kg mass and spring scale are being lifted so that the 1.0-kg mass is being accelerated in the positive upward direction at 1.0 m/s². What is the net force acting on the mass?

a. 0 N   **b.** +1 N   **c.** −1 N   **d.** +20 N

11. In problem 10, what is the relationship among the magnitudes of the forces acting on the mass?

a. $F_{net} = F_{scale} + F_g$
b. $F_{net} = F_{scale} - F_g$
c. $F_{net} = -(F_{scale} + F_g)$
d. $F_{net} = F_g - F_{scale}$

12. In problem 10, what is the spring scale reading?

a. < 10 N   **b.** 10 N   **c.** >10 N

13. If the scale is accidentally dropped, the net force acting on the 1.0-kg mass is _____.

a. 0 N   **b.** +10 N   **c.** −10 N   **d.** +20 N

14. If the scale is accidentally dropped, the reading of the spring scale as it falls is _____.

a. 0 N   **b.** +10 N   **c.** −10 N   **d.** +20 N

---

6 Study Guide

In your textbook, read about the friction force.

For each of the statements below, write true or rewrite the italicized part to make the statement true.

___true___ **15.** The force of friction *opposes* the motion of an object sliding on a surface.

___parallel___ **16.** The force of friction acts in a direction that is *perpendicular* to the surface on which the object slides.

___opposite___ **17.** The force of friction acts in the *same* direction as the direction of the sliding object.

___true___ **18.** Static friction opposes the *start* of an object's motion.

___does not___ **19.** The static friction force *does* depend on the area of the surfaces in contact.

___does not___ **20.** The kinetic friction force *does* depend on the speed of the relative motion of the surfaces.

In your textbook, read about periodic motion.

Read the sentence below and answer the following questions, using complete sentences.

A stone attached to a spring is oscillating vertically.

21. What is the direction of the stone's acceleration when it is at the lowest point of its oscillation?

The direction of the stone's acceleration is upward.

22. At what point in its oscillation does the stone have the greatest downward acceleration?

It has the greatest downward acceleration at the highest point of its oscillation.

23. At what point does the stone have an acceleration of zero in its downward motion?

It has an acceleration of zero at a displacement of zero, which is the midpoint of its oscillation.

24. At what point does the stone have its maximum upward and downward velocities?

It has its maximum upward and downward velocities at the midpoint of its oscillation.

25. What causes the stone to move through the midpoint of its oscillation?

The inertia of the stone carries it through the midpoint.

6 Study Guide

Section 6.3: Interaction Forces

In your textbook, read about interaction pairs.
Refer to the diagram below to complete the table.

40 N
50 N
Book 1
Book 2

Table 1		
Force	Magnitude	Direction
$F_{\text{book 1 on book 2}}$	40 N	down
$F_{\text{book 2 on book 1}}$	40 N	up
$F_{\text{book 2 on desktop}}$	50 N	down
$F_{\text{desktop on book 2}}$	50 N	up
$F_{\text{books 1 and 2 on desktop}}$	90 N	down
$F_{\text{desktop on books 1 and 2}}$	90 N	up

In your textbook, read about the four fundamental forces.
For each answer given below, write an appropriate question.

1. Answer: an attractive force due to the masses of objects
   Question: **What is the gravitational interaction?**

2. Answer: the electromagnetic interaction
   Question: **What force holds atoms and molecules together?**

3. Answer: two forces that occur within the nucleus of the atom
   Question: **What are the strong nuclear interaction and the weak nuclear interaction?**

4. Answer: the strong nuclear interaction
   Question: **What force acts between the protons and the neutrons that hold the nucleus together?**

5. Answer: the force apparent in some kinds of radioactive decay
   Question: **What is the weak nuclear interaction?**

---

7 Study Guide

Forces and Motion in Two Dimensions

Vocabulary Review

Write the term that correctly completes each statement. Use each term once.

centripetal acceleration
centripetal force
coefficient of kinetic friction
equilibrant
equilibrium
flight time
lever arm
maximum height
normal force
period
projectile
range
rigid rotating object
torque
trajectory
uniform circular motion

1. **lever arm** The perpendicular distance from the axis of rotation to a line along which a force acts is the _____.

2. **trajectory** The path of a projectile is the _____.

3. **equilibrium** A force that produces equilibrium is the _____.

4. **range** The horizontal distance traveled by a projectile is the _____.

5. **centripetal force** A force that acts toward the center of a circle is the _____.

6. **maximum height** The height of a projectile when its vertical velocity is zero is the _____.

7. **rigid rotating object** A mass that rotates around its own axis is a(n) _____.

8. **flight time** The time a projectile is in the air is the _____.

9. **centripetal acceleration** Acceleration toward the center of a circle is the _____.

10. **projectile** An object that has been launched by an initial thrust is a(n) _____.

11. **normal force** A contact force that acts perpendicular to and away from a surface is a(n) _____.

12. **torque** The product of a force and the lever arm is the _____.

13. **uniform circular motion** The movement of an object or a point mass at constant speed around a circle with a fixed radius is _____.

14. **equilibrium** When the net sum of the forces acting on an object is zero, the object is in _____.

15. **coefficient of kinetic friction** The ratio of the force of kinetic friction to the normal force is the _____.

16. **period** The time needed to complete one cycle of motion is a(n) _____.

7 Study Guide

Section 7.1: Forces in Two Dimensions

In your textbook, read about the equilibrant.

For each of the statements below, write true or rewrite the italicized part to make the statement true.

equal to   1. Equilibrium occurs when the resultant of two or more forces equals *a net force greater than zero.*

true   2. An object in equilibrium is motionless or has a *constant velocity.*

true   3. The *equilibrant* is a force that places an object in equilibrium when added to the resultant of all the forces on the object.

true   4. The equilibrant is *equal* in magnitude to the resultant force.

opposite direction   5. The equilibrant acts in the *same direction* as the resultant force.

Refer to the diagram below. Circle the letter of the choice that best completes each statement.

6. Angle θ is ___.
a. 57.5°   (b.) 65°   c. 115°   d. 230°

7. The force equation that represents equilibrium is ___.
a. $F_A - F_B - F_g = 0$ c. $F_A = F_B$
b. $F_A = 2F_g$ (d.) $F_A + F_B - F_g = 0$

8. $F_A \cos \theta =$ ___.
a. $F_A \sin \theta$ (b.) $-F_B \cos \theta$ c. F_g d. $F_g /2$

9. $F_B \sin \theta =$ ___.
a. $F_A \cos \theta$ b. $F_B \cos \theta$ c. F_g (d.) $F_g /2$

10. As θ increases, the tension on each rope ___.
a. increases   (b.) decreases   c. remains the same

---

7 Study Guide

In your textbook, read about motion along an inclined plane.

Draw a free-body diagram representing the situation below. Label angle θ and the horizontal and vertical components of the weight force.

A trunk is placed on a frictionless inclined plane that is at angle θ from the horizontal.

For each situation below, write the letter of the matching item.

e   **11.** calculation of F_{gx}

c   **12.** calculation of F_{gy}

g   **13.** calculation of F_N

b   **14.** calculation of F_g

f   **15.** component of weight force that increases as angle θ increases

a   **16.** component of weight force that decreases as angle θ increases

d   **17.** calculation of acceleration along incline

a. perpendicular component of weight force

b. mg

c. $-F_g \cos \theta$

d. $-g \sin \theta$

e. $-F_g \sin \theta$

f. parallel component of weight force

g. $-F_{gy}$

18. Draw a free-body diagram representing the situation below. Label the +x-axis in the direction of motion. Label the +y-axis. Then draw and label items a–f.

An 82-N trunk is accelerating along a plank inclined at 26.0° from the horizontal. The coefficient of kinetic friction of the trunk and plank is 0.20.

a. horizontal component of the weight force

b. vertical component of the weight force

c. angle of 26.0°

d. normal force

e. force of kinetic friction

f. net force

7 Study Guide

19. Refer to the free-body diagram you drew in problem 18. Complete the table below. Then answer the following questions. Note: sin 26.0° = 0.44; cos 26.0° = 0.90.

20. What will happen to the acceleration of the trunk if the elevated end of the plank is raised? Why?
The acceleration will increase. At a greater angle, F_{gx} increases and F_{gy} decreases.

Because F_{gy} decreases, F_N decreases, causing F_f to decrease also. Because F_{gx} increases and F_f decreases, F_{net} increases, causing a greater acceleration.

Table 1

Variable	Value	Variable	Value
F_g	+82 N	F_N	−74 N
F_{gx}	+36 N	F_f	−15 N
F_{gy}	+74 N	F_{net}	+21 N

21. What will happen to the motion of the trunk if it reaches a section of the plank where the coefficient of sliding friction makes the frictional force equal to the magnitude of the horizontal component of the weight force?
The trunk will slide at a constant speed.

Section 7.2: Projectile Motion

In your textbook, read about solving projectile-motion problems.

Read each problem and complete the table by writing the value of the variable, an X if the variable is not necessary to answer the problem, or a question mark for the unknown. (Assume that the coordinate system has the +y-axis pointing up.) Briefly explain how you would solve the problem.

1. A ball rolls off a horizontal shelf at 2.0 m/s and falls to the floor 1.8 m below. How far from the shelf does the ball land?

Table 2

Variable	Vertical Component	Horizontal Component
acceleration $a = F_{net}/m$	$a_y = -9.8 \text{ m/s}^2$	$a_x = 0.0 \text{ m/s}^2$
velocity $v = v_0 + at$	$v_{y0} = 0.0 \text{ m/s}$	$v_{x0} = 2.0 \text{ m/s}$
	$v_y = \text{X}$	$v_x = 2.0 \text{ m/s}$
position $d = d_0 + v_0 t + \frac{1}{2}at^2$	$y_0 = 1.8 \text{ m}$	$x_0 = 0.0 \text{ m}$
	$y = 0.0 \text{ m}$	$x = \text{?}$

From the vertical displacement equation, find the time for the ball to fall through a displacement of −1.8 m with an initial velocity of 0.0 m/s. Using the time, find the horizontal position of the ball starting at 0.0 m by multiplying its constant horizontal velocity (2.0 m/s) by the time.

---

7 Study Guide

2. A javelin leaves the thrower's hand at a velocity of 21 m/s at an angle of 43° above the horizontal. What is the maximum height the javelin will reach? Note: (21 m/s)(sin 43°) = 14 m/s; (21 m/s)(cos 43°) = 15 m/s.

Table 3

Variable	Vertical Component	Horizontal Component
acceleration $a = F_{net}/m$	$a_y = -9.8 \text{ m/s}^2$	$a_x = \text{X}$
velocity $v = v_0 + at$	$v_{y0} = 14 \text{ m/s}$	$v_{x0} = \text{X}$
	$v_y = 0.0 \text{ m/s}$	$v_x = \text{X}$
position $d = d_0 + v_0 t + \frac{1}{2}at^2$	$y_0 = 0.0$	$x_0 = \text{X}$
	$y = \text{?}$	$x = \text{X}$

From the vertical velocity equation, find the time for the javelin to reach a vertical velocity of 0.0 m/s. Substitute the time in the vertical displacement equation to determine the upward displacement of the javelin with an initial vertical velocity of 14 m/s.

3. A person at the edge of a vertical 12-m cliff throws a rock down at a velocity of 8.5 m/s, 55° below the horizontal. How far from the base of the cliff does the rock land? Assume a coordinate system in which the upward direction is positive. Note: (8.5 m/s)(sin 55°) = 7.0 m/s; (8.5 m/s)(cos 55°) = 4.9 m/s.

Table 4

Variable	Vertical Component	Horizontal Component
acceleration $a = F_{net}/m$	$a_y = -9.8 \text{ m/s}^2$	$a_x = 0.0 \text{ m/s}^2$
velocity $v = v_0 + at$	$v_{y0} = -7.0 \text{ m/s}$	$v_{x0} = 4.9 \text{ m/s}$
	$v_y = \text{X}$	$v_x = 4.9 \text{ m/s}$
position $d = d_0 + v_0 t + at^2$	$y_0 = 12 \text{ m}$	$x_0 = 0.0 \text{ m}$
	$y = 0.0 \text{ m}$	$x = \text{?}$

From the vertical displacement equation, find the time for the rock to move through a vertical displacement of −12 m with an initial velocity of −7.0 m/s. Using the time, find the position of the rock starting at 0.0 m by multiplying its constant horizontal velocity (4.9 m/s) by the time.

7 Study Guide

Section 7.3: Circular Motion

In your textbook, read about circular motion.

Write the term that correctly completes each statement. Use each term once.

center	directions	length	straight line
centripetal	directly	perpendicular	tangent
constant	inversely	radius	

An object is moving in uniform circular motion if the radius of its path and its speed are (1) **constant**. The velocity of an object in uniform circular motion is (2) **perpendicular** to the radius and (3) **tangent** to the circular path.

The velocity vectors have the same (4) **length** but different (5) **directions**. The direction of the centripetal acceleration vector lies along the (6) **radius** and points toward the (7) **center**. The centripetal acceleration is (8) **directly** proportional to the square of the velocity and (9) **inversely** proportional to the radius of the circle. The force that causes the centripetal acceleration is the (10) **centripetal** force. If this force ceases to act on the object in uniform circular motion, the object will travel in a (11) **straight line** tangent to the circle.

In your textbook, read about torque.

The diagrams below represent a force of 65 N applied at three different angles to a wrench 0.25 m long and connected to the head of a bolt. In each diagram, construct the lever arm and label it. Then answer the following questions.

A   B   C

12. In which diagram is the torque the greatest?
The torque is the greatest in diagram A.

13. At what angle θ will the torque be maximal?
The torque will be greatest when θ is 90° or 270°.

14. At what angle θ will the torque be minimal?
The torque will be smallest when θ is 0° or 180°.

8 Study Guide

Universal Gravitation

Vocabulary Review

Write the term that correctly completes each statement. Use each term once.

black hole	inertial mass
centripetal acceleration	inverse square law
gravitational field	Kepler's laws of planetary motion
gravitational mass	law of universal gravitation
	Newton's universal gravitational constant
	period

Kepler's laws of planetary motion

1. The behavior of every planet and satellite is described by ___.

2. **law of universal gravitation** The ___ states that the gravitational force between two objects depends directly on the product of their masses and inversely on the square of the distance between the centers of the masses.

3. **inertial mass** The ___ of an object is $\frac{F_{net}}{a}$, where F_{net} is the net force exerted on an object and a is its acceleration.

4. **gravitational mass** The ___ of an object is defined as $\frac{r^2 F_{grav}}{Gm}$ where F_{grav} is the gravitational force exerted on an object by another object of mass m at a distance r, and G is a universal constant.

5. **gravitational field** The ___ is a property of the region surrounding an object, is due to the object's mass, and interacts with other objects, resulting in a force of attraction.

6. **black hole** A massive and dense object in which light leaving the object is totally bent back to the object, resulting in no light escaping is a(n) ___.

7. **period** The time needed to repeat one complete cycle of motion is a(n) ___.

8. **centripetal acceleration** The direction of ___ is toward the center of motion.

9. **inverse square law** A relationship in which one variable is inversely proportional to the square of another variable is the basis of a(n) ___.

10. **Newton's universal gravitational constant** ___ is the same number for any two masses anywhere.

Name _____

8 Study Guide

Section 8.1: Motions in the Heavens and on Earth

In your textbook, read about observed motion and Kepler's laws.
For each statement below, write true or rewrite the italicized part to make the statement true.

1. Tycho Brahe believed that Earth was the center of the universe.
true

2. Johannes Kepler believed *the sun* was the center of the universe.
true

3. From studying Brahe's astronomical data, Kepler developed three *physical* laws of planetary motion.
mathematical

4. Kepler's first law states that the paths of the planets are *ellipses*.
true

5. In the first law, *the planet* is located at one focus of the planet's orbit.
the sun

6. The second law states that an imaginary line extending from the sun to the planet sweeps out equal *distances* in equal times.
areas

7. The third law states that the *product* of the squares of the periods of any two planets revolving about the sun is equal to the cube of the ratio of their average distances from the sun.
ratio

8. Kepler's *first, second, and third* laws apply to each planet, moon, or satellite individually.
first and second

In your textbook, read about Kepler's laws.
Refer to the diagram to answer the following questions.

9. The shaded portions of planet A's orbit represent areas swept out by an imaginary line from the sun between times t_1 and t_2 and between times t_3 and t_4. If the time intervals $t_2 - t_1$ and $t_4 - t_3$ are equal, what statement can be made about the two shaded areas?
The two areas are equal.

Name _____

8 Study Guide

10. At which of the indicated points in planet B's orbit is its speed the greatest?
Point 1

11. Io, one of Jupiter's moons, has a period of 1.8 days. What information would you need to apply Kepler's third law to determine how far Io is from the center of Jupiter?
You would have to know the period and the distance from the center of Jupiter of another of Jupiter's moons.

In your textbook, read about observed motion and universal gravitation.
For each term on the left, write the letter of the matching item.

c 12. German mathematician who developed three laws of planetary motion

a 13. Danish astronomer who recorded the exact positions of the planets and stars for over 20 years

d 14. English physicist who proposed that gravitational attraction keeps planets and satellites in their orbits

b 15. Italian scientist who discovered the moons of Jupiter

a. Brahe
b. Galileo
c. Kepler
d. Newton

In your textbook, read about universal gravitation.
Refer to the diagram and complete the table for the new values of distance and mass.

Table 1

Distance	Mass A	Mass B	Force
16. d	m_A	$2m_B$	2F
17. d	$2m_A$	m_B	2F
18. d	$2m_A$	$2m_B$	4F
19. $2d$	m_A	m_B	F/4
20. $d/2$	m_A	m_B	4F

8 Study Guide

Read about universal gravitation and weighing the earth.
Answer the following questions, using complete sentences.

21. What apparatus did Cavendish use to find a value for Newton's universal gravitational constant?
Cavendish used a rod and two small spheres suspended on a wire, and two large spheres of lead placed near the smaller spheres.

22. How did Cavendish get an experimental value for gravitational force, *F*, to use in Newton's law of gravitational force?
He measured the angle of rotation of the dumbbell (two small spheres on a rod) in isolation and near the large lead balls, to determine *F*.

23. The gravitational force between two 1.00-kg masses whose centers are 1.00 m apart is defined as 6.67×10^{-11} N. Show that the value of Newton's universal gravitational constant is 6.67×10^{-11} N·m²/kg².

$$F = G\frac{m_1 m_2}{d^2} \qquad G = F\frac{d^2}{m_1 m_2}$$
$$= \frac{(6.67 \times 10^{-11}\ \text{N})(1.00\ \text{m})^2}{(1.00\ \text{kg})(1.00\ \text{kg})}$$
$$= 6.67 \times 10^{-11}\ \text{N} \cdot \text{m}^2/\text{kg}^2$$

8 Study Guide

Section 8.2: Using the Law of Universal Gravitation

In your textbook, read about the motion of planets and satellites.
Write the term that correctly completes each statement.

If a cannonball is fired horizontally from a cannon high atop a mountain, its (1) **motion (velocity)** has both horizontal and vertical components. During the first second of its flight, the cannonball falls (2) **4.9 m**. If fired at the right horizontal velocity, the cannonball will fall 4.9 m at a point where Earth's surface has curved 4.9 m from the (3) **horizontal**. Thus, the cannonball is at the same (4) **height** above Earth as it was initially. The curvature of the cannonball's path will continue to just match the (5) **curvature** of Earth. As a result, the cannonball is said to be in (6) **orbit** of Earth. A horizontal speed of 8 km/s will keep the cannonball at the same altitude, and it will circle Earth as an artificial (7) **satellite**.

In your textbook, read about the gravitational field.
Refer to the diagram on the right to answer the following questions.

8. Draw the vector representing the direction and magnitude of the gravitational field at each of the points 1–5. Indicate the scale you used. Label each gravitational field vector with its magnitude.

9. What is the weight of a 10.0-kg mass located at point 4?
$$F = mg = 10\ \text{kg} \left(\frac{9.8\ \text{m/s}^2}{4}\right) = 25\ \text{N}$$

In your textbook, read about two kinds of masses.
For each term on the left, write the letter of the matching item.

c 10. definition of inertial mass
e 11. definition of gravitational mass
a 12. property of inertial mass
d 13. property of gravitational mass
b 14. hypothesis that inertial and gravitational masses are identical

a. resistance to acceleration
b. principle of equivalence
c. $\dfrac{F_{net}}{a}$
d. attraction toward other masses
e. $\dfrac{r^2 F_{grav}}{Gm}$

8 Study Guide

In your textbook, read about Einstein's theory of gravity.
Circle the letter of the choice that best completes each statement.

15. The effect of gravity can be explained by the _____
    a. equivalence principle
    b. gravitational field
    c. general theory of relativity
    d. inertial field

16. The origin of gravity is proposed in _____
    a. the law of universal gravitation
    b. the gravitational field
    c. the general theory of relativity
    d. the inertial field

17. According to Einstein, gravity is _____
    a. an effect of space
    b. a force
    c. a property of mass
    d. energy

18. The mass of an object causes the space around it to become _____.
    a. more dense
    b. less dense
    c. heated
    d. curved

19. Objects _____ because they follow the shape of the space surrounding a massive object.
    a. are repulsed
    b. become visible
    c. lose mass
    d. undergo accelerations

20. The effect of mass on space _____
    a. accounts for the deflection of light by massive objects
    b. explains the existence of black holes
    c. models gravitational attraction
    d. all of these

---

9 Study Guide

Momentum and Its Conservation

Vocabulary Review

Write the term that correctly completes each statement. Use each term once.

angular momentum	impulse-momentum theorem	law of conservation of momentum	Newton's third law
closed system	internal forces	linear momentum	recoil
external forces	isolated system	Newton's second law	torque
impulse			vector

1. **Newton's second law** — The acceleration of a body is directly proportional to the net force on it and inversely proportional to its mass; this is a statement of _____.

2. **Newton's third law** — When one object exerts a force on a second object, the second exerts a force on the first that is equal in magnitude but opposite in direction; this is a statement of _____.

3. **vector** — A quantity that has magnitude and direction is a(n) _____.

4. **impulse** — The product of the average force exerted on an object and the time interval through which it acts is the _____.

5. **linear momentum** — The product of the mass and velocity of a body is its _____.

6. **impulse-momentum theorem** — The _____ states that the impulse on an object is equal to the change of momentum that it causes.

7. **angular momentum** — The quantity of motion used with objects rotating about a fixed axis is _____.

8. **closed system** — A(n) _____ does not gain or lose mass.

9. **internal forces** — Forces within a closed system are _____.

10. **external forces** — All the forces that act on the system from outside the system are _____.

11. **isolated system** — A closed system in which the net external force on the system is zero is a(n) _____.

12. **law of conservation of momentum** — The _____ states that the momentum of any closed system with no net external force acting on it does not change.

13. **recoil** — The backward motion of part of an isolated, closed system due to an internal force is _____.

14. **torque** — The product of force and a lever arm is _____.

9 Study Guide

•••••••••••••

Section 9.1: Impulse and Momentum

In your textbook, read about relating impulse and momentum.

The diagram below shows the force-time graph of a force acting on an 8.0-kg cart initially at rest on a frictionless surface. Circle the letter of the choice that best completes each statement.

Force (N) vs Time (s)

1. The magnitude of the force acting on the cart is _____.
   a. +2.0 N   **c.** +10.0 N
   (b.) +8.0 N   **d.** +20.0 N

2. The force acted on the cart for a duration of _____.
   a. 2.0 s   **c.** 8.0 s
   (b.) 6.0 s   **d.** 10.0 s

3. The shaded area of the graph represents _____.
   a. force   **c.** momentum
   (b.) impulse   **d.** acceleration

4. The shaded area of the graph is represented algebraically by _____.
   (a.) $F\Delta t$ **c.** $F/\Delta t$
   b. mv **d.** m/v

5. The impulse acting on the cart is _____.
   a. 0 N·s
   b. +2.0 N·s
   c. +8.0 N·s
   (d.) +48 N·s

6. The momentum of the cart is represented algebraically by _____.
   a. $F\Delta t$ **c.** $F/\Delta t$
   (b.) mv **d.** m/v

7. The change of momentum of the cart is _____.
   a. 0 kg·m/s   **c.** +8.0 kg·m/s
   b. +2.0 m/s   **(d.)** +48 kg·m/s

8. The final velocity of the cart is _____.
   a. 0 m/s   **c.** 12 m/s
   (b.) 6.0 m/s   **d.** 48 m/s

---

9 Study Guide

•••••••••••••

In your textbook, read about using the impulse-momentum theorem.

Read each of the statements below. In the diagrams, draw and label the velocities of the sport utility van before and after the event described. In the vector diagram section, draw and label the momentum vectors p_1 and p_2, and the impulse vector $F\Delta t$.

9. The van has a velocity of +30 km/h and uniformly comes to a stop in 15 s.

Before   After   Vector diagram

10. The van, initially at rest, uniformly reaches a velocity of +30 km/h in 20 s.

Vector diagram

11. In 5 s, the van uniformly backs up to a speed of 5 km/h.

Vector diagram

12. The van has a velocity of −5 km/h and uniformly comes to a stop in 5 s.

Vector diagram

9 Study Guide

In your textbook, read about the impulse-momentum theorem as it applies to air bags.

Answer the following questions, using complete sentences.

13. In what two ways can impulse be increased?

Increase the size of the force or increase the time during which the force is acting.

14. In terms of impulse, how does an air bag reduce injuries that would be caused by the steering wheel during an accident?

Both a steering wheel and an air bag deliver the same magnitude impulse to stop similar drivers braking from the same speed under similar conditions. The impulse of the steering wheel consists of a large force that is delivered in a very short time. The impulse of the air bag consists of a small force that is delivered over a longer time. So the force of the air bag on the driver is less than the force of a steering wheel.

In your textbook, read about angular momentum.

For each of the statements below, write true or rewrite the italicized part to make the statement true.

true	15. The speed of a rotating object changes only if *torque* is applied to it.
angular	16. The quantity of angular motion that is used with rotating objects is called *linear* momentum.
true	17. When a *torque* acts on an object, its angular momentum changes.
perpendicular	18. Angular momentum is the product of the object's mass, displacement from the center of rotation, and the component of its velocity *parallel* to that displacement.
increases	19. If the angular momentum of a rotating object is constant and its distance to the center of rotation decreases, then its velocity *decreases*.
true	20. The torque on the planets orbiting the sun is zero because the gravitational force is directed toward the sun and, therefore, is not *perpendicular* to its velocity.
constant	21. Because the torque on each planet is zero, each planet's angular momentum is *zero*.
faster	22. When a planet's distance from the sun becomes smaller, the planet moves *slower*.

---

9 Study Guide

Section 9.2: The Conservation of Momentum

In your textbook, read about two-particle collisions.

Read the sentence below and answer the following questions, using complete sentences.

Two balls of unequal mass traveling at different speeds collide head-on and rebound in opposite directions.

1. How does the force that ball A exerts on ball B compare to the force that ball B exerts on ball A?

The two forces are equal in magnitude but opposite in direction.

2. How do the impulses received by both balls compare?

The impulses must be equal in magnitude but opposite in direction.

3. How do the sums of the momenta of the balls before and after the collision compare?

The sums of the momenta of the balls before and after the collision are equal.

Write the term that correctly completes each statement. Use each term once.

change	conditions	interaction	isolated system
closed system	external forces	internal forces	law of conservation of momentum

A system that doesn't gain or lose mass is a(n) **(4)** _**internal forces**_ . All the forces within a closed system are **(5)** _**external forces**_ . All the forces outside the system are **(6)** _**isolated system**_ . When the net external force on a closed system is zero, the system is a(n) **(7)** _____. The **(8)** _**law of conservation of momentum**_ states that the momentum of any closed system with no net external forces does not **(9)** _**change**_ . Using this law, you can connect **(10)** _**conditions**_ before and after an interaction without knowing any of the details of the **(11)** _**interaction**_ .

In your textbook, read about explosions.

Read the paragraph below. Then circle the letter of the choice that best completes each statement.

Two in-line skaters are skating on such a smooth surface that there are no external forces. They both start from rest. Skater A gives skater B a push in the *positive* direction.

12. The momentum of the system before the push is _____.

   a. >0   **b.** 0   c. <0

13. The momentum of the system after the push is _____.

   a. >0   **b.** 0   c. <0

14. The momentum of skater B after the push, p_{B2}, is _____.

   a. >0   b. 0   c. <0

10 Study Guide

Use with Chapter 10.

Energy, Work, and Simple Machines

Vocabulary Review

Write the term that correctly completes each statement. Use each term once.

compound machine	kinetic energy	system
efficiency	machine	watt
effort force	mechanical advantage	work
energy	power	work-energy theorem
ideal mechanical advantage	resistance force	
joule	simple machine	

1. _____ kinetic energy _____   The energy resulting from motion of an object is called _____.

2. _____ work-energy theorem _____   The _____ states that the work done on an object is equal to the object's change in kinetic energy.

3. _____ effort force _____   The force exerted on a machine is called the _____.

4. _____ efficiency _____   The ratio of the output work to the input work is a machine's _____.

5. _____ joule _____   The SI unit of work is the _____.

6. _____ watt _____   The unit of power equal to 1 J of energy transferred in 1 s is the _____.

7. _____ resistance force _____   A machine exerts _____.

8. _____ work _____   The product of the applied force and the distance through which the force is applied is _____.

9. _____ energy _____   The ability of an object to produce a change in itself or its surroundings is _____.

10. _____ power _____   The rate of doing work is _____.

11. _____ machine _____   A device that changes the magnitude or direction of a force is a(n) _____.

12. _____ ideal mechanical advantage _____   The ratio of effort distance to resistance distance is a machine's _____.

13. _____ mechanical advantage _____   The ratio of resistance force to effort force is a machine's _____.

14. _____ compound machine _____   A device that consists of two or more simple machines linked so that the resistance force of one machine becomes the effort force of the second machine is a(n) _____.

15. _____ system _____   A defined group of objects is called a(n) _____.

16. _____ simple machine _____   A lever, pulley, wheel and axle, inclined plane, wedge, or screw is a(n) _____.

---

9 Study Guide

15. The momentum of skater A after the push, p_{A2}, is _____.

 a. $+p_{B2}$ **b.** 0   **c.** $-p_{B2}$

16. If the velocity of skater B after the push is represented by v_{B2}, the velocity of skater A after the push, v_{A2}, is _____.

 a. $+\left(\dfrac{m_A}{m_B}\right)v_{B2}$ **c.** $-\left(\dfrac{m_B}{m_A}\right)v_{B2}$

 b. 0   **d.** $-\left(\dfrac{m_A}{m_B}\right)v_{B2}$

In your textbook, read about two-dimensional collisions.

Read the paragraph below. Label the momentum diagram, indicating the final momentum of the system p_2, the momenta of both balls after the collision p_{A2} and p_{B2}, and the 50.0° angle.

A 4.0-kg ball, A, is moving at a speed of 3.0 m/s. It collides with a stationary ball, B, of the same mass. After the collision, ball A moves off in a direction of 50.0° to the left of its original direction. Ball B moves off in a direction of 90.0° to the right of ball A's final direction.

For each situation below, write the letter of the matching item.

 d **17.** initial momentum of the system

 b **18.** magnitude of final momentum of the system

 a **19.** magnitude of ball A's momentum after the collision

 c **20.** magnitude of ball B's momentum after the collision

 a. $(12\ \text{kg·m/s})(\cos 50.0°)$

 b. $12\ \text{kg·m/s}$

 c. $(12\ \text{kg·m/s})(\sin 50.0°)$

 d. p_A

10 Study Guide

· · · · · · · · · · · · · ·

Section 10.1: Energy and Work

In your textbook, read about energy.

For each phrase on the left, write the letter of the matching item.

__f__   **1.** symbol for kinetic energy

__c__   **2.** calculation of kinetic energy

__a__   **3.** symbol for work

__b__   **4.** calculation of work

__d__   **5.** statement that the work done on an object is equal to the object's change in kinetic energy

__e__   **6.** equivalent to 1 kg · $\dfrac{m^2}{s^2}$

a. W

b. Fd

c. $\dfrac{mv^2}{2}$

d. $\Delta K = W$

e. 1 J

f. K

In your textbook, read about energy transfer and calculating work.

Circle the letter of the choice that best completes each statement.

7. Through the process of doing work, energy can move between the environment and the system as the result of _____.

   (a.) forces

   b. matter

   c. momentum

   d. impulse

8. If the environment does work on the system, the quantity of work is _____.

   a. negative

   (b.) positive

   c. zero

   d. undetermined

9. If the environment does work on the system, the energy of the system _____.

   a. decreases

   (b.) increases

   c. remains the same

   d. cannot be determined

10. If the system does work on the environment, the energy of the system _____.

   (a.) decreases

   b. increases

   c. is undetermined

   d. remains the same

11. In the equation $W = Fd$, Fd holds only for _____ forces exerted in the direction of displacement.

   (a.) constant

   b. frictional

   c. gravitational

   d. positive

12. In the equation $W = Fd \cos\theta$, angle θ is the angle between F and the _____.

   a. x-axis

   b. y-axis

   (c.) direction of the displacement

   d. vertical direction

---

10 Study Guide

· · · · · · · · · · · · · ·

For each situation shown, write its letter next to the number of the correct expression.

13. __B, E, F__ $W > 0$

14. __A, D__ $W = 0$

15. __C__ $W < 0$

The diagram below is the force-displacement graph of a crate that was pushed horizontally. Answer the following questions.

16. What was the magnitude of the force acting on the crate?

   30.0 N

17. How far did the crate move horizontally?

   0.5 m

18. What does the area under the curve of this graph represent?

   The area represents the work done on the crate.

19. How much work was done in moving the crate 0.1 m?

   3.0 J

For each term on the left, write the letter of the matching item.

__a__   **20.** rate of doing work

__c__   **21.** unit of power

__e__   **22.** symbol for power

__b__   **23.** calculation of power

__d__   **24.** 1000 watts

a. power

b. $\dfrac{W}{t}$

c. watt

d. kW

e. P

10 Study Guide

Section 10.2: Machines

In your textbook, read about mechanical advantage and efficiency.

For each of the statements below, write true or rewrite the italicized part to make the statement true.

1. *A machine* makes doing a task easier.

true

2. A machine eases the load by changing either the magnitude or the direction of *energy*.

a force

3. Work is the transfer of *energy* by mechanical means.

true

4. A machine *cannot* create energy.

true

5. The force that is exerted on a machine is the *effort force.*

true

6. The *product* of the resistance force and the effort force is the mechanical advantage of the machine.

ratio

7. When the mechanical advantage of a machine is greater than one, the machine *decreases* the effort force.

increases

8. A real machine *cannot* have a mechanical advantage that is less than one.

can

9. The *ideal mechanical advantage* of a machine can be used to calculate the distance the effort force moves compared to the distance the resistance force moves.

true

10. If a machine transfers all of the energy applied to it, then the output work is *less than* the input work.

equal to

11. The IMA of most machines is fixed by their *design.*

true

12. The efficiency of a machine is the *ratio* of work output to work input.

true

13. An ideal machine has an efficiency *greater than* 100 percent.

equal to

---

10 Study Guide

14. A real machine has an efficiency *equal to* 100 percent.

less than

15. The *lower* the efficiency of a machine, the greater the effort force needed to produce the same resistance force.

true

In your textbook, read about simple machines.

The numbers below correspond to the numbers in the diagram. For each number, write the letter of the matching term from the right column. A term may be used more than once.

16. **f**

17. **e**

18. **b**

19. **d**

20. **c**

21. **g**

22. **f**

23. **a**

24. **d**

25. **b**

26. **e**

27. **c**

a. axle
b. F_e
c. F_r
d. pivot point
e. r_e
f. r_r
g. wheel

Refer to the machine on the left in the diagram above. Circle the letter of the choice that best completes the statement or answers the question.

28. What is the value of the MA?

a. **>1**
b. = 1
c. <1
d. cannot be determined

29. What is the value of the IMA?

a. **>1**
b. = 1
c. <1
d. cannot be determined

30. To increase the IMA of the machine, you would _____.

a. increase r_r
b. **increase r_e**
c. decrease r_e
d. decrease F_r

---

10 Study Guide

Name _____

In your textbook, read about compound machines.
Refer to the diagram below. For each term on the left, write the letter of the matching item.

Rear sprocket
Front sprocket
$F_{\text{on pedal}}$
Pedal
$F_{\text{on chain}}$
$F_{\text{by chain}}$
Rear wheel
$F_{\text{on road}}$

g   **31.** MA of pedal and front sprocket

c   **32.** IMA of pedal and front sprocket

b   **33.** MA of rear sprocket and rear wheel

a   **34.** IMA of rear sprocket and rear wheel

d   **35.** MA of pedal and rear wheel

f   **36.** IMA of pedal and rear wheel

a. $\dfrac{\text{rear sprocket radius}}{\text{wheel radius}}$

b. $\dfrac{F_{\text{on road}}}{F_{\text{by chain}}}$

c. $\dfrac{\text{pedal radius}}{\text{front sprocket radius}}$

d. $\dfrac{F_{\text{on road}}}{F_{\text{on pedal}}}$

e. $\dfrac{\text{pedal radius}}{\text{wheel radius}}$

f. $\dfrac{\text{rear sprocket radius}}{\text{front sprocket radius}} \times \dfrac{\text{pedal radius}}{\text{wheel radius}}$

g. $\dfrac{F_{\text{on chain}}}{F_{\text{on pedal}}}$

Refer to the diagram above. Write the value <1, $=1$, or >1 to complete the table below.

Table 1

Machine	MA Value	IMA Value
pedal and front sprocket	**37.** >1	**38.** >1
rear sprocket and rear wheel	**39.** <1	**40.** <1
pedal and rear wheel	**41.** <1	**42.** <1

Date _____ Period _____ Name _____

Use with Chapter 11.

11 Study Guide

Energy

Vocabulary Review

Write the term that correctly completes each statement. Use each term once.

closed system   inelastic collision   mechanical energy
elastic collision   isolated system   momentum
elastic potential energy   joule   reference level
energy   kinetic energy   work
gravitational potential energy   law of conservation of energy   work-energy theorem

1. kinetic energy — The energy of an object resulting from motion is _____.

2. work-energy theorem — The _____ states that the work done on an object is equal to the object is change in kinetic energy.

3. elastic potential energy — The energy in a compressed spring is _____.

4. closed system — A system that does not gain or lose mass is a(n) _____.

5. elastic collision — A collision in which the kinetic energy doesn't change is a(n) _____.

6. joule — The SI unit of work is the _____.

7. inelastic collision — A collision in which kinetic energy decreases is a(n) _____.

8. gravitational potential energy — Energy stored in the Earth-object system as a result of gravitational interaction between the object and Earth is _____.

9. work — The product of the applied force and the distance through which the force is applied is _____.

10. energy — The ability of an object to produce a change in itself or its surroundings is _____.

11. law of conservation of energy — Within a closed, isolated system, energy can change form, but the total amount of energy is constant; this is a statement of the _____.

12. mechanical energy — The sum of the kinetic energy and gravitational potential energy is _____.

13. isolated system — A closed system in which the net external force on the system is zero is a(n) _____.

14. reference level — The position at which the potential energy is defined to be zero is a(n) _____.

15. momentum — The product of the mass and velocity of an object is its _____.

11 Study Guide

Section 11.1: The Many Forms of Energy

In your textbook, read about modeling the work-energy theorem.

The diagram below shows changes to your finances for the first week in October. Circle the choice that best completes the statement or answers the question.

1. How much money did you have on hand on Monday morning, October 1?
   a. $85   c. $40
   (b.) $45   d. $0

2. How much money did you have on hand on Tuesday?
   a. $85   c. $40
   (b.) $45   d. $0

3. By the end of the day on Wednesday, how much money did you have on hand?
   (a.) $85   b. $45   c. $40   d. $0

4. On Thursday, what happened to the amount of money you had on hand?
   a. It increased.   (b.) It decreased.   c. It remained unchanged.

5. By the end of the day on Saturday, how much money had you spent during the week?
   a. $75   b. $50   (c.) $40   d. $0

6. How much money did you have on hand on the morning of Monday, October 8?
   a. $75   (b.) $55   c. $40   d. $0

Read the following situations and draw before-and-after energy diagrams in the space provided.

7. A partially loaded shopping cart has a kinetic energy of 60 J. A short time later the cart's kinetic energy is 60 J.

8. A partially loaded shopping cart has a kinetic energy of 60 J. You do 20 J of work on the cart.

---

11 Study Guide

9. You do 50 J of work on a shopping cart at rest.

10. A partially loaded shopping cart has a kinetic energy of 60 J. You do −40 J of work on the cart.

11. You do 70 J of work on a partially loaded shopping cart, giving it a total kinetic energy of 80 J.

12. A partially filled shopping cart has a kinetic energy of 80 J. The work you do on the cart stops it.

11 Study Guide

In your textbook, read about kinetic energy.
Circle the letter of the choice that best answers each question. Refer to Table 11-1 on page 250 of your textbook.

13. What accounts for the aircraft carrier having a greater kinetic energy than the orbiting satellite?
    (a.) mass   b. speed   c. mass and speed

14. What accounts for the pitched baseball having a greater kinetic energy than the falling nickel?
    a. mass   b. speed   (c.) mass and speed

15. What accounts for the bumblebee having more kinetic energy than the snail?
    a. mass   (b.) speed   c. mass and speed

16. How much work would have to be done to the truck starting from rest to give it half the listed kinetic energy?
    a. 0 J   b. 2.2×10^3 J   c. 5.7×10^5 J   (d.) 1.1×10^6 J

17. How fast would the truck be moving if it had half the listed kinetic energy?
    a. -52 km/h   b. 0 km/h   (c.) 71 km/h   d. 118 km/h

In your textbook, read about gravitational and elastic potential energies.
For each statement below, write true or rewrite the italicized part to make the statement true.

18. __true__ If a juggler's ball is considered a system, work is done on it by gravity and *the juggler's hand.*

19. __true__ On the way up, the work done on the ball by gravity is *-mgh.*

20. __increases__ On the way down, the work done on the ball by gravity *decreases* the ball's kinetic energy.

21. __equal to__ When the ball returns to the height of the juggler's hand, its kinetic energy is *more than* the kinetic energy it had when it left the juggler's hand.

22. __gravitational potential energy__ If you choose a system consisting of the juggler's ball and Earth, energy is stored in the system as *kinetic energy.*

23. __is constant__ In a system consisting of the juggler's ball and Earth, the sum of the kinetic and potential energies *changes* because no work is done on the system.

24. __equal to__ If the height of the juggler's hand is the reference point, when the ball returns to that height, its gravitational potential energy is *less than* 0 J.

25. __elastic potential energy__ When a running pole-vaulter plants the end of a pole into a socket in the ground, the vaulter's kinetic energy is stored as *gravitational potential energy* in the bent pole.

---

11 Study Guide

Section 11.2: Conservation of Energy

In your textbook, read about the conservation of mechanical energy.
The diagram below shows the position of two identical balls initially at rest. Complete the following table, assuming there is neither air resistance nor frictional forces on either ball. Using the table as a guide, construct graphs of E, U_g, and K versus d for ball A on the grid. Then answer the following question.

Table 1

Location (d)	Ball A			Ball B		
	E	U_g	K	E	U_g	K
1.00 m	6.0 J	6.0 J	0 J	6.0 J	6.0 J	0 J
0.50 m	6.0 J	3.0 J	3.0 J	6.0 J	3.0 J	3.0 J
0.00 m	6.0 J	0 J	6.0 J	6.0 J	0 J	6.0 J

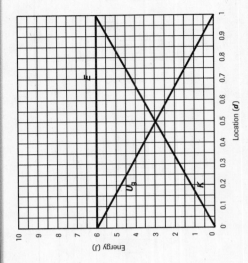

1. How would the graphs of E, U_g, and K versus d for ball B compare with the graphs you constructed for ball A?
   __They would be the same.__

12 Study Guide

Thermal Energy
Vocabulary Review

Write the term that correctly completes each statement. Use each term once.

absolute zero	heat of fusion	second law of thermodynamics
calorimeter	heat of vaporization	specific heat
conduction	kelvin melting point	thermal energy
entropy	kinetic-molecular theory	thermodynamics
first law of thermodynamics	melting point	thermometer
heat engine	radiation	

1. __thermometer__   A device that measures temperature is a(n) _____.

2. __conduction__   The transfer of kinetic energy when particles collide is _____.

3. __second law of thermodynamics__   The _____ states that natural processes go in a direction that maintains or increases the universe's total entropy.

4. __kinetic-molecular theory__   The _____ states that matter is made up of particles that are always in motion.

5. __heat engine__   A device that continuously converts thermal energy to mechanical energy is a(n) _____.

6. __melting point__   The temperature at which a substance changes from solid to liquid is called the _____.

7. __absolute zero__   The lowest possible temperature is _____.

8. __calorimeter__   A device that measures changes in thermal energy is a(n) _____.

9. __radiation__   The transfer of energy by electromagnetic waves is _____.

10. __specific heat__   The amount of energy that must be added to raise the temperature of a unit mass one unit is the _____ of a material.

11. __kelvin__   The unit of temperature on the Kelvin scale is the _____.

12. __heat of fusion__   The amount of energy needed to melt 1 kg of a substance is the _____ of the substance.

13. __first law of thermodynamics__   The _____ states that the total increase in thermal energy of a system is the sum of the work done on it and the heat added to it.

14. __entropy__   The disorder in a system is _____.

15. __thermodynamics__   The study of heat is _____.

16. __thermal energy__   The overall energy of motion of the particles that make up the object is the _____ of the object.

17. __heat of vaporization__   The amount of thermal energy needed to change 1 kg of liquid to a gas is the _____.

---

11 Study Guide

In your textbook, read about analyzing collisions.

The diagrams below show the motion of two identical 2.0 kg boxes before and after they collide. Sketch bar graphs of the energy of each system before and after the collision. Circle the letter of the choice that best completes each statement.

2. The conservation of momentum occurs in collisions _____.
   a. A and B   **b.** A and C   **c.** B and C   **(d.)** A, B, and C

3. An elastic collision occurs in collision _____.
   (a.) A   **b.** B   **c.** C

4. An inelastic collision occurs in collision _____.
   a. A   **b.** B   **(c.)** C

5. A superelastic collision occurs in collision _____.
   a. A   **(b.)** B   **c.** C

6. The conservation of energy occurs in collisions _____.
   a. A and B   **b.** A and C   **c.** B and C   **(d.)** A, B, and C

Name _____

12 Study Guide

• • • • • • • •

Section 12.1: Temperature and Thermal Energy

In your textbook, read about the theory and measurement of thermal energy.

For each of the statements below, write true or rewrite the italicized part to make the statement true.

1. _____ **true** _____ In a hot body, particles tend to move *faster* than in a cooler body.

2. _____ **an average** _____ At a given temperature, all the particles in a body have *the same energy*.

3. _____ **does** _____ The thermal energy in an object *doesn't* depend on the number of particles in it.

4. _____ **true** _____ Two bodies are in *thermal* equilibrium if they are at the same temperature.

5. _____ **true** _____ A kelvin is equal in size to a *Celsius* degree.

6. _____ **−273.15°C or 0 K** _____ Absolute zero is equal to *0°C*.

7. _____ $T_c + 275.15 = T_k$ _____ The equation that allows conversion of a Celsius temperature to a Kelvin temperature is $T_k + 273.15 = T_c$.

8. _____ **kinetic-molecular** _____ The *caloric* theory could successfully explain why objects become warm when they are rubbed together.

In your textbook, read about temperature measurement.

Express each temperature in the scale indicated.

9. The freezing point of water, in degrees Celsius _____ **0°C**

10. The freezing point of water, in kelvins _____ **273.15 K**

11. The boiling point of water, in degrees Celsius _____ **100°C**

12. The boiling point of water, in kelvins _____ **373.15 K**

13. The lowest possible temperature, in degrees Celsius _____ **−273.15°C**

14. The lowest possible temperature, in kelvins _____ **0 K**

In your textbook, read about thermal-energy transfer.

For each term on the left, write the corresponding symbol.

Q	**15.** heat
°C	**16.** degree Celsius
K	**17.** kelvin
C	**18.** specific heat
ΔE	**19.** energy change
ΔT	**20.** temperature change

Name _____

12 Study Guide

• • • • • • • •

In your textbook, read about thermal-energy transfer and specific heat.

Answer the following questions.

21. Describe the typical direction of heat transfer when a cooler body is in contact with a warmer one.

Heat flows from the warmer body to the cooler one.

22. Write the equation for calculating the amount of heat transferred, given the mass, specific heat, and temperature change.

$Q = mC\Delta T$

23. Name the three means of thermal transfer.

Thermal transfer takes place through conduction, convection, and radiation.

24. How does the specific heat of liquid water compare in general with that of most other substances?

Water's specific heat is higher than that of most other substances.

In your textbook, read about calorimetry.

The diagram below shows a calorimeter just after addition of an object and after thermal equilibrium is reached. Refer to the diagram to answer the following questions.

25. What is the approximate value of T_f?

40°C

26. What is the approximate value of T_i?

25°C

27. Is the value of ΔT for the water positive or negative?

positive

28. Has heat flowed from the object to the water, or to the object from the water?

Heat flowed from the object to the water.

29. Is Q for the object positive or negative?

negative

30. Is Q for the water positive or negative?

positive

31. Assuming no heat loss to the surroundings, how do the ΔE values for the water and the object compare?

They are equal but opposite in sign—negative for the object and positive for the water.

12 Study Guide

Section 12.2: Change of State and Laws of Thermodynamics

In your textbook, read about changes of state.

Circle the letter of the choice that best completes the statement or answers the question.

1. The energy needed to melt 1 kg of a substance is called the _____.
   a. heat of vaporization
   b. entropy
   c. (heat of fusion) ← circled
   d. melting point

2. The temperature at which all added thermal energy converts a material from liquid to gas is the _____.
   a. melting point
   b. (boiling point) ← circled
   c. heat of fusion
   d. heat of vaporization

3. How do the specific heats of ice, liquid water, and steam compare?
   a. They are equal.
   b. That of ice is highest.
   c. That of steam is highest.
   d. (That of liquid water is highest.) ← circled

4. Which equation correctly relates heat, mass, and heat of vaporization?
   a. $Q = m/H_v$
   b. $Q = H_v/m$
   c. $Q = m + H_v$
   d. ($Q = mH_v$) ← circled

5. Is Q positive or negative for a melting solid and for a freezing liquid?
   a. negative in both cases
   b. positive in both cases
   c. (positive for the melting solid, negative for the freezing liquid) ← circled
   d. negative for the melting solid, positive for the freezing liquid

---

12 Study Guide

In your textbook, read about changes of state.

For each of the statements below, write true or rewrite the italicized part to make it true.

6. **absorbs**   When a liquid changes to a gas, it *releases* thermal energy.

7. **true**   During melting, the kinetic energy of the particles *does not change.*

8. **true**   An increase in the range of particle speeds in an object represents an *increase* in entropy.

9. **does**   The heat required to melt a solid *does not* depend on the mass of the sample.

10. **true**   In a plot of temperature versus heat added, the portion of the graph representing the boiling process is *horizontal*.

In your textbook, read about the first and second laws of thermodynamics.

Decide whether each statement relates more closely to the first law of thermodynamics or to the second law. Write first law or second law.

11. Total entropy tends to increase.
    second law

12. Energy is neither created nor destroyed.
    first law

13. Thermal-energy increases depend on the work done and the heat added.
    first law

14. Heat does not flow from a cold body to a hot body.
    second law

15. Waste heat is generated whenever thermal energy is converted into mechanical energy.
    second law

16. Energy can be converted from one form to another.
    first law

17. The total amount of useful energy tends to decrease.
    second law

Physics: Principles and Problems

13 Study Guide

States of Matter

Vocabulary Review

Write the term that correctly completes each statement. Use each term once.

adhesion	capillary action	evaporation	pressure
amorphous solid	cohesive force	fluid	surface tension
Archimedes' principle	condensation	pascal	thermal expansion
Bernoulli's principle	crystal lattice	Pascal's principle	volatile
buoyant force		plasma	

1. **pascal** — The SI unit of pressure is the _____.

2. **buoyant force** — An upward force on an object in a liquid is a(n) _____.

3. **plasma** — A _____ contains electrons and positively charged ions.

4. **crystal lattice** — A fixed pattern of particles within a solid is a(n) _____.

5. **thermal expansion** — An increase in temperature may cause _____.

6. **Archimedes' principle** — "The magnitude of the buoyant force on an object equals the weight of fluid displaced by the object" is a statement of _____.

7. **Pascal's principle** — "A change in pressure at any point on a confined fluid is transmitted undiminished throughout the fluid" is a statement of _____.

8. **surface tension** — The tendency of the surface of a liquid to contract to the smallest possible area is _____.

9. **volatile** — A liquid that evaporates quickly is _____.

10. **elasticity** — The ability of an object to return to its original form when external forces are removed is _____.

11. **Bernoulli's principle** — "As the velocity of a fluid increases, the pressure exerted by the fluid decreases" is a statement of _____.

12. **evaporation** — The escape of particles from a liquid's surface is _____.

13. **pressure** — Force divided by area equals _____.

14. **adhesion** — The attractive force between particles of different substances is _____.

15. **amorphous solid** — A substance that has definite volume and shape but no regular crystal structure is a(n) _____.

16. **capillary action** — The rise of a liquid up a narrow tube is due to _____.

17. **condensation** — The change of a gas to a liquid is _____.

18. **cohesive force** — An attractive force between particles of the same substance, caused by electromagnetic attraction, is a(n) _____.

19. **fluid** — A _____ flows and has no definite shape of its own.

---

12 Study Guide

In your textbook, read about devices that convert energy.
For each of the statements below, write true or rewrite the italicized part to make it true.

18. A heat engine converts thermal energy to mechanical energy.
    true

19. A heat engine requires a low-temperature receptacle into which *mechanical* energy can be delivered.
    thermal

20. An automobile internal combustion engine is an example of *a heat pump.*
    heat engine

21. Using mechanical energy, a refrigerator removes thermal energy from a warmer body.
    true

22. A heat pump is a refrigerator that can run in *one direction.*
    two directions

In your textbook, read about entropy.
Decide whether the process is likely to occur spontaneously. Write yes or no.

23. A hot body absorbs thermal energy from a cooler one. **no**

24. A set of particles becomes more orderly. **no**

25. An engine generates waste heat. **yes**

26. Gas particles collect in one corner of a container. **no**

27. Total entropy increases. **yes**

28. Usable energy increases. **no**

13 Study Guide

Section 13.1: The Fluid States

In your textbook, read about measures and equivalents for pressure.
For each term on the left, write the corresponding symbol.

Answer	#	Term
P	1.	symbol for pressure
F_g	2.	symbol for weight
A	3.	symbol for surface area
Pa	4.	unit of pressure
N	5.	unit of weight
F/A	6.	definition of pressure
$1\ N/m^2$	7.	equivalent to 1 Pa
101 kPa	8.	atmospheric pressure at sea level

In your textbook, read about pressure and fluids.
For each of the statements below, write true or rewrite the italicized part to make the statement true.

9. The shape of a container *does not affect* the pressure at any given depth of the fluid it contains.
true

10. The buoyant force on an object depends on the weight of the *object*.
displaced fluid

11. The *apparent weight* of an object in water is equal to its actual weight minus the upward buoyant force.
true

12. Fluids flow and have no definite *volume*.
shape

13. The pressure of the water on a body beneath its surface equals *phg*.
true

14. Bernoulli's principle applies to *turbulent* flow only.
streamlined

---

13 Study Guide

In your textbook, read about Bernoulli's principle, Archimedes' principle, and Pascal's principle.
Complete the table below by writing the name of the principle that is most clearly illustrated in each situation.
Choose among Bernoulli's principle, Archimedes' principle, and Pascal's principle.

Situation	Principle Illustrated
15. A man uses the hydraulic brake to stop his truck.	Pascal's principle
16. An airplane rises into the air.	Bernoulli's principle
17. An ice cube floats in water.	Archimedes' principle
18. A piece of paper rises when wind blows across it.	Bernoulli's principle
19. A fish uses its air bladder to move downward in water.	Archimedes' principle
20. Ketchup rises up in a squeezed plastic bottle.	Pascal's principle
21. A person feels lighter in water than on land.	Archimedes' principle
22. Curved airfoils help hold down the rear wheels of race cars.	Bernoulli's principle

Write the term that correctly completes each statement.

The relationship between the (23) **velocity** of a moving fluid and the (24) **pressure** exerted by the fluid is described by Bernoulli's principle.

Airfoils are devices that use this principle to produce (25) **lift**, a net force in a(n) (26) **upward** direction, when moving through a(n) (27) **fluid**. An airplane wing is curved so that the (28) **top** surface has a greater curve than the (29) **bottom** surface. Air moving over the top of the wing moves a(n) (30) **greater** distance, and therefore travels at a greater speed. The air pressure over the wing is (31) **less** than the pressure under the wing. The flow of a fluid can be represented by a set of lines called (32) **streamlines**. The closer the lines are to each other, the greater is the (33) **velocity** and the lower is the (34) **pressure** of the fluid. Swirling of such lines indicates that the fluid flow is (35) **turbulent**, and Bernoulli's principle does not apply to the situation.

13 Study Guide

In your textbook, read about cohesive and adhesive forces.

The diagram on the left shows water molecules in a glass tube. The diagram on the right shows mercury atoms in a glass tube. The longer the vector arrows are, the greater is the force between the particles. Refer to the diagrams to answer the following questions. Use complete sentences.

Molecules near a glass tube wall

36. Which arrows represent cohesive forces?
The arrows between the water molecules and those between the mercury atoms represent cohesive forces.

37. Which arrows represent adhesive forces?
The arrows between the water molecules and the glass and those between the mercury atoms and the glass represent adhesive forces.

38. For the water molecules, how do the cohesive forces compare to the adhesive forces?
The adhesive forces are greater.

39. For the mercury atoms, how do the cohesive forces compare to the adhesive forces?
The cohesive forces are greater.

40. Explain how the behavior of mercury would compare to that of water if a thin glass tube were placed in each liquid.
The water would rise, but the mercury would not. Capillary action can occur only if the adhesive forces drawing the liquid up the glass are stronger than the cohesive forces holding the liquid particles together.

41. Would the top surface of mercury in a glass container be the same shape as the top surface of water in a similar container? Give the reason for your answer.
The mercury surface would be lower at the edges and higher in the center because the adhesive forces are weaker than the cohesive forces. The water surface would be higher at the edges and lower in the center because the adhesive forces are stronger than the cohesive forces.

---

13 Study Guide

Section 13.2: The Solid State

In your textbook, read about solids and thermal expansion of solids.
For each of the statements below, write true or false.

false 1. The particles in a crystalline solid do not move at all.

true 2. Butter and glass are examples of amorphous solids.

true 3. Elasticity is the ability of an object to return to its original form when external forces are removed.

true 4. Malleability and ductility depend upon elasticity.

false 5. Copper is a nonductile metal.

true 6. Gold is a malleable metal.

true 7. The symbol for the coefficient of linear expansion is α.

false 8. Water is most dense at 0°C.

true 9. Metals used in a bimetallic strip have different rates of thermal expansion.

In your textbook, read about solids and thermal expansion.
Circle the letter of the choice that best completes the statement or answers the question.

10. For what substances is the solid state less dense than the liquid state?
a. no liquids
b. most liquids other than water
c. water
d. all liquids

11. A substance that can be flattened and shaped into thin sheets by hammering is ___.
a. inelastic
b. adhesive
c. ductile
d. malleable

12. A substance that can be pulled into thin strands of wire is said to be ___.
a. inelastic
b. ductile
c. adhesive
d. malleable

13. The change in volume of a material due to thermal expansion equals ___.
a. $\beta V \Delta T$
b. $\beta V / \Delta T$
c. $\alpha V \Delta T$
d. $\alpha V / \Delta T$

14. The coefficient of linear expansion equals ___.
a. $\Delta T \Delta L$
b. $L_1 / \Delta L \Delta T$
c. $\Delta T / \Delta L$
d. $\Delta L / L_1 \Delta T$

14 Study Guide

Use with Chapter 14.

Waves and Energy Transfer

Vocabulary Review

Write the term that correctly completes each statement. Use each term once.

antinode   destructive   node   transverse wave
constructive   interference   normal   trough
interference   interference   standing wave   wave
crest   longitudinal wave   surface wave   wave pulse
   mechanical wave

1.	**trough**	Any of the low points of a wave is a(n) _____
2.	**destructive interference**	Superposition of waves with opposite amplitudes causes _____
3.	**wave**	Any rhythmic disturbance that carries energy through matter or space is a(n) _____
4.	**standing wave**	A wave that appears to be standing still is a(n) _____
5.	**mechanical wave**	A wave that requires a physical medium is a(n) _____
6.	**wave pulse**	A single bump or disturbance that travels through a medium is a(n) _____
7.	**constructive interference**	Superposition of waves with displacements in the same direction causes _____
8.	**node**	An unmoving point at which destructively interfering pulses meet is a(n) _____
9.	**longitudinal wave**	In a(n) _____, the disturbance moves parallel to the direction of motion of the wave.
10.	**antinode**	A point of largest displacement caused by the constructive interference of waves is a(n) _____
11.	**crest**	Any of the high points of a wave is a(n) _____
12.	**interference**	The result of any superposition of two or more waves is _____
13.	**surface wave**	In a(n) _____, the particles move in a direction that is both parallel and perpendicular to the direction of wave motion.
14.	**transverse wave**	In a(n) _____, the particles vibrate in a direction perpendicular to the direction of motion of the wave.
15.	**normal**	A line that is at a right angle to a barrier is a(n) _____

---

13 Study Guide

In your textbook, read about thermal expansion of solids.
For each term on the left, write the corresponding symbol.

ΔL	**15.** change of length	ΔT
β	**16.** coefficient of volume expansion	α
α	**17.** coefficient of linear expansion	ΔV
ΔT	**18.** change of temperature	$(\,^{\circ}\mathrm{C})^{-1}$
ΔV	**19.** change of volume	ΔL
(°C)⁻¹	**20.** unit for coefficient of linear expansion	β

In your textbook, read about plasma and thermal expansion of liquids.
Use the terms below to complete the passage. You may need to use terms more than once.

electrons   gas   liquid   temperature
fluid   ions   plasma

Heating a solid substance eventually turns it to a **(21)** **liquid** and then
to a **(22)** **gas** . Further increases in **(23)** **temperature**
eventually cause collisions between particles to become violent enough that
(24) **electrons** are pulled off the atoms. The resulting state of matter is called
(25) **plasma** . Along with liquids and gases, matter in this state is a
(26) **fluid** . It contains positively charged **(27)** **ions** and
negatively charged **(28)** **electrons** . The main difference between a gas and a plasma
is that only the **(29)** **plasma** can conduct electricity.

Name _____

14 Study Guide

Section 14.1: Wave Properties

In your textbook, read about different kinds of waves.

Circle the letter of the choice that best completes each statement.

1. Waves typically transmit _____.
   a. matter only
   b. both matter and energy
   c. energy only
   d. neither matter nor energy

2. Water waves, sound waves, and waves that travel down a spring are all examples of _____.
   a. mechanical waves *(circled)*
   b. transverse waves
   c. electromagnetic waves
   d. longitudinal waves

3. If a wave moves in a leftward direction but the particles of the medium move up and down, the wave must be a _____.
   a. mechanical wave
   b. transverse wave *(circled)*
   c. surface wave
   d. longitudinal wave

4. A surface wave has characteristics of _____.
   a. longitudinal waves only
   b. transverse waves only
   c. both longitudinal and transverse waves *(circled)*
   d. neither longitudinal nor transverse waves

For each of the statements below, write true or rewrite the *italicized part* to make the statement true.

5. Sound is an example of a *transverse wave*.
   longitudinal

6. Fluids usually transmit only *longitudinal* waves.
   true

7. Waves at the top of a lake or an ocean are examples of *surface waves*.
   true

8. Energy from the sun reaches Earth by means of *longitudinal* electromagnetic waves.
   transverse

9. Waves that travel down a rope are examples of *surface* waves.
   mechanical

Name _____

14 Study Guide

In your textbook, read about amplitude and frequency.

For each of the statements below, write true or rewrite the *italicized part* to make it true.

10. *One hertz is equal to one oscillation per second.*
    true

11. The speed of a wave generally depends only on the *source*.
    medium

12. Waves with larger amplitudes tend to transmit *less* energy than do waves with smaller amplitudes.
    more

13. The frequency of a wave does not depend on the *medium*.
    true

14. A wave of *high* frequency also has a long period.
    low

15. The higher the frequency of a wave is, the *longer* the period is.
    shorter

In your textbook, read about measuring waves.

For each term on the left, write the matching symbol from the list on the right.

λ 16. wavelength Δd

T 17. period v

v 18. speed T

f 19. frequency Δt

Δd 20. displacement of wave peak f

Δt 21. time interval λ

In your textbook, read about the relationship of speed to wave attributes.

Use symbols to write the equation that combines the attributes on the left.

22. frequency and period $f = \dfrac{1}{T}$

23. speed, displacement, and time interval $v = \dfrac{\Delta d}{\Delta t}$

24. speed, wavelength, and frequency $v = \lambda f$

25. speed, wavelength, and period $v = \dfrac{\lambda}{T}$

14 Study Guide

Name _____

In your textbook, read about measuring waves.
Write the terms that correctly completes the passage.

The **(26)** __amplitude__ of a wave is its maximum displacement from its position of rest. Doubling the amplitude of a wave increases the rate of energy transfer by a factor of **(27)** __four__. The time it takes for the motion of an oscillator to repeat itself in generating a wave is the **(28)** __period__ of the wave. Because the motion keeps repeating, such a wave is a(n) **(29)** __continuous__ wave. The number of complete oscillations per second is the **(30)** __frequency__ and is measured in units called **(31)** __hertz__. Both period and frequency of a wave depend only on its **(32)** __source__. A material that carries the energy of a mechanical wave is a(n) **(33)** __medium__.

In your textbook, read about the attributes of a wave.
Refer to the drawing below to answer the following questions.

34. Which of the lettered distances represents the wavelength of wave 1?
D

35. Which of the distances represents the amplitude of wave 1?
A

36. Which of the two waves has the greater wavelength?
wave 1

37. Which of the two waves has the smaller amplitude?
wave 2

38. Assuming that the two waves move at equal speed, which has the higher frequency?
wave 2

39. Assuming that the two waves move at equal speed, which has the greater period?
wave 1

---

14 Study Guide

Name _____

Section 14.2: Wave Behavior

In your textbook, read about wave reactions to boundaries.
For each of the statements below, write true or rewrite the italicized part to make it true.

sometimes 1. When a wave encounters the boundary of the medium in which it is traveling, the wave *always* reflects completely back into the medium.

true 2. A wave that strikes a boundary is called the *incident* wave.

true 3. If a wave passes from a lighter, more flexible spring to a heavier, stiffer one, the resulting reflected wave will be *inverted*.

almost all 4. If a wave pulse is sent down a spring connected to a rigid wall, *almost none* of the wave's energy is reflected back.

Answer the following questions, using complete sentences.

5. What happens to the wavelength of water waves as they move from deep to shallow water?
The wavelength decreases.

6. What happens to the frequency of water waves as they move from deep to shallow water?
The frequency remains the same.

7. What happens to the speed of water waves as they move from deep to shallow water? Describe an equation that would show this change.
The speed decreases. The equation $v = \lambda f$ shows that if wavelength (λ) decreases but frequency stays the same, speed must decrease.

In your textbook, read about wave interference.
For each of the statements below, write true or rewrite the italicized part to make it true.

sum of 8. According to the principle of superposition, the medium's displacement caused by two or more waves is the algebraic *difference between* the displacements caused by the individual waves.

larger 9. In constructive interference, the resulting wave has an amplitude *smaller* than that of any of the individual waves.

can 10. Two waves *cannot* exist in the same medium at the same time.

standing 11. A *continuous* wave appears to be standing still.

true 12. If the trough of one wave occurs at the same point as the crest of another wave, the two may cancel out, producing zero amplitude at that point.

quickly 13. When a continuous wave crosses a boundary and moves more *slowly*, the amplitude increases.

14 Study Guide

In your textbook, read about two-dimensional waves.

Answer the following questions, using complete sentences.

14. What is a ray?

A ray is a line drawn at a right angle to the crests of waves.

15. What is a ripple tank?

A ripple tank contains a thin layer of water and has sources of vibration to produce waves.

16. State the law of reflection, and explain how each of the two kinds of angles involved are measured.

The law states the angle of incidence equals the angle of reflection. The angle of incidence is the angle between the incident ray and the normal, and the angle of reflection is the angle between the reflected ray and the normal.

17. What is meant by refraction?

Refraction is a change in the direction of waves at the boundary between two media.

18. In how many dimensions do the waves travel in the following three cases: a wave moving along a rope, a wave on the surface of water, and a sound wave.

A wave moving along a rope travels in one dimension. A wave on the surface of water travels in two dimensions. A sound wave travels in three dimensions.

In your textbook, read about diffraction and interference of waves.

Write the terms that correctly complete the passage.

When waves reach a small opening in a barrier, they form waves that have a(n) **(19)** **circular** shape. This effect is an example of **(20)** **diffraction**. The smaller the **(21)** **wavelength** is, compared to the size of the barrier, the **(22)** **less** pronounced this effect is. When there are two closely spaced openings in a barrier, two sets of **(23)** **interfering** waves are produced. Nodes lie along lines between lines of **(24)** **antinodes**. Nodes form where there is **(25)** **destructive** interference.

---

15 Study Guide

Sound

Vocabulary Review

Write the term that correctly completes each statement. Use each term once.

beat	dissonance	harmonic	sound level
consonance	Doppler shift	octave	timbre
decibel	fundamental	pitch	

1. **sound level** The amplitude of sound, as measured on a logarithmic scale, is called _____.

2. **harmonic** Any higher frequency that is a multiple of the fundamental frequency is a(n) _____.

3. **beat** An oscillation of wave amplitude caused by the sounding of two nearly identical frequencies is called a(n) _____.

4. **decibel** A unit used to measure sound level is the _____.

5. **dissonance** A jarring combination of pitches is called _____.

6. **octave** Two frequencies in a 1:2 ratio differ by a(n) _____.

7. **fundamental** The lowest frequency that will resonate in a pipe is the _____.

8. **Doppler shift** The apparent change in pitch caused by the motion of a sound source is called the _____.

9. **pitch** The apparent highness or lowness of a note, associated with frequency of vibration is called _____.

10. **timbre** Tone color or tone quality is called _____.

11. **consonance** A pleasant combination of pitches is called _____.

15 Study Guide

· · · · · · · · · · · · · ·

Section 15.1: Properties of Sound

In your textbook, read about sound waves.

Write the term that correctly completes each statement.

Sound waves move in the same direction as the particles of the medium and are therefore
(1) __longitudinal__ waves. The waves are caused by variations in
(2) __pressure__ relating to the different **(3)** __velocities__ of
molecules. Therefore, sound cannot travel through a(n) **(4)** __vacuum__. The
(5) __frequency__ of a sound wave is the number of pressure oscillations per second.
The **(6)** __wavelength__ is the distance between successive regions of high or low
pressure. The speed of a sound wave in air depends on the **(7)** __temperature__ of the
air. At 20°C, sound moves through air at sea level at a speed of **(8)** __343__ m/s.
In general, the speed of sound is **(9)** __greater__ in liquids and solids than in gases.
Reflected sound waves are **(10)** __echoes__. The reflection of sound waves can be
used to find the **(11)** __distance__ between a source and a reflecting surface.
Sound waves can **(12)** __interfere__, producing nodes, where little sound is heard.
Sound waves can also be **(13)** __diffracted__; they spread outward after passing
through a narrow opening. The equation that relates velocity, frequency, and wavelength is
(14) __$v = \lambda f$__.

In your textbook, read about loudness.

For each of the statements below, write true or rewrite the italicized part to make the statement true.

15. Sound level is measured on a *logarithmic* scale. __true__

16. The ear detects *pressure* variations as sound. __true__

17. Hearing loss can result from long exposure to *dissonant* sound levels. __high__

18. Sound level is measured in *hertz.* __decibels__

19. Loudness, as perceived by the human ear, is directly proportional to *length* of a pressure wave.
__amplitude__

20. A *40-dB* increase is perceived as roughly a doubling of the loudness of a sound. __10-dB__

---

15 Study Guide

· · · · · · · · · · · · · ·

In your textbook, read about sound waves and loudness.

For each term on the left, write the corresponding symbol from those on the right. Some symbols may be used more than once.

__s__ 21. period   dB

__dB__ 22. amplitude   Hz

__m/s__ 23. speed   m

__Hz__ 24. frequency   m/s

__dB__ 25. loudness   s

__Hz__ 26. pitch

__m__ 27. wavelength

In your textbook, read about pitch and the Doppler effect.

State whether the process would make the apparent pitch of a sound higher, lower, or have no effect on it.

28. moving the listener away from the sound source __lower__

29. decreasing the frequency __lower__

30. increasing the number of decibels __no effect__

31. decreasing the wavelength, at constant wave speed __higher__

32. increasing the wavelength, at constant wave speed __lower__

33. moving the sound source toward the listener __higher__

34. decreasing the wave amplitude __no effect__

35. increasing the wavelength, at constant frequency __no effect__

36. decreasing the period __higher__

In your textbook, read about the Doppler shift.

The drawing below shows the crests of sound waves produced by a point source, S, that is moving. The two ears represent two listeners at different positions. Refer to the drawing to answer the following questions.

37. Which direction is the point source moving? Give a reason for your answer.
__It's moving toward A. The crests are crowded together__
__above S and spread apart below S.__

38. How do the apparent wavelengths at A and B compare?
__The apparent wavelength is greater at B.__

---

15 Study Guide

39. How does the speed of the sound waves compare at A and B?
The speeds are equal.

40. How does the apparent frequency at point A compare to that at point B? Give a reason for your answer, in terms of the meaning of the word *frequency* and of the equation relating frequency to speed and wavelength.
It is higher at point A. The number of apparent oscillations per second is higher: v is constant, but $λ$ is lower at A in the equation $v = λ f$, which means that f must be higher.

41. How loud is the sound heard at A compared to that heard at B when A and B are equally far from the source? Give a reason for your answer.
The sounds are equally loud because the amplitude of the waves is not affected by the motion.

42. Is the sound heard at A higher or lower pitch than that heard at B? Give a reason for your answer.
The sound would seem to have a higher pitch at A because pitch is related to frequency.

43. If the point source began to move faster in the same direction, would the apparent sound at A and B change? If yes, how would it change?
The pitch would become higher at A and lower at B.

44. If the point source stopped moving, how would the apparent sound at A and B change, if at all? At A, the sound would lower to the pitch corresponding to the actual frequency at the point source, and at B it would rise to that pitch.
source, and at B it would rise to that pitch.

45. Suppose B started to move downward while the point source continued to move in its original direction. How would the apparent sound at B change, if at all?
The pitch would become lower.

---

15 Study Guide

Section 15.2: The Physics of Music

In your textbook, read about pipe resonators and other sources of sound.
Circle the letter of the choice that best completes the statement or answers the question.

1. Sound is produced when there are _____.
   a. increases in pressure
   (b.) oscillations in pressure
   c. increases in temperature
   d. electromagnetic waves

2. The frequencies of vibrating air that will be set into resonance are determined by an air column's _____.
   a. radius   (b.) length   c. mass   d. width

3. Resonance occurs when _____.
   a. any constructive interference occurs
   b. any destructive interference occurs
   (c.) a standing wave is created.
   d. no nodes are formed

4. In which kind of resonator is the pressure of the reflected wave inverted?
   a. closed-pipe only
   (b.) open-pipe only
   c. both open- and closed-pipe
   d. neither open- nor closed-pipe

5. In a standing sound wave in a pipe, nodes are regions of _____.
   a. maximum or minimum pressure and low displacement
   b. maximum or minimum pressure and high displacement
   (c.) mean atmospheric pressure and low displacement
   d. mean atmospheric pressure and high displacement

6. In a standing sound wave in a pipe, two antinodes are separated by _____.
   a. one-quarter wavelength
   b. one wavelength
   (c.) one-half wavelength
   d. two wavelengths

In your textbook, read about resonance frequencies in pipes.
For each of the statements below, write true or false.

false	7.	A closed pipe can't have resonance unless it has antinodes at both ends.
true	8.	In a closed pipe, a column of length $λ/4$ will be in resonance with a tuning fork.
true	9.	An open pipe can't have resonance unless it has nodes at both ends.
false	10.	In an open pipe, a column of length $3λ/4$ will be in resonance with a tuning fork.
true	11.	For both open and closed pipes, resonance lengths are spaced at half-wavelength intervals.

15 Study Guide

In your textbook, read about sound detectors.

Answer the following questions, using complete sentences.

12. Briefly describe energy conversion by a microphone.

   A microphone's thin disk vibrates in response to sound waves and produces an electrical signal, thus converting sound energy into electrical energy.

13. Describe the pathway that sound waves follow as they enter the ear and eventually lead to the sensation of sound.

   Sound waves enter the ear through the auditory canal. The waves cause the tympanic membrane (eardrum) to vibrate. The vibrations pass to three tiny bones and then to a liquid in the cochlea. Tiny hairs in the cochlea pick up certain frequencies of the vibrations and stimulate nerve cells, which send an impulse to the brain.

In your textbook, read about sound qualities and beat.

For each of the statements below, write true or true or rewrite the italicized part to make the statement true.

14. **lowest**	The *highest* frequency that will resonate in a musical instrument is called the fundamental.
15. **true**	In a *closed-pipe* instrument, such as a clarinet, the harmonics are odd-number multiples of the fundamental frequency.
16. **frequency**	A sound spectrum of an instrument is a graph of wave *amplitude* versus *speed*.
17. **true**	Sounds perceived as *consonant* in most Western cultures tend to have frequencies that are in small, whole-number ratios.
18. **beat**	Interference between two nearly identical frequencies causes a *consonance*.
19. **true**	A beat is an oscillation of wave amplitude.
20. **true**	The frequency of the beat equals the magnitude of *difference* between the frequencies of the two waves.

In your textbook, read about musical intervals.

Write the frequency ratio for the pitches in each musical interval.

21. octave **1:2**

22. fifth **2:3**

23. major third **4:5**

24. fourth **3:4**

Physics: Principles and Problems

---

16 Study Guide

Use with Chapter 16.

Light

Vocabulary Review

Write the term that correctly completes each statement. Use each term once.

complementary color	luminous	polarized	secondary pigment
dye	luminous flux	primary pigment	spectrum
illuminance	luminous intensity	ray model	translucent
illuminated	opaque	secondary color	transparent
light	pigment		

1. **illuminance** — The illumination of a surface is _____.

2. **complementary color** — The _____ of a given color forms white light when it combines with that color.

3. **luminous intensity** — The _____ of a point source is the luminous flux that falls on 1 m^2 of a sphere with a 1-m radius.

4. **luminous flux** — A measure of the total rate at which light is emitted from a source is _____.

5. **polarized** — Light that vibrates in a particular plane is _____.

6. **secondary color** — A color formed from two primary colors of light is a(n) _____.

7. **light** — The range of frequencies of electromagnetic waves that stimulates the retina of the eye is _____.

8. **ray model** — The _____ uses straight lines to describe how light behaves.

9. **transparent** — A material that transmits light without distorting it is _____.

10. **spectrum** — The ordered arrangement of colors from red through violet is the _____.

11. **pigment** — A colored material that is made up of particles larger than molecules is a(n) _____.

12. **dye** — A molecule that absorbs certain wavelengths and transmits others is a(n) _____.

13. **primary pigment** — A(n) _____ absorbs only one primary color from white light.

14. **secondary pigment** — A(n) _____ absorbs two primary colors of light.

15. **translucent** — A material that transmits light, but objects cannot be seen clearly through it is a(n) _____ material.

16. **opaque** — A material that transmits no incident light is a(n) _____ material.

17. **illuminated** — A(n) _____ body does not emit light but simply reflects light produced by a source.

18. **luminous** — A(n) _____ body emits light waves.

Physics: Principles and Problems

Physics: Principles and Problems   Teacher Guide and Answers   **45T**

16 Study Guide

Section 16.1: Light Fundamentals

In your textbook, read about characteristics of light.
For each of the statements below, write true or rewrite the italicized part to make the statement true.

true	1. Light waves have wavelengths from about 400 nm to about 700 nm.
violet	2. The shortest wavelengths of light are seen as *red* light.
true	3. Light travels in a *straight* line in a vacuum.
3.00 × 10⁸ m/s	4. The speed of light in a vacuum is approximately 3.00×10^{10} m/s.

In your textbook, read about characteristics of light.
Circle the letter of the choice that best completes the statement or answers the question.

5. Light behaves like _____.
a. particles only
b. waves only
c. both particles and waves *(circled)*
d. neither particles nor waves

6. Geometric optics studies light by means of _____.
a. ray diagrams *(circled)*
b. the wave model
c. ripple tanks
d. a particle-wave model

7. The fact that sharp shadows are cast by the sun is an indication that light _____.
a. is a wave.
b. travels in straight lines *(circled)*
c. is made up of colors
d. travels in a curved path

8. A straight line that represents the path of a very narrow beam of light is _____.
a. normal
b. a complement
c. a ray *(circled)*
d. a wave

9. The orbital period of which of the following was studied in the seventeenth century to determine the speed of light?
a. Io *(circled)*
b. Saturn
c. Jupiter
d. Earth's moon

10. How long does light take to cross Earth's orbit?
a. 2 s
b. 8 min
c. 16 min *(circled)*
d. 22 min

11. Light of which of the following colors has the longest wavelength?
a. red *(circled)*
b. yellow
c. blue
d. violet

---

16 Study Guide

In your textbook, read about measures of light.
Complete the table below.

Table 1

Quantity	Name of Unit	Symbol for Unit
illuminance	lux	lx
luminous flux	lumen	lm
luminous intensity	candela	cd

In your textbook, read about sources of light.
Write the term that correctly completes each statement.

A body that (12) __emits__ light waves is luminous, and a body that (13) __reflects__ light waves given off by a source is illuminated. A(n) (14) __incandescent__ object emits light as a result of its high temperature. The official SI unit from which all light intensity units are calculated is the (15) __candela__.

Luminous flux expresses the (16) __rate__ at which light is given off. Illuminance is the (17) __illumination__ of a surface. If the distance from a surface to a point source of light is doubled, the illumination reaching the surface is only (18) __one-fourth__ as great. The relationship between illuminance and luminous flux is given by the equation (19) $E = P/4\pi d^2$, where the distance to the surface is represented by the symbol (20) __d__. This equation is valid only if the light from the source is traveling (21) __perpendicularly__ to the surface. It is also valid only for sources small enough or far away enough to be (22) __point__ sources.

In your textbook, read about light sources and quantities.
For each situation below, write the letter of the matching item.

d   23. symbol for the speed of light
c   24. area of the surface of a sphere
g   25. symbol for luminous flux
e   26. symbol for illuminance
f   27. equivalent to the speed of light
a   28. equivalent to 1 lx
b   29. proportional to illumination
h   30. equivalent to luminous intensity

a. 1 lm/m²
b. $1/r^2$
c. $4\pi r^2$
d. c
e. E
f. λf
g. P
h. P/4π

16 Study Guide

Section 16.2: Light and Matter

In your textbook, read about the additive color process.

The diagram below represents three overlapping circles of equally intense light of different pure colors. Assume that the circles are projected onto a white screen in an otherwise completely dark room.

1. What color (if any) would region A be?
   black

2. What color would region B be?
   magenta

3. What color would region C be?
   cyan

4. What color would region D be?
   yellow

5. What color would region E be?
   white

6. What color types of light—primary or secondary—are red, blue, and green light?
   All are primary.

7. What color type of light would be in region B? Give a reason for your answer.
   Region B; it is a secondary color, produced by the mixing of two primary colors.

8. What color type of light would be in region C?
   secondary

9. What color type of light would be in region D?
   secondary

10. The color in region B is the complementary color to which color?
    green

11. What happens if two complementary colors are projected together at the correct intensities onto a white screen?
    White light would be formed.

12. The color in region C is complementary to which color?
    red

13. The color in region D is complementary to which color?
    blue

---

16 Study Guide

In your textbook, read about pigments.

Answer the following questions, using complete sentences.

14. What does a primary pigment absorb from white light?
    It absorbs one primary color.

15. What does a secondary pigment absorb from white light?
    It absorbs two primary colors.

16. Is the absorption of light to form pigment colors an additive or a subtractive process?
    It is subtractive.

17. What color are the three primary pigments?
    The colors are yellow, cyan, and magenta.

18. What color are the three secondary pigments?
    The colors are red, green, and blue.

19. What color(s) does yellow pigment absorb from light?
    It absorbs blue.

20. What color(s) does yellow pigment reflect?
    It reflects red and green.

21. What colors does red pigment absorb from light?
    It absorbs green and blue.

22. What is the complementary pigment to cyan pigment?
    The complementary pigment is red.

23. What color would result from the mixing of two complementary pigments?
    Black would result.

In your textbook, read about thin films.

For each of the statements below, write true or rewrite the italicized part to make the statement true.

24. _____ **true** _____ The colors produced by an oil film on water result from thin-film *interference.*

25. _____ **thinner** _____ When a soap film is held vertically, it is *thicker* at the top than at the bottom.

26. _____ **true** _____ When a light wave traveling through the air reaches the top surface of a soap film, the wave that is reflected there is *inverted.*

27. _____ **not inverted** _____ When a light wave that has traveled into a soap film reaches the back surface, the wave that is reflected there is *inverted.*

28. _____ **reinforces** _____ When a soap film has a thickness of $\lambda/4$, the wave reflected from the back surface *destructively interferes* with the wave reflected from the top surface.

17 Study Guide

Reflection and Refraction

Vocabulary Review

Write the term that correctly completes each statement. Use each term once.

angle of incidence   dispersion   refraction
angle of reflection   index of refraction   regular reflection
angle of refraction   normal   Snell's law
critical angle   optically dense   total internal reflection
diffuse reflection

1. **diffuse reflection**   When light bounces off surfaces that are not very smooth, _____ occurs.

2. **normal**   A line perpendicular to a surface is a(n) _____.

3. **total internal reflection**   When light passes from one medium to a less optically dense medium at an angle so great that there is no refracted ray, _____ occurs.

4. **dispersion**   The separation of light into its spectrum is _____.

5. **regular reflection**   When light bounces off surfaces that are extremely smooth, so that the light returns to the observer in parallel beams, _____ occurs.

6. **angle of incidence**   The angle that an incoming beam makes with the normal is the _____.

7. **Snell's law**   The relationship of the angle of incidence to the angle of refraction is stated in _____.

8. **optically dense**   If the angle of refraction is smaller than the angle of incidence, the medium in which the angle is smaller is more _____.

9. **angle of refraction**   The angle that a refracted ray makes with the normal is the _____.

10. **index of refraction**   For light going from a vacuum into another medium, the constant n is the _____.

11. **angle of reflection**   The angle made with the normal by a beam of light that has bounced off a surface is the _____.

12. **refraction**   The bending of light at the boundary between two media is _____.

13. **critical angle**   The _____ describes a refracted ray that lies along the boundary of a substance.

---

16 Study Guide

29. **true**   When a soap film has a thickness of 5λ/4, the wave reflected from the back surface *reinforces* the wave reflected from the top surface.

30. **different colors**   In a soap film, the λ/4 requirement is met at the same locations for *all colors* of light.

31. **ray**   The explanation of thin-film interference does not require a *wave* model of light.

In your textbook, read about polarization.
For each of the statements below, write true or rewrite the italicized part to make the statement true.

32. **one plane**   Light that has been polarized vibrates in *all planes*.

33. **true**   Polaroid material allows electromagnetic waves vibrating in one direction to pass through, while absorbing waves vibrating in the *perpendicular* direction.

34. **reflection**   Light can be polarized by *refraction*.

35. **true**   Photographers use polarizing filters to block *reflected* light.

17 Study Guide

Section 17.1: How Light Behaves at a Boundary

In your textbook, read about reflection and refraction.

For each of the statements below, write true or rewrite the italicized part to make it true.

1. __normal__ The angle of incidence is the angle between the incoming light beam and the *surface*.

2. __does__ The velocity of light *does not depend* on the medium through which the light is traveling.

3. __true__ The angle of incidence equals the angle of *reflection*.

4. __regular__ A mirror causes *diffuse reflection*.

5. __Refraction__ *Reflection* involves a bending of light.

6. __true__ The angle of incidence *differs* from the angle of refraction.

Write the term that correctly completes each statement.

When a beam of light strikes a rough surface, it reflects at (7) __many__ angles, producing (8) __diffuse__ reflection. When a beam of light strikes a very smooth surface, the reflected rays are (9) __parallel__ to each other, producing (10) __regular__ reflection. If a light beam is not reflected, but is bent instead, the light is (11) __refracted__. The angle of incidence is measured between the (12) __incident__ ray and the (13) __normal__. The angle of refraction is measured between the (14) __refracted__ ray and the (15) __normal__. Refraction does not occur if the angle of incidence is (16) __zero__ degrees. When a light ray enters a medium that is more (17) __optically__ dense, its speed (18) __decreases__, and the refracted ray bends (19) __toward__ the normal. If a light ray passes into a medium in which it travels faster, the refracted ray bends (20) __away from__ the normal.

---

17 Study Guide

In your textbook, read about Snell's law and the effect of different media on light.

The diagram below represents a light ray passing through two media. Refer to the diagram to answer the following questions. Use complete sentences.

21. Which labeled line represents the incident ray? How can you tell?

    B is the incoming ray, given the arrow.

22. Which line represents the refracted ray? How can you tell?

    D is the ray that has passed into (been refracted by) the second medium.

23. Which line represents the boundary between the two media?

    C is the boundary.

24. Which line represents the normal? How can you tell?

    A; is at right angles to the boundary.

25. Which labeled angle represents the angle of incidence? How can you tell?

    E; is the angle between the incident ray and the normal.

26. Which labeled angle represents the angle of refraction? How can you tell?

    H; is the angle between the refracted ray and the normal.

27. Which is greater: the angle of incidence or the angle of refraction?

    The angle of refraction is greater.

28. Which medium is more optically dense? How can you tell?

    Medium 1 is denser. The angle between the ray and the normal is smaller in medium 1 than in medium 2.

29. Which medium has the lower refractive index? How can you tell?

    Medium 2 has the lower refractive index. In it, the light is bent farther from the normal.

30. Write an equation for Snell's law.

    $n_i \sin \theta_i = n_r \sin \theta_r$

17 Study Guide

31. Using Snell's law, complete the following equation, showing the ratio of the indices of refraction for medium 1 and medium 2: $n_2/n_1 = $ _____.

$n_2/n_1 = \sin\theta_1/\sin\theta_2$

32. In which medium does the light travel faster? How can you tell? **In medium 2, light travels faster. The refractive index there is lower.**

In your textbook, read about the index of refraction and speed of light. Match each quantity on the left with the correct symbol.

Answer			Symbol
θ_r	**33.**	angle of refraction	c
θ_i	**34.**	angle of incidence	θ_r
c	**35.**	speed of light in a vacuum	n
v	**36.**	speed of light in a medium	sin
f	**37.**	frequency of light	f
λ	**38.**	wavelength of light	θ_i
n	**39.**	index of refraction	v
sin	**40.**	sine	λ

Circle the letter of the choice that best completes each statement.

41. Compared to its speed in air, the speed of light in glass is _____.
a. the same   b. faster   (c.) slower   d. not measurable

42. Which of the following has the highest index of refraction?
a. a vacuum   b. air   (c.) diamond   d. crown glass

43. For most practical purposes, the index of refraction of air can be considered _____.
a. 0   (b.) 1.00   c. infinite   d. equal to that of the other medium involved

44. The wavelength of light in a given material equals _____.
a. the speed of light in the material times frequency
b. frequency times the speed of light in the material
c. the speed of light in the material divided by frequency
(d.) frequency divided by the speed of light in the material

45. Which expression equals the index of refraction of a given medium?
(a.) c/v_{medium} b. v_{medium}/c c. $c - v_{medium}$ d. $v_{medium} - c$

---

17 Study Guide

Section 17.2: Applications of Reflected and Refracted Light

In your textbook, read about total internal reflection.
For each of the statements below, write true or false.

true **1.** The critical angle is the incident angle that causes the refracted ray to lie along the boundary.

true **2.** The sine of the critical angle for a substance from which light is passing into air is equal to $1.00/n_i$.

false **3.** Total internal reflection cannot be achieved for light that is passing from water to air.

false **4.** All substances have the same critical angle.

true **5.** Plants can use total internal reflection for light transport.

true **6.** A single bundle of optical fibers can carry thousands of telephone conversations at once.

false **7.** Total internal reflection occurs whenever light passes from one medium to a less optically dense medium.

false **8.** When incident light is at the critical angle, θ_r equals 0°.

false **9.** The core of an optical fiber is metal.

true **10.** Each time light moving through an optical fiber strikes the surface, the angle of incidence is larger than the critical angle.

true **11.** Cladding covers the outside of an optical fiber.

true **12.** Optical fibers are flexible.

In your textbook, read about the effects of refraction.
Circle the letter of the choice that best completes the statement or answers the question.

13. As temperature increases, the index of refraction of air _____.
a. increases   (b.) decreases   c. remains constant   d. becomes negligible

14. The mirage effect is caused by _____.
a. total internal reflection   b. polarization   (c.) temperature differences in index of refraction   d. differences in the speeds of different colors of light

15. Which of the following is correct regarding sunlight?
a. It reaches us only after the sun has actually risen.
(b.) It continues to reach us after the sun has actually set.
c. It stops reaching us before the sun has actually set.
d. It corresponds exactly to sunrise and sunset.

18 Study Guide

Use with Chapter 18.

Mirrors and Lenses

Vocabulary Review

Write the term that correctly completes each statement. Use each term once.

achromatic lens   convex lens   focal point   principal axis
chromatic aberration   convex mirror   lens/mirror equation   real image
concave lens   erect image   magnification   spherical aberration
concave mirror   focal length   object   virtual image

1. **real image** — An image at which light rays actually converge is a(n) _____.
2. **concave mirror** — A(n) _____ reflects light from its inwardly curving surface.
3. **principal axis** — The straight line perpendicular to the surface of a mirror at its center is the _____.
4. **lens/mirror equation** — The mathematical relationship between focal length, distance of object, and distance of image is expressed by the _____.
5. **concave lens** — A transparent refracting device that is thinner in the middle than at the edges is a(n) _____.
6. **convex lens** — A transparent refracting device that is thicker in the middle than at the edges is a(n) _____.
7. **focal length** — The distance between the focal point and the mirror or lens is the _____.
8. **object** — Any source of diverging light rays is a(n) _____.
9. **virtual image** — An image at which light rays do not actually converge is a(n) _____.
10. **focal point** — The place at which light rays parallel to the principal axis of a concave mirror converge is the _____.
11. **chromatic aberration** — An undesirable effect in which an object viewed through a lens appears to be ringed with color is _____.
12. **erect image** — An image that is not inverted is a(n) _____.
13. **spherical aberration** — An undesirable effect in which the parallel rays reflected in a concave mirror fail to meet at a point is _____.
14. **convex mirror** — A spherical mirror that reflects light from its outwardly curving surface is a(n) _____.
15. **achromatic lens** — A lens constructed so as to avoid undesirable color effects is a(n) _____.
16. **magnification** — The ratio of the size of an image to the size of the object that produces it is the _____.

---

17 Study Guide

16. When all the colors of light are combined, _____.
    a. black results
    b. the frequencies add together, producing light of higher frequency
    c. the colors completely cancel out because of destructive interference
    d. white light is produced *(d circled)*

17. Which color of light is bent most as it goes through a prism?
    a. red   b. yellow   c. green   d. violet *(d circled)*

18. The color of light that has the lowest index of refraction is _____.
    a. red *(circled)*   b. yellow   c. green   d. violet

19. Diamond has _____.
    a. a low refractive index and little color variation in the index
    b. a low refractive index and lots of color variation in the index
    c. a high refractive index and little color variation in the index
    d. a high refractive index and lots of color variation in the index *(d circled)*

20. Which description fits the spectrum of light from an incandescent lamp?
    a. a continuous band only *(a circled)*
    b. bright lines only
    c. both a continuous band and bright lines
    d. neither a continuous band nor bright lines

21. Which description fits the spectrum of light from a fluorescent lamp?
    a. a continuous band only
    b. bright lines only
    c. both a continuous band and bright lines *(c circled)*
    d. neither a continuous band nor bright lines

22. Production of a rainbow by water droplets depends on _____.
    a. differences of angles of incidence for lights of different colors
    b. differences of angles of refraction for lights of different colors *(b circled)*
    c. differences of speed for lights of different colors
    d. equality of index of refraction for lights of all colors

23. A puddle mirage seen by a motorist is actually light from _____.
    a. the ground underneath the puddle
    b. the ground surrounding the puddle
    c. the sky *(circled)*
    d. passing vehicles.

18 Study Guide

Section 18.1: Mirrors

In your textbook, read about concave mirrors.

For each of the statements below, write true or false or rewrite the italicized part to make the statement true.

parallel 1. Rays *perpendicular* to the principal axis of a concave mirror converge at or near the focal point.

true 2. The focal length of a concave mirror is *half* the radius of curvature.

true 3. If the object is *farther out* than the center of curvature of a concave mirror, its image appears between the focus and the center of curvature.

In your textbook, read about real images formed by concave mirrors.

Circle the letter of the choice that best answers each question.

virtual and real 4. Concave mirrors can produce *only virtual* images.

can 5. Concave mirrors *cannot* act as magnifiers.

6. Which of the following correctly states the lens/mirror equation?

   a. $f = d_i + d_o$
   c. $f = 1/d_i + 1/d_o$
   b. $1/f = d_i + d_o$
   (d.) $1/f = 1/d_i + 1/d_o$

7. Which of the following is a correct relationship?

   a. $m = h_i + h_o$
   (c.) $m = h_i/h_o$
   b. $m = h_i - h_o$
   d. $m = h_o/h_i$

8. Which of the following indicates that an image produced by a concave mirror is upright?

   (a.) a positive value for h_i
   c. a positive value for d_i
   b. a negative value for h_i
   d. a negative value for d_i

9. To which of the following is m equal?

   a. d_o/d_i
   c. d_i/d_o
   b. $-d_o/d_i$
   (d.) $-d_i/d_o$

In your textbook, read about virtual images and image defects in concave mirrors.

Circle the letter of the choice that best answers each question.

10. Which of the following indicates that an image produced by a concave mirror is virtual?

    a. a positive value for h_i
    c. a positive value for d_i
    b. a negative value for h_i
    (d.) a negative value for d_i

11. If an object is placed at the focal point of a concave mirror, where will the image be?

    a. also at the focal point
    (c.) at infinity
    b. at the center of curvature
    d. at the surface of the mirror

---

18 Study Guide

12. Which of the following posed a problem for the Hubble Space Telescope?

    a. improperly ground lenses
    (c.) spherical aberration
    b. chromatic aberration
    d. cracked spherical mirrors

13. Why don't parabolic mirrors have trouble with spherical aberration?

    (a.) All parallel rays are reflected to a single spot.
    c. They use a secondary mirror for correction.
    b. All parallel rays focus on infinity.
    d. They have a virtual focus point.

In your textbook, read about real images formed by concave mirrors.

The diagram below shows a concave mirror and an object. Refer to the diagram to answer the following questions.

Bottle

C F

Concave mirror

14. What does the letter F stand for?

    F is the focal point.

15. What does the dashed line represent?

    The dashed line is the principal axis.

16. Under what condition will rays be reflected through point F?

    They will be reflected through F if they are parallel to the principal axis.

17. Relative to points C and E, roughly where will the image be?

    The image will be between C and F.

18. Will the value of d_i be positive or negative? Why?

    It will be positive because the image is on the same side of the mirror as the object.

19. Will the image be real or virtual? Why?

    It will be real; light actually converges there because d_i is positive.

20. Will the image be reduced or enlarged?

    It will be reduced.

21. Will the value of h_i be greater or less than that of h_o?

    h_i will be less.

18 Study Guide

22. Will the image be erect or inverted?
The image will be inverted.

23. Will the value of h_i be positive or negative? Why?
h_i will be negative because the image is inverted.

24. If the object was moved closer to C but still remained to the left of it, what would happen to the image?
It would move closer to C and become larger.

25. What would happen to the image if the object was moved to C?
The image would become the same size as the object and would also be at C, but inverted.

In your textbook, read about convex mirrors.
For each of the statements below, write true or rewrite the italicized part to make the statement true.

26.	**true** — The focal length of a convex mirror is *negative*.
27.	**diverge** — Rays reflected from a convex mirror always *converge*.
28.	**true** — Convex mirrors reflect an *enlarged* field of view.
29.	**virtual** — The images produced by convex mirrors are *real* images.
30.	**inverted** — When the magnification is negative, an image will be *erect*.
31.	**smaller** — Compared to the size of the corresponding objects, the images produced by convex mirrors are always *the same size*.

Section 18.2: Lenses

In your textbook, read about real images formed by convex lenses.
Circle the letter of the choice that best completes the statement or answers the question.

1. Convex lenses typically have ___.
 a. one focal point
 b. two focal points
 c. a virtual focal point
 d. no focal point

2. For a convex lens, if an object is between f and $2f$, the image will be ___.
 a. smaller than the object
 b. larger than the object
 c. the same size as the object
 d. at infinity

3. For a lens, which of the following relationships is correct?
 a. $m = h_o/h_i$
 b. $m = d_i/d_o$
 c. $m = -h_o/h_i$
 d. $m = -d_i/d_o$

18 Study Guide

4. The relationship $1/f = 1/d_i + 1/d_o$ is ___.
 a. valid for any lens
 b. not valid for lenses
 c. valid for convex lenses only
 d. valid for concave lenses only

5. What kinds of images can convex lenses produce?
 a. real only
 b. virtual only
 c. both real and virtual
 d. neither real nor virtual

6. What is the principal advantage of using a large convex lens rather than a small one?
 a. elimination of spherical aberration
 b. elimination of chromatic aberration
 c. increasing the size of the focal point
 d. collection of more light rays

7. If an object is placed at the focal point of a convex lens, the refracted rays will ___.
 a. emerge in a parallel beam
 b. converge at the other focal point
 c. converge at the lens surface
 d. diverge

In your textbook, read about virtual images formed by convex lenses.
Answer the following questions, using complete sentences.

8. What type of lens can be used as a magnifying glass?
A convex lens can act as a magnifying glass.

9. When a lens is used as a magnifying glass, where is the object placed?
The object is between F and the lens.

10. When a lens is used as a magnifying glass, what sign(s) do d_i and h_i have?
d_i is negative and h_i is positive.

In your textbook, read about concave lenses and lens defects.
For each of the statements below, write true or rewrite the italicized part to make the statement true.

11.	**erect** — The images produced by concave lenses are always *inverted*.
12.	**true** — A concave lens is *thinner* in the center than at the edges.
13.	**diverge** — Concave lenses refract light rays so that the rays *converge*.
14.	**virtual and reduced** — The images produced by concave lenses are *virtual and enlarged*.
15.	**true** — Lenses suffer from spherical aberration because the rays that pass through *do not* all pass through the focus.
16.	**true** — The edges of a lens act like a *prism*, scattering light in a ring of color.
17.	**chromatic aberration** — You can reduce *spherical aberration* by joining a concave lens with a convex lens.

18 Study Guide

• • • • • • • • • • • • • •

In your textbook, read about microscopes and telescopes.

Circle the letter of the choice that best completes the statement or answers the question.

18. The objective lens of a microscope is used to produce an image located _____.

   a. at the ocular lens

   (b.) between the ocular lens and its focal point

   c. at the focal point of the ocular lens

   d. beyond the ocular lens and its focal point

19. What kind of image is a telescope designed to produce for the viewer?

   a. real and inverted

   b. real and erect

   (c.) virtual and inverted

   d. virtual and erect

20. An astronomical refracting telescope uses _____.

   a. two concave lenses

   b. a combination of concave and convex lenses

   (c.) two convex lenses

   d. a variety of lenses and mirrors

19 Study Guide

• • • • • • • • • • • • • •

Diffraction and Interference of Light

Vocabulary Review

Write the term that correctly completes each statement. Use each term once.

coherent waves   diffraction grating   monochromatic light

constructive interference   first-order line   Rayleigh criterion

corpuscular model   grating spectrometer   resolving power

destructive interference   interference fringes   wavelet

diffraction

1. **diffraction grating**   A(n) _____ has parallel slits that diffract light and form an interference pattern.

2. **monochromatic light**   Light of only one wavelength is _____.

3. **diffraction**   The slight spreading of light around barriers is _____.

4. **coherent waves**   Waves that are in phase are _____.

5. **interference fringes**   The patterns of bright and dark bands produced when light passes through a double slit are _____.

6. **Rayleigh criterion**   The _____ indicates whether two closely spaced star images will be resolved.

7. **resolving power**   The ability of an instrument, such as a telescope, to reveal the separateness of closely spaced images is its _____.

8. **constructive interference**   When crests of waves overlap, _____ occurs.

9. **first-order line**   A bright band directly on either side of the central band is a(n) _____.

10. **wavelet**   A repeating disturbance produced when the crest of a wave is replaced by a wave source is a(n) _____.

11. **destructive interference**   When crests of one wave overlap troughs of another wave, _____ occurs.

12. **grating spectrometer**   An instrument used to measure light wavelengths produced by a diffraction grating is a(n) _____.

13. **corpuscular model**   The theory that light is made up of tiny particles is called the _____.

19 Study Guide

Section 19.1: When Light Waves Interfere

In your textbook, read about diffraction and the properties of light.

Circle the letter of the choice that best completes the statement or answers the question.

1. One sign that the corpuscular model of light isn't entirely correct is that light _____.
   a. travels in absolutely straight lines
   b. produces fuzzy shadow edges
   c. produces sharp shadow edges
   d. adds energy to matter

2. The crest of any wave can be replaced by a series of _____.
   a. equally spaced wave sources that are in step with each other
   b. equally spaced wave sources that interfere with each other
   c. unequally spaced wave sources that are in step with each other
   d. unequally spaced wave sources that interfere with each other

3. Interference fringes result from _____.
   a. constructive and destructive interference
   b. particle interactions
   c. wavelet creation
   d. refraction

4. A monochromatic light source emits light of _____.
   a. all frequencies
   b. one wavelength
   c. different wavelengths that interfere constructively
   d. one refractive index

5. How many slits were present in the barrier Young used to observe interference fringes?
   a. none
   b. one
   c. two
   d. three

6. Wave crests that reach the same points at the same times are said to be _____.
   a. out of phase
   b. in phase
   c. noncoherent
   d. diffractive

7. Where two wave crests overlap, _____.
   a. a bright band is created
   b. a dark band is created
   c. diffraction occurs
   d. a colored band is created

8. Where a wave crest and a wave trough overlap, _____.
   a. a bright band is created
   b. a dark band is created
   c. diffraction occurs
   d. a colored band is created

9. In a two-slit experiment that uses monochromatic light, what appears at the center of the screen?
   a. bands of two different colors
   b. a dark band
   c. a complete spectrum
   d. a bright band

---

19 Study Guide

10. In a two-slit experiment that uses white light, what appears at the center of the screen?
    a. bands of two different colors
    b. a dark band
    c. a complete spectrum
    d. a bright band

11. In a two-slit experiment that uses white light, what types of bands appear away from the center of the screen?
    a. bright bands only
    b. dark bands only
    c. colored spectra
    d. monochromatic bands

In your textbook, read about measuring wavelength with two-slit diffraction.

For each term on the left, write the matching item.

w	12.	width of a single slit
λ	13.	wavelength
d	14.	separation of two slits
L	15.	distance between the screen and slits
P_0	16.	location of the central bright band
P	17.	location of the first-order line
x	18.	distance between the central bright line and first-order line

d	
L	
λ	
P	
P_0	
w	
x	

The diagram below shows a two-slit experimental setup. Refer to the diagram to answer the following questions. Use complete sentences.

19. Describe the band that appears on the screen at point A. What kind of interference is occurring there?
    It is a bright central band, caused by constructive interference.

20. What kind of band appears at point B? What kind of interference is occurring there?
    It is a dark band caused by destructive interference.

21. Describe the band that appears on the screen at point C. What kind of interference is occurring there?
    A bright, first-order band appears at C, caused by constructive interference.

---

19 Study Guide

Name _____

22. What does the length E represent?
It represents the distance between the central band and the first-order line.

23. Explain how the wavelength of the light can be calculated from the two-slit setup.
Multiply the distance between the central line and first-order line by the distance between the slits, and divide by the distance between the screen and the slits.

24. Write an equation calculating wavelength, first using the labels from the diagram, and then using the standard symbols.
λ = EF/D; λ = xd/L

In your textbook, read about single-slit diffraction.
Circle the letter of the choice that best completes the statement or answers the question.

25. Which of the following is true of the diffraction of light compared to that of sound?
   a. Light is diffracted more because it has smaller wavelengths.
   b. Light is diffracted more because it has larger wavelengths.
   c. Sound is diffracted more because it has smaller wavelengths.
   d. Sound is diffracted more because it has larger wavelengths.

26. If light is passed through a single slit, _____.
   a. it is not diffracted
   b. a pattern of equally spaced bright bands results
   c. a wide, bright central band with dimmer bands on either side is produced
   d. a narrow, dim central band with brighter bands on either side is produced

27. In a single-slit situation, the distance between the central band and the first dark band is equal to
   a. $\lambda L/w$
   b. wL/λ
   c. $\lambda w/L$
   d. $w/\lambda L$

---

19 Study Guide

Name _____

Section 19.2: Applications of Diffraction

In your textbook, read about diffraction gratings.
For each of the statements below, write true or write or rewrite the italicized part to make the statement true.

1. **spectra** — When white light falls on a diffraction grating, *white bands* are produced.

2. **true** — Diffraction gratings are made by using a diamond to scratch fine *lines on glass*.

3. **1000 nm** — The spacing between the lines on diffraction gratings is typically about *1 mm*.

4. **can** — Wavelength *cannot* be measured as precisely with diffraction gratings as with double slits.

Write the term that correctly completes each statement. Use each term once.

θ	colors	interference
λ/d	diffract	narrower
angle	distance	wavelengths
broader	grating spectrometer	

A diffraction grating has many parallel slits that (5) **diffract** light and form a(n) (6) **interference** pattern. This pattern has bright bands that are (7) **narrower** than those produced by a double slit, and the dark regions are (8) **broader**. The pattern makes it easier to distinguish individual (9) **colors** and to measure (10) **wavelengths** more precisely.

The equation used in the calculation states that x/L is equal to (11) **λ/d**, where the variable in the denominator is the (12) **distance** between the grating's lines. Instead of measuring the distance from the central band to the first bright band, most laboratory instruments measure the (13) **angle** between them. The symbol for that quantity is (14) **θ**. The instrument used for the measurement is called a (15) **grating spectrometer**.

19 Study Guide

In your textbook, read about determining wavelength with diffraction gratings.
Circle the letter of the choice that best completes the statement or answers the question.

16. For a diffraction grating, the wavelength equals _____.
   a. sin d b. sin $d\theta$ c. d/sin θ **d. d sin θ** *(circled)*

17. When monochromatic light is used with a diffraction grating, what is produced?
   a. no diffraction pattern
   b. no central band, but bright bands to the left and right
   c. a bright central band with bright bands to the left and right *(circled)*
   d. a dark central band with white bands to the left and right

18. How do the screen locations of the red lines produced by red light shone on a diffraction grating compare with the locations of the red lines produced by white light?
   a. Those produced by the red light are above.
   b. Those produced by the red light are to the left.
   c. Those produced by the white light are closer together.
   d. They are in the same places. *(circled)*

19. The sine of the angle between bright bands is approximately equal to _____.
   a. d/L b. L/x **c. x/L** *(circled)*   d. d/x

20. Which quantity is read directly from the calibrated base of a grating spectrometer?
   a. θ *(circled)*   b. λ c. f d. c

In your textbook, read about telescope and microscope resolution.
For each of the statements below, write true or rewrite the italicized part to make the statement true.

21. **wider** — Decreasing the width of a lens used in a telescope causes the diffraction pattern to become *narrower*.

22. **true** — Two stars will be just resolved if the central bright band of one star falls on the *first dark band* of the second star.

23. **narrower** — The diffraction pattern formed by blue light in a microscope is *wider* than that formed by red light.

24. **telescopes only** — Using a larger lens is practical in reducing effects of diffraction on the resolving power of *both microscopes and telescopes*.

25. **true** — *White light would be more useful than green light in reducing diffraction patterns formed in a microscope.*

26. **more spread out** — Telescope diffraction causes light from a star to appear *brighter*.

---

20 Study Guide

Static Electricity
Vocabulary Review

Write the term that correctly completes each statement. Use each term once.

charged	coulomb	elementary charge
charging by conduction	Coulomb's law	insulators
charging by induction	electroscope	neutral
conductors	electrostatics	plasma

1. **insulators** — Materials through which charges will not move easily are electrical _____.

2. **electrostatics** — The study of electrical charges that can be collected and held in one place is _____.

3. **electroscope** — A(n) _____ is a device used to determine charge.

4. **elementary charge** — The magnitude of the charge of an electron is the _____.

5. **charging by induction** — Separating the charges in an object without touching the object is _____.

6. **conductors** — Materials such as metals are electrical _____. They allow charges to move about easily.

7. **neutral** — The positive charge in _____ objects exactly balances the negative charge.

8. **charging by conduction** — Giving a neutral body a charge by touching it with a charged body is _____.

9. **Coulomb's law** — The magnitude of the force between charge q_A and charge q_B separated by a distance d, is proportional to the magnitude of the charges and inversely proportional to the square of the distance; this is a statement of _____.

10. **coulomb** — The _____ is the SI standard unit of charge.

11. **plasma** — A(n) _____ is a gaslike state of negatively charged electrons and positively or negatively charged ions.

12. **charged** — An object that exhibits electrical interaction after rubbing is said to be _____.

Name ____

20 Study Guide

Section 20.1: Electrical Charge

In your textbook, read about charged objects.
Circle the letter of the choice that best completes each statement.

1. Electricity caused by rubbing is ____.
   a. static electricity *(circled)*
   b. lightning
   c. current electricity
   d. charge

2. An object that exhibits electrical interaction after rubbing is said to be ____.
   a. positive
   b. electrical
   c. charged *(circled)*
   d. negative

3. Two objects with the same type of charge ____.
   a. have no affect on each other
   b. repel each other *(circled)*
   c. attract each other
   d. have to be positive

4. Two objects with opposite charges ____.
   a. have no affect on each other
   b. repel each other
   c. attract each other *(circled)*
   d. have to be negative

5. Two types of charges are ____.
   a. yellow and green
   b. top and bottom
   c. attractive and repulsive
   d. positive and negative *(circled)*

In your textbook, read about charged objects.
Complete the chart below by marking the appropriate column for the charge on each material after it is rubbed.

Table 1

Material	Positively charged	Negatively charged
6. plastic		x
7. wool	x	
8. hard rubber		x
9. fur	x	
10. glass	x	

In your textbook, read about the microscopic reasons for charge.
Answer the following questions.

11. What are the negative and positive parts of an atom?
The electrons are negative and the nucleus is positive.

Name ____

20 Study Guide

12. How can an atom become charged?
An atom becomes charged by losing or gaining electrons.

13. What happens when two neutral objects, such as rubber and fur, are rubbed together?
Electrons from atoms in the fur are transferred to the rubber.

In your textbook, read about conductors and insulators.
Decide whether the examples below are insulators or conductors. Mark the correct column.

Table 2

Example	Insulator	Conductor
14. a material through which a charge will not move easily	x	
15. glass	x	
16. air as a plasma		x
17. aluminum		x
18. an object, held at the midpoint and rubbed only one end, becomes charged only at the rubbed end	x	
19. copper		x
20. dry wood	x	
21. a material through which charges move about easily		x
22. graphite		x
23. charges removed from one area are not replaced by charges from another area	x	
24. most plastics	x	
25. dry air	x	
26. charges applied to one area spread quickly over the entire object		x

Section 20.2: Electrical Force

In your textbook, read about forces on charged bodies and lightning.
For each of the statements below, write true or rewrite the italicized part to make the statement true.

1. There are *two kinds* of electrical charges, positive and negative.
true

2. Charges *cannot* exert force on other charges over a distance.
can

3. The force between two charged objects is *weaker* when the objects are closer together.

stronger

4. *Opposite* charges repel.

Like

5. If an electroscope is given a *positive* charge, the leaves will spread.

true

6. Neutral objects can attract charged objects because of separation of charge in the *charged* object.

neutral

7. Lightning bolts *discharge* clouds.

true

In your textbook, read about electroscopes.
Refer to the drawings to answer the following questions.

8. What is the net charge on the electroscope?

The net charge is negative.

9. By what method is the electroscope being charged?

The electroscope is being touched by a charged object, so it

is being charged by conduction.

10. The electroscope has a net negative charge. What will happen if the electroscope is touched with an object that has a negative charge?

The leaves will spread farther apart.

11. What will happen if the electroscope is touched with an object that has a positive charge?

The leaves will fall.

12. What is the charge on the metal sphere A?

It has a positive charge.

13. By what method are these metal spheres being charged?

They are being charged by induction.

In your textbook, read about Coulomb's law.
Circle the letter of the choice that best completes each statement.

According to Coulomb's law, the magnitude of the force on a charge q_A caused by charge q_B a distance d away can be written $F = K(q_A q_B/d^2)$.

14. The force, F, _____ with the square of the distance between the centers of two charged objects.

   a. varies directly
   b. varies inversely
   c. varies negatively
   d. doesn't vary

15. The force, F, _____ with the charge of two charged objects.

   a. varies directly
   b. varies inversely
   c. varies negatively
   d. doesn't vary

16. When the charges are measured in coulombs, the distance is measured in meters, and the force is measured in newtons, the constant, K, is _____

   a. 1
   b. 1.60×10^{-19} C
   c. 9.0×10^9 N·m²/C²
   d. unknown

21 Study Guide

Use with Chapter 21.

Electric Fields
Vocabulary Review

Circle the letter of the choice that best completes each statement.

1. The unit used to measure the electric potential difference is the _____.
   - **a.** volt
   - **b.** voltmeter
   - **c.** coulomb
   - **d.** joule

2. The _____ of a charged object exerts force on other charged objects.
   - **a.** charge
   - **b.** capacitance
   - **c.** electric field
   - **d.** voltage

3. The ratio of charge to potential difference of an object is its _____.
   - **a.** capacitance
   - **b.** capacity
   - **c.** voltage
   - **d.** electric potential difference

4. The instrument that measures potential difference is the _____.
   - **a.** voltmeter
   - **b.** ammeter
   - **c.** potential difference meter
   - **d.** capacitor

5. The direction and strength of an electric field are depicted by _____.
   - **a.** tangents
   - **b.** electric field lines
   - **c.** spokes
   - **d.** magnetic field lines

6. The change in potential energy per unit charge is _____.
   - **a.** volt
   - **b.** work
   - **c.** electric potential difference
   - **d.** capacitance

7. Touching an object to Earth to eliminate excess charge is _____.
   - **a.** connecting
   - **b.** equalizing
   - **c.** recharging
   - **d.** grounding

8. A device that stores charge by having a specific capacitance is a(n) _____.
   - **a.** charge holder
   - **b.** battery
   - **c.** capacitor
   - **d.** electric field

9. Capacitance is measured in _____.
   - **a.** coulombs
   - **b.** volts
   - **c.** ohms
   - **d.** farads

10. Electric charge may be visible as a(n) _____ on a power line.
    - **a.** corona
    - **b.** electric field line
    - **c.** electric vector
    - **d.** plasma

---

20 Study Guide

17. Coulomb's law can be used to determine _____ of an electrical force.
    - **a.** the direction
    - **b.** the magnitude
    - **c.** the charge
    - **d.** both the magnitude and the direction

In your textbook, read about the application of electrical forces on neutral bodies.
Answer the following questions.

18. According to Newton's third law of motion, how is a neutral object affected by a charged object?
    A neutral object is attracted toward the charged object.

    _____

    _____

19. Give two examples of applications of electrical forces on neutral particles.
    Answers will vary. Sample answer: These forces can be used to collect soot in smokestacks to
    reduce air pollution. Static electricity is also used in photocopy machines.

    _____

    _____

    _____

21 Study Guide

Section 21.1: Creating and Measuring Electric Fields

In your textbook, read about electric fields.

Answer the following questions, using complete sentences.

11. What produces an electric field?

An electric charge produces an electric field.

12. Why must you use a test charge to observe an electric field?

An electric field can be observed only when it produces forces on other charges.

13. How does Coulomb's law relate to test charges?

The force exerted on a test charge in an electric field is proportional to the size of the test

charge.

14. If arrows represent electric field vectors in a picture of an electric field, how are the magnitude and direction of the field shown?

The length of the arrow is used to show the magnitude of the field. The direction of the arrow

shows the field direction.

15. How do you find the electric field from two charges?

Add the fields from the individual charges vectorially.

16. Why should an electric field be measured only by a small test charge?

The test charge exerts a force on q. It is important that the force exerted by the test charge

doesn't move q to a new location, and thus change the force on q' and the electric field being

measured.

In your textbook, read about models for electric fields.

Answer the following questions.

17. Explain what a Van de Graaff machine is and one way it can be used to show field lines.

A Van de Graaff machine transfers large amounts of charge from one part of the machine to

the top metal terminal. A person touching the terminal is charged electrically. The charges on

the person's hairs repel each other, causing the hairs to follow the field lines.

18. Do field lines and electric fields really exist? How are field lines and electric fields useful?

Field lines do not really exist, but electric fields do. Field lines provide a model of an electric

field. Electric fields provide a method of calculating the force on a charged body.

Physics: Principles and Problems

---

21 Study Guide

In your textbook, read about electric field vectors.

Refer to the illustration to answer the following questions.

19. At what point is the magnitude of the electric field the greatest? Explain how you can tell from the drawing that this is true.

The magnitude of the electric field is greatest at

point A. The arrow representing the field at this point

is the longest.

20. Points B and C are the same distance from the field charge. What could cause the force measured on a test charge at point B to be twice as large as the force measured on a test charge at point C?

If the test charge used at point B is twice as large as the test charge used at point C, the force

measured at point B would be twice as large.

21. If an arrow representing the electric field were drawn at point D, how long would it be relative to the other arrows in the drawing? Why?

It would be shorter than all the other arrows because it is farthest from the field charge.

In your textbook, read about electric field lines.

Answer the following questions.

22. Draw two electric charges, one positive and one negative. Assume they are so far apart that there is no interaction between the charges.

23. Draw electric field lines around each charge. Show that the field around the negative charge is twice as strong as the field around the positive charge.

Physics: Principles and Problems

Physics: Principles and Problems

Teacher Guide and Answers **61T**

Name _____

21 Study Guide

Section 21.2: Applications of Electric Fields

In your textbook, read about electric potential.

Circle the letter of the choice that best completes the statement or answers the question.

1. Which equation defines the electric potential difference?
   a. $E = F/q$
   b. (circled) $\Delta V = \Delta V_e/q'$
   c. $V = J/C$
   d. $q = mg/E$

2. When you do positive work on a two-charge system, the electric potential energy _____
   a. (circled) increases
   b. decreases
   c. does not change
   d. always disappears

3. Only _____ electric potential can be measured.
   a. points of
   b. absolute values of
   c. (circled) differences in
   d. attractions between

4. The electric potential _____ when a positive charge is moved toward a negative charge.
   a. increases
   b. stays the same
   c. (circled) decreases
   d. becomes positive

5. A positive test charge is located at point A. If the test charge is moved to some point B and then back to point A, what is the change in the electric potential?
   a. The electric potential increases.
   b. The electric potential decreases.
   c. The electric potential becomes zero.
   d. (circled) The electric potential does not change.

In your textbook, read about electric potential and uniform fields.

For each of the statements below, write true or false or rewrite the italicized part to make the statement true.

6. Two large, flat conducting plates parallel to each other can create a constant electric force and field. *Both are charged negatively.*
   One is charged negatively and one is charged positively.

7. The direction of an electric field between two parallel conducting plates is *from the positive plate to the negative plate.*
   true

8. The *electrical* difference between two points a distance d apart in a uniform field is represented by the equation $\Delta V = Ed$.
   potential

9. The potential increases in the direction *opposite* the electric field direction.
   true

10. The potential is *lower* near the positively charged plate.
    higher

124   Study Guide   Physics: Principles and Problems

Name _____

21 Study Guide

In your textbook, read about Millikan's oil-drop experiment.

Write the term that correctly completes each statement. Use each term once.

charged	gravitational field	multiple
electric field	ionized	potential difference
electron	magnitude	suspended
		uniform

Millikan used a(n) (11) **uniform** electric field between two parallel plates to measure the charge on an electron. (12) **Charged** oil drops between the plates fell from the air unless the (13) **potential difference** between the two plates was adjusted. When the top plate was positive enough, an oil drop was (14) **suspended** between the plates. At this adjustment, the force of Earth's (15) **gravitational field** and the force of the (16) **electric field** were the same magnitude. From the (17) **magnitude** of the electric field, the charge on the drop was calculated. When Millikan (18) **ionized** the air to add or remove electrons from the drops, the change in the charge of a drop was always a (19) **multiple** of 1.6×10^{-19} C. Therefore, Millikan proposed that each (20) **electron** always carried that charge.

In your textbook, read about objects sharing a charge.

Refer to the illustration. For each of the statements below, write true or false or rewrite the italicized part to make the statement true.

Metal spheres of equal size

21. In drawing A, the electric potential of *sphere 1* is high.
    true

22. When the spheres touch, negative charges flow from *sphere 2 to sphere 1.*
    sphere 1 to sphere 2

23. When the spheres touch, the potential of sphere 2 *decreases* and the potential of sphere 1 *decreases.*
    increases

24. In drawing B, the potential of sphere 1 now *equals* the potential of sphere 2.
    true

25. If sphere 2 were smaller than sphere 1, the two spheres *would not* have reached the same potential by touching.
    would

Physics: Principles and Problems   Study Guide   125

21 Study Guide

In your textbook, read about grounding and conductors.

Answer the following questions.

26. Why can an object be touched to Earth to eliminate excess charge on a body?

Earth is such a large sphere that almost any amount of charge can flow into Earth without

changing Earth's potential. So, all the excess charge on a body can flow into Earth.

27. Give one example of an object that requires grounding to prevent damage or injury.

Answers will vary. Sample answer: Gasoline trucks can acquire charge through friction. If they

were not grounded, the charge could jump to Earth through gasoline vapor and cause an

explosion.

28. Explain why people inside a car are protected from electric fields generated by lightning.

A car is a closed, hollow metal container, so excess charges move to the outer surface.

29. Explain how a lightning rod works.

Because lightning rods are pointed, the electric field is strong near the end of the rod. Air mol-

ecules are pulled apart and start a conducting path from the rods to the clouds. Charges in

the clouds spark to the rod rather than to high points on the house. A conductor from the rod

grounds the charges.

In your textbook, read about capacitance and capacitors.

Circle the letter of the answer that best completes each statement.

30. A small device invented by Pieter Van Musschenbroek that can store a large electric charge is the

a. capacitor   c. resistor

(b.) Leyden jar   d. electric field

31. For a given shape and size of an object, the ratio of charge stored to ——— is a constant.

a. resistance   c. current

(b.) potential difference   d. size

32. All capacitors are made up of two ———, separated by an insulator.

a. insulators   b. plates   (c.) conductors   d. wires

33. Capacitors are used in electric circuits to store ———.

(a.) charge   b. current   c. resistance   d. capacitance

34. The capacitance of a capacitor is ——— the charge on it.

a. dependent on   b. linked to   c. changed by   (d.) independent from

22 Study Guide

Current Electricity

Vocabulary Review

For each description on the left, write the letter of the matching item.

e   **1.** a closed loop though which charges can flow

d   **2.** the flow of positive charge

j   **3.** a variable resistor or rheostat

f   **4.** a flow of charged particles

k   **5.** the property that determines how much current is present

b   **6.** a flow of 1 C/s

m   **7.** a circuit diagram

a   **8.** a device that measures current

c   **9.** several voltaic cells connected together

l   **10.** device designed to have a specific resistance

n   **11.** a connection that provides only one path for a current

o   **12.** a device that measures the potential difference of a circuit

h   **13.** a connection of two or more electric devices that provides more than one current path

i   **14.** a device that converts light energy to electric energy

g   **15.** 100 watts of electric energy delivered continuously and used for 1 h

a. ammeter
b. ampere
c. battery
d. conventional current
e. electric circuit
f. electric current
g. kilowatt-hour
h. parallel connection
i. photovoltaic cell
j. potentiometer
k. resistance
l. resistor
m. schematic
n. series connection
o. voltmeter

22 Study Guide

Section 22.1: Current and Circuits

In your textbook, read about electric circuits.

Circle the letter of the choice that best completes the statement or answers the question.

1. If two conductors at different potential differences are connected by another conductor, charges flow from the conductor with the _____ potential difference to the conductor with the _____ potential difference.

   a. higher, lower   **b.** lower, higher   **c.** negative, positive   **d.** medium, higher

2. If two conductors, A and B, are connected by another conductor, when does the flow of charge stop?

   a. when the potential difference of A is lower than the potential difference of B

   b. when the potential difference of A is higher than the potential difference of B

   c. when the potential difference of all conductors is equal

   d. never

3. Batteries and generators are both sources of _____.

   a. light   **c.** photovoltaic cells

   b. electric energy   **d.** kinetic energy

4. A(n) _____ is a closed loop that consists of a charge pump connected to a device that reduces the potential energy of the flowing charges.

   a. electric circuit   **c.** resistor

   b. generator   **d.** potentiometer

5. The potential energy lost by the charges moving through a device in a circuit is represented by _____.

   a. ΔV **c.** PE

   b. E **d.** qV

6. A general term that could refer to a battery, photovoltaic cell, or generator in a circuit is _____.

   a. ammeter   **c.** charge pump

   b. resistor   **d.** current

7. No generator is 100 percent efficient, and the kinetic energy that is not converted to electric energy usually _____.

   a. stays electric energy   **c.** becomes light energy

   b. becomes thermal energy   **d.** disappears

8. Because q is conserved, the net change in potential energy of the charges going completely around the circuit _____.

   a. must be zero

   b. is higher at the beginning than at the end

   c. is lower at the beginning than at the end

   d. is a negative number

---

22 Study Guide

In your textbook, read about electric power.

Write the term that correctly completes each statement. Use each term once.

ammeter	coulomb	energy	power
ampere	electric current	potential difference	watts
charge			

Power measures the rate at which **(9)** _____ energy _____ is transferred. The energy carried by an electric current depends on the **(10)** _____ charge _____ transferred and the potential difference across which it moves. The unit used for quantity of electric charge is the **(11)** _____ coulomb _____. Thus, the rate of flow of electric charge, or **(12)** _____ electric current _____, is measured in coulombs per second. One coulomb per second is a(n) **(13)** _____ ampere _____. A(n) **(14)** _____ ammeter _____ is used to measure current. The **(15)** _____ power _____ of an electric device is found by multiplying the **(16)** _____ potential difference _____ by the current. The power, or energy delivered to the electric device per second, is measured in joules per second, or **(17)** _____ watts _____.

In your textbook, read about resistance.

For each of the statements below, write true or rewrite the italicized part to make the statement true.

18. _____ almost no current _____ If you put a glass rod between two conductors that have a potential difference between them, you will have *a very large current.*

19. _____ true _____ *Resistance* is measured by placing a potential difference across two points on a conductor and measuring the current.

20. _____ current _____ Resistance is the ratio of the potential difference to the *charge.*

21. _____ true _____ The resistance of a conductor is measured in *ohms.*

22. _____ true _____ One ohm, 1Ω, is the resistance that permits a current of 1 A when a *potential difference of 1 V is applied* across the resistance.

23. _____ constant resistance _____ A device that has a *changing resistance* and appears to be independent of the potential difference is said to obey Ohm's law.

24. _____ small volume _____ To reduce current, you need a large resistance in a *large volume.*

25. _____ zero _____ Superconductors are materials that have *high resistance.*

Name ___

22 Study Guide

In your textbook, read about control of current.
Answer the following questions.

26. How does voltage affect the current that passes through a resistor?
The larger the voltage that passes through a resistor, the larger is the current that passes through it.

27. How can the current be reduced if the voltage is kept constant?
The current is reduced when the resistance is increased.

28. Explain how a variable resistor, or potentiometer, works.
A variable resistor consists of a coil of resistance wire and a sliding contact point. By moving the contact point to various positions along the coil, the amount of wire in the circuit varies. As more wire is included in the circuit, the resistance of the circuit increases.

In your textbook, read about symbols used in schematic diagrams.
Complete the table below by writing the correct symbols or the names of components.

Component	Symbol	Component	Symbol
capacitor	⊣⊢	electric connection	──
conductor	──	no electric connection	──
fuse	(symbol)	switch	(symbol)
lamp	(symbol)		

Name ___

22 Study Guide

In your textbook, read about schematic diagrams of circuits.
Complete the schematic diagrams below.

29. Label the components of the schematic diagram below.

lamp
resistor
battery
ammeter

30. Draw a schematic diagram for the circuit in the drawing below.

Current flow
30 V
10 Ω
3A

$I = \dfrac{V}{R}$
$= \dfrac{30\ V}{10\ \Omega}$
$= 3\ A$

31. Draw a schematic diagram for a circuit that has a battery, a lamp, a motor, a switch, and an ammeter, with a voltmeter across the motor.

22 Study Guide

Name _____

Section 22.2: Using Electrical Energy

In your textbook, read about resistors used to turn electric energy into thermal energy.
Circle the letter of the choice that best completes each statement.

1. A space heater, a hot plate, and the heating element in a hair dryer are designed to convert almost all the electric energy into _____.
   a. kinetic energy
   b. potential energy
   c. thermal energy
   d. solar energy

2. Household appliances that convert electric energy into thermal energy act as _____ when they are in a circuit.
   a. resistors
   b. motors
   c. ammeters
   d. voltage dividers

3. When a charge moves through a resistor, its _____ is reduced.
   a. current
   b. potential difference
   c. resistance
   d. charge

4. The _____ dissipated in a resistor is proportional to the square of the current that passes through it and to the resistance.
   a. voltage
   b. power
   c. current
   d. kinetic energy

5. A resistor gets hot because the power that cannot pass through it is changed _____.
   a. from thermal energy to electric energy
   b. from kinetic energy to thermal energy
   c. from electric energy to kinetic energy
   d. from electric energy to thermal energy

In your textbook, read about transmission of electric energy and power companies.
For each of the statements below, write true *or rewrite the italicized part to make the statement true.*

6. ___true___ When power is transmitted over long distances, energy is lost as *thermal energy.*

7. ___resistance___ To reduce the loss of energy during transmittal of power over long distances, either the current or the *voltage* must be reduced.

8. ___true___ All *wires* have some resistance, even though the resistance is small.

9. ___large___ Cables of high conductivity and *small* diameter are used to transmit power long distances to reduce the resistance and reduce loss of energy as thermal energy.

10. ___true___ Current can be reduced without reducing power, by increasing the *voltage.*

11. ___kilowatt-hours___ Electric companies measure their energy sales in *joules per second times seconds.*

---

23 Study Guide

Series and Parallel Circuits

Vocabulary Review

For each description on the left, write the letter of the matching item.

__h__ 1. circuit in which all current travels though each device

__e__ 2. short piece of metal that melts if too large a current passes through it

__i__ 3. occurs when a circuit forms that has a very low resistance

__g__ 4. circuit in which there are several different paths for a current

__b__ 5. automatic switch that opens a circuit when the current reaches some set value

__c__ 6. circuit that has some resistors in parallel and some in series

__d__ 7. value of a single resistor that could replace all resistors in a circuit without changing the current

__a__ 8. device used to measure the current in part of a circuit

__k__ 9. device used to measure the potential drop across some part of a circuit

__f__ 10. detects small differences in current caused by an extra current path and opens the circuit

__j__ 11. series circuit used to produce a voltage source from a higher-voltage battery

a. ammeter
b. circuit breaker
c. combination series-parallel circuit
d. equivalent resistance
e. fuse
f. ground-fault interpreter
g. parallel circuit
h. series circuit
i. short circuit
j. voltage divider
k. voltmeter

23 Study Guide

Section 23.1: Simple Circuits

In your textbook, read about current in series circuits.

Circle the letter of the choice that best completes the statement or answers the question.

1. The current is _____ a series circuit.
   a. higher at the beginning of
   b. (the same everywhere in)
   c. lower at the beginning of
   d. variable in

2. In an electric circuit, the increase in voltage provided by the generator or other energy source, ΔV_{source}, is equal to the _____ of voltage drops across the resistors.
   a. subtraction
   b. multiplication
   c. (sum)
   d. average

3. Which of the following equations is not correct?
   a. $I = \dfrac{\Delta V_{source}}{(R_1 + R_2)}$
   b. $I = \dfrac{\Delta V_{source}}{R}$
   c. $I = \dfrac{\Delta V_{source}}{(R_1 + R_2 + R_3)}$
   d. $\left(I = R_3 + \dfrac{\Delta V_{source}}{(R_1 + R_2)} \right)$

4. Which of the following equations correctly computes the equivalent resistance for a series circuit with four resistors?
   a. $\left(R = R_1 + R_2 + R_3 + R_4 \right)$
   b. $R = R_1 \times R_2 \times R_3 \times R_4$
   c. $\dfrac{1}{R} = \dfrac{1}{R_1} + \dfrac{1}{R_2} + \dfrac{1}{R_3} + \dfrac{1}{R_4}$
   d. $R = \dfrac{(R_1 \times R_2)}{(R_3 \times R_4)}$

5. In a series circuit, the equivalent resistance is _____ any single resistance.
   a. (larger than)
   b. determined by
   c. equal to
   d. smaller than

6. If the battery voltage does not change, adding more devices in series _____ the current.
   a. sometimes decreases
   b. (always decreases)
   c. sometimes increases
   d. always increases

7. Given the voltage of a series circuit, you first calculate _____ to find the current through the circuit.
   a. the voltage
   b. (the equivalent resistance)
   c. the power
   d. the equivalent voltage

23 Study Guide

In your textbook, read about voltage drops in series circuits.

Answer the following questions, using complete sentences.

8. Why must the net change in potential be zero as current moves through a circuit?
   As current passes through the resistors of a circuit, the energy source (the battery or genera-tor) raises the potential an amount equal to the total voltage drops across the resistors.

9. How do you find the potential drop across an individual resistor?
   Multiply the current in the circuit by the resistance of that resistor.

10. What type of circuit is used in a voltage divider?
    A series circuit is used in a voltage divider.

11. What is the purpose of a voltage divider?
    A voltage divider produces a voltage source from a higher-voltage battery.

12. What determines the resistance of a photoresistor?
    The resistance of a photoresistor depends on the amount of light that strikes it.

13. Why are photoresistors often used in voltage dividers? In what special devices can they be used?
    The output voltage of a voltage divider that uses a photoresistor depends on the amount of light striking the photoresistor sensor. It can be used as a light meter.

23 Study Guide

In your textbook, read about parallel circuits.

Refer to the circuit diagram below. Circle the letter of the best answer for each question.

14. What type of circuit does this diagram represent?

  a. series circuit

  (b.) parallel circuit

  c. combination series-parallel circuit

  d. tandem circuit

15. How many current paths are in this circuit?

  a. one

  b. four

  (c.) three

  d. five

16. How would you calculate the total current of this circuit?

  a. Total current is found by computing the average of the currents through each path.

  (b.) Total current is found by adding the currents through each path.

  c. Total current is found by subtracting the currents through each path.

  d. Total current cannot be calculated for this circuit.

17. If the 10-Ω resistor were removed from the circuit, which of the following would *not* be true?

  a. The current through the 20-Ω resistor would be unchanged.

  b. The sum of the current in the branches of the circuit would change.

  c. The total current through the generator would change.

  (d.) The current through the 50-Ω resistor would change.

18. Which of the following is true for this circuit?

  (a.) The equivalent resistance of this circuit is smaller than 10 Ω.

  b. $R = R_1 + R_2 + R_3$

  c. $R = \dfrac{1}{R_1} + \dfrac{1}{R_2} + \dfrac{1}{R_3}$

  d. $R = R_1 \times R_2 \times R_3$

---

23 Study Guide

Section 23.2: Applications of Circuits

In your textbook, read about safety devices.

For each of the statements below, write true or rewrite the italicized part to make it true.

1. When appliances are connected in *parallel*, each additional appliance placed in operation reduces the equivalent resistance in the circuit and causes more current to flow through the wires.

  true

2. The *length* of the metal in a fuse determines the amount of current that will melt the fuse and break the circuit.

  thickness

3. When a circuit breaker *opens*, it allows current to flow.

  closes

4. Ground-fault interrupters can be used as safety devices on circuits in which the current flows along *a single path* from the power source into the electric outlet and back to the source.

  true

5. Electric wiring in homes uses only *series* circuits.

  parallel

6. Low resistance causes the current to be very *small* and may result in a short circuit.

  large

In your textbook, read about combined series-parallel circuits.

Circle the letter of the choice that best answers the question.

7. Which diagram represents a combined series-parallel circuit in which a 30-Ω resistor and a 75-Ω resistor are connected in parallel to a 125-V source through a 2-Ω resistor in series?

23 Study Guide

In your textbook, read about ammeters and voltmeters.
Redraw the circuit diagram below according to the following directions.

125 V

10 Ω

20 Ω

60 Ω

Question 8

125 V

10 Ω

(A)

(V)

20 Ω

60 Ω

Question 10

(A) **Question 9**

8. Insert an ammeter in the circuit that would measure the current of the entire circuit.
   See answer to problem 10.

9. Insert an ammeter in the circuit that would measure the current that flows through the 60-Ω resistor.
   See answer to problem 10.

10. Insert a voltmeter that would measure the voltage drop across the 10-Ω resistor.

Write the term that correctly completes each statement. Use each term once.

| ammeter | low | series |
| high | parallel | voltmeter |

A(n) **(11)** _____ **ammeter** _____ measures current. It is placed in

(12) _____ **series** _____ with the resistor if you want to measure the current through

a resistor. So that it will change the current as little as possible, its resistance should be as

(13) _____ **low** _____ as possible. A(n) **(14)** _____ **voltmeter** _____ measures the

voltage drop across a resistor. It should be connected in **(15)** _____ **parallel** _____ with a

resistor to measure the potential drop across that resistor. So that it will change the current as little as

possible, its resistance should be as **(16)** _____ **high** _____ as possible.

---

24 Study Guide

Magnetic Fields

Vocabulary Review

For each description on the left, write the letter of the matching item.

d 1. a current-carrying coil of wire that has a north pole and a south pole

j 2. the strength of a magnetic field

e 3. used to find the direction of the magnetic field around a current-carrying wire

b 4. the combined magnetic fields of electrons in a group of atoms

l 5. used to find the direction of the magnetic field around an electromagnet

n 6. used to find the direction of the force on a current-carrying wire in a magnetic field

f 7. a device used to measure very small currents

i 8. the number of magnetic field lines passing through a surface

k 9. having a north pole and a south pole

g 10. the magnetic forces that exist around magnets

h 11. imaginary lines used to help visualize a magnetic field

m 12. a long coil of wire consisting of many loops

c 13. a device that converts electrical energy to kinetic energy

a 14. several rotating loops of wire in an electric motor

a. armature
b. domain
c. electric motor
d. electromagnet
e. first right-hand rule
f. galvanometer
g. magnetic field
h. magnetic field lines
i. magnetic flux
j. magnetic induction
k. polarized
l. second right-hand rule
m. solenoid
n. third right-hand rule

24 Study Guide

Section 24.1 Magnets: Permanent and Temporary

In your textbook, read about magnets.

For each of the statements below, write true or rewrite the italicized part to make it true.

north-south	When a magnet is allowed to swing freely, it comes to rest lined up in *an east-west* direction.

1. _____

2. **true** — A *compass* is a small magnet mounted so that it is free to turn.

3. **repel** — Like poles *attract* each other.

4. **always** — Magnets *do not always* have two opposite poles.

5. **true** — If Earth is considered a giant magnet, the south pole of the Earth-magnet is near Earth's *geographic north pole.*

6. **an iron alloy** — Many permanent magnets are made of *pure iron.*

In your textbook, read about magnetic fields.

Answer the following questions, using complete sentences.

7. Describe one method for showing the magnetic field around a magnet.
Answers will vary. The description should include the use of iron filings that become small magnets by induction. The filings rotate until each is parallel to the magnetic field.

8. What does *magnetic flux* mean in terms of both magnetic field lines and magnetic field strength? Where is it greatest on a magnet?
Magnetic flux is the number of magnetic field lines passing through a surface. The flux per unit area is proportional to the strength of the magnetic field. The magnetic flux is greatest at the poles of a magnet.

9. Describe the direction and shape of magnetic field lines of a bar magnet.
Outside the magnet, the field lines come out of the N-pole and loop around the outside, entering at the S-pole. Inside the magnet, they continue from the S-pole to the N-pole to form closed loops.

10. Describe three things that happen when a sample made of iron, cobalt, or nickel is placed in the magnetic field of a permanent magnet.
The field lines become concentrated within the sample; the end of the sample closest to the magnet's N-pole becomes the sample's S-pole; and the sample is attracted to the magnet.

---

24 Study Guide

In your textbook, read about magnetic fields around current-carrying wires and electromagnets.

Answer the following questions, using complete sentences.

11. In the drawing at the right, what is the direction of the conventional current?
The direction of the conventional current is down.

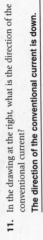

12. Is the strength of the magnetic field greater at point A or point B?
The strength of the magnetic field is greater at point A.

13. Describe the direction of the magnetic field inside and outside of the loop, shown at the right.
Inside the loop, the direction of the field is down, into the page. Outside the loop, it is up, out of the page.

14. In the drawing of an electromagnet shown below, which end is the magnetic north pole?
The left end is the magnetic north pole.

15. Describe two ways to increase the strength of the magnetic field around an electromagnet, besides placing an iron rod inside the coil.
Increasing the number of loops and increasing the current will increase the strength of the magnetic field.

In your textbook, read about domains in magnetic materials.

For each of the statements below, write true or false.

16. **false** The magnetic fields of the electrons in a group of neighboring atoms cannot combine together.

17. **true** When a piece of iron is not in a magnetic field, the domains point in random directions.

18. **false** In permanent magnets, the domains point in random directions.

19. **false** The material on the tape for a recorder is chosen so that the alignment of the domains is only temporary.

20. **true** The direction of the magnetization in different rocks on the seafloor varies, indicating that the north and south poles of Earth have exchanged places many times.

In your textbook, read about uses of the force on a current-carrying wire in a magnetic field.
For each of the following statements, write true or false.

false 8. A loudspeaker changes sound energy into electrical energy.

true 9. The amplifier driving the loudspeaker sends a current through a coil of wire mounted on a paper cone and placed in a magnetic field.

false 10. The force exerted on the coil of wire in a magnetic field in a loudspeaker pushes the coil into or out of the field, depending on the magnitude of the current.

false 11. The forces exerted on a current-carrying loop of wire in a magnetic field cannot be used to measure current.

false 12. In an electric motor, the loop of current-carrying wire must rotate 180°.

In your textbook, read about galvanometers.
Write the term that correctly completes each statement. Use each term once.

current	loop	proportional	torque
direction	magnetic fields	series	voltmeter
down	multiplier	spring	wire
galvanometers	parallel		

(13) **Magnetic fields** that exert forces on a loop of wire carrying a current can be used to measure very small currents. A small loop of (14) **wire** that is carrying a current is placed in the strong magnetic field of a permanent magnet. The current passing through the (15) **loop** goes in one end and out the other. The (16) **direction** of the force on the wire resulting from the magnetic field can be determined by using the third right-hand rule. One side of the loop is forced (17) **down**; the other side of the loop is forced up. The resulting (18) **torque** rotates the loop. The magnitude of the torque acting on the loop is proportional to the magnitude of the (19) **current**. This principle is used in (20) **galvanometers** to measure small currents. A small spring in a galvanometer exerts a torque that opposes the torque resulting from the current; thus the amount of torque is (21) **proportional** to the current. A galvanometer can be used as a(n) (22) **voltmeter** or an ammeter. A galvanometer can be converted to an ammeter by connecting it in (23) **parallel** with a resistor having a resistance smaller than that of the galvanometer. To convert the galvanometer to a voltmeter, the galvanometer is connected in (24) **series** with a resistor called a (25) **multiplier**.

Section 24.2: Forces Caused by Magnetic Fields

In your textbook, read about forces on current-carrying wires in magnetic fields.
Circle the letter of the choice that best completes each statement.

1. The force on a current-carrying wire in a magnetic field is ____ both the direction of the magnetic field and the direction of current.
   a. parallel to   **b.** at right angles to   c. opposite   d. independent of

2. The magnitude of the force on a current-carrying wire in a magnetic field is proportional to ____.
   a. the strength of the field, the current in the wire, and the length of the wire in the magnetic field
   b. only the strength of the field
   c. only the strength of the field and the current in the wire
   d. the strength of the field, the current in the wire, and the voltage in the wire

3. Magnetic induction is measured in ____.
   a. newtons   **b.** teslas   c. amperes   d. volts

4. The direction of Earth's magnetic field is toward the ____.
   a. equator   b. north magnetic pole   **c.** south magnetic pole   d. surface

In your textbook, read how to find the direction of force on a current-carrying wire in a magnetic field.
Answer the following questions, using complete sentences.

5. In the drawing at the right, what is the direction of the force on the current-carrying wire?
   The force is down.

6. In the drawing at the right, what is the direction of the force on the current-carrying wire?
   The force is up.

7. Are the current-carrying wires in the drawing at the right attracted or repelled?
   They are attracted.

25 Study Guide

Electromagnetic Induction

Vocabulary Review

Circle the letter of the choice that best completes each statement.

1. The induction of EMF in a wire carrying changing current is _____.
   a. mutual inductance
   b. magnetic induction
   c. electromotive force
   d. self-inductance

2. The part of a transformer that is connected to a source of AC voltage is the _____.
   a. armature
   b. primary coil
   c. secondary coil
   d. core

3. The potential difference given to charges by a charge pump is the _____.
   a. electromotive force
   b. current
   c. electronic force
   d. eddy current

4. The law that states that the direction of the induced current is such that the magnetic field resulting from the induced current opposes the change in the field that caused the induced current is _____.
   a. Ohm's law
   b. Newton's law
   c. Faraday's law
   d. Lenz's law

5. Generating a current in a circuit by relative motion between a wire and a magnetic field is _____.
   a. electromagnetic induction
   b. magnetism
   c. electric induction
   d. current induction

6. A device that increases the voltage is a _____.
   a. step-down transformer
   b. step-up transformer
   c. capacitor
   d. generator

7. A varying EMF is induced in the _____ of a transformer.
   a. primary coil
   b. secondary coil
   c. tertiary coil
   d. armature

8. A(n) _____ increases or decreases AC voltages.
   a. generator
   b. armature
   c. transformer
   d. electric motor

9. The induction of an EMF in one coil as a result of a varying magnetic field in another coil is _____.
   a. self-inductance
   b. electric induction
   c. mutual inductance
   d. magnetic induction

10. A(n) _____ converts mechanical energy to electric energy.
   a. electric generator
   b. electric motor
   c. transformer
   d. capacitor

11. A(n) _____ is used to decrease voltage.
   a. step-up transformer
   b. step-down transformer
   c. electric generator
   d. electric motor

12. When a piece of metal moves through a magnetic field, _____ are produced. They produce a magnetic field that opposes the motion that caused them.
   a. resistances
   b. electromagnets
   c. permanent magnets
   d. eddy currents

24 Study Guide

In your textbook, read about force exerted on charged particles by magnetic fields.

Answer the following questions, using complete sentences.

26. Explain how pictures form on the screen of a cathode-ray tube in a computer monitor or television set.
   In a cathode-ray tube, electric fields pull electrons off atoms in the cathode. Other electric fields gather, accelerate, and focus the electrons into a narrow beam. Magnetic fields are used to control the motion of the beam across the screen of the tube. The screen is coated with a phosphor that glows when it is struck by the electrons, producing the picture.

27. On what does the force produced by a magnetic field on a single electron depend?
   The force depends on the velocity of the electron, the strength of the field, and the angle between the direction of the velocity and the field.

28. Why is the direction of the force on an electron in a magnetic field opposite to the direction given by the third right-hand rule?
   The electron has a negative charge, and conventional current has a positive charge.

29. Why does a charged particle in a uniform magnetic field have a circular path?
   The magnetic field exerts a force on the particle that is always perpendicular to the particle's velocity. This force causes the particle to continually change direction, creating a circular path.

30. What do high-energy nuclear-particle accelerators use magnets for, and how does this process work?
   The magnetic fields force the charged particles to travel in a circle.

31. Explain what causes the aurora borealis.
   Electrons and positive ions trapped in the magnetic field of Earth form the Van Allen belts. Solar storms send high-energy charged particles toward Earth, disturbing Earth's magnetic field and dumping electrons out of the Van Allen belts. These electrons excite atoms of nitrogen and oxygen in Earth's atmosphere, making them emit the colors of the aurora borealis.

25 Study Guide

•••••••••••••

Section 25.1: Creating Electric Current from Changing Magnetic Fields

In your textbook, read about production of an electric current with a magnetic field.
Circle the letter of the choice that best completes each statement.

1. Michael Faraday found that _____ could be produced by moving a wire through a magnetic field.

   a. a resistance   **b.** a current   c. charge   d. magnetism

2. When a wire is held stationary or moved _____ to a magnetic field, no current flows.

   a. parallel   b. perpendicular   c. tangent

3. An electric current is generated in a wire in a magnetic field only when _____.

   a. the wire is stationary in the field

   b. the wire cuts magnetic field lines

   c. the wire is moved parallel to the field

   d. a small current exists in the wire before it is placed in the magnetic field

4. To generate a current in a wire in a magnetic field, _____.

   a. the conductor must move through the magnetic field while the magnetic field remains stationary

   b. the magnetic field must move past the conductor while the conductor remains stationary

   c. there must be relative movement between the wire and the magnetic field

   d. there must be a battery connected to the wire

5. Electromotive force is not a force; it is a _____.

   a. current   b. resistance   c. charge   **d.** potential difference

6. *EMF* is measured in _____.

   a. volts   b. amperes   c. ohms   d. newtons

7. The *EMF* produced in a wire moving in a magnetic field depends only on the _____.

   a. field strength

   b. current in the wire

   c. magnetic field strength, the length of the wire in the field, and the velocity of the wire in the field

   d. magnetic field strength, the length of the wire in the field, and the current in the wire

8. If a wire moves through a magnetic field at an angle to the field, only the component of the wire's velocity that is _____ generates *EMF*.

   a. positive

   b. parallel to the direction of the magnetic field

   c. negative

   d. perpendicular to the direction of the magnetic field

Physics: Principles and Problems

---

25 Study Guide

•••••••••••••

In your textbook, read about microphones and generators.
Answer the following questions, using complete sentences.

9. Explain how *EMF* is produced in a microphone.
   In a microphone, a diaphragm is attached to a coil of wire that is free to move in a magnetic field. Sound waves vibrate the diaphragm, which moves the coil in the magnetic field. The motion of the coil induces an *EMF* across the ends of the coil.

10. Explain how a sound wave is converted to an electric signal in a microphone.
    The induced *EMF* varies as the frequency of the sound varies.

11. What is the purpose of an electric generator?
    An electric generator turns mechanical energy into electric energy.

12. Describe how an electric generator works.
    As the armature of the electric generator turns, the wire loops cut through the magnetic field lines, inducing an *EMF*.

13. What is one way to increase the induced *EMF* produced by a generator?
    The induced *EMF* can be increased by increasing the number of loops of wire in the armature.

14. Explain why the strength of the electric current changes as the armature of an electric generator turns.
    The current is greatest when the loop is in a horizontal position because the component of the loop's velocity perpendicular to the magnetic field is greatest. As the loop rotates from the horizontal position to the vertical, it moves through the magnetic field lines at an ever-increasing angle and cuts through fewer magnetic field lines per unit time.

15. Explain why the direction of the electric current changes as the armature of an electric generator turns.
    As the loop turns, the segments of the loop alternate between moving up and moving down. When a segment that has been moving up begins to move down, the direction of the force felt by the charges in the wire changes, and thus the current changes.

16. Compare and contrast electric generators and electric motors.
    A generator converts mechanical energy to electric energy, while a motor converts electric energy to mechanical energy. In a generator, mechanical energy turns an armature in a magnetic field. The induced voltage makes current flow. In a motor, a voltage is placed across an armature coil in a magnetic field. The voltage makes current flow in the coil, so that the armature turns, producing mechanical energy.

Physics: Principles and Problems

Physics: Principles and Problems

Teacher Guide and Answers **73T**

25 Study Guide

• • • • • • • • • • • • •

Section 25.2: Changing Magnetic Fields Induce *EMF*

In your textbook, read about Lenz's law.

For each of the statements below, write true or rewrite the italicized part to make the statement true.

1. _true_ — When a current is produced in a wire by electromagnetic induction, the direction of the current is such that the magnetic field produces a force on the wire that *opposes* the original motion of the wire.

2. _the change in the field_ — The direction of an induced current is such that the magnetic field resulting from the induced current opposes *the field* that caused the induced current.

3. _repels_ — If the N-pole of a magnet is moved toward the right end of the coil, the right end of the coil *attracts* the magnet and becomes an N-pole.

4. _true_ — If a generator produces a larger current, then the armature will be *more difficult* to turn.

5. _true_ — The opposing force on an armature means that mechanical energy must be supplied to the generator to produce electric energy; this fact is consistent with *the law of conservation of energy*.

In your textbook, read about applications of Lenz's law.

Answer the following questions, using complete sentences.

6. Explain why a large current flows when an electric motor is first turned on but is reduced as the motor begins to turn.

When a motor is first turned on, a large current flows because of the low resistance of the motor. As the motor begins to turn, the motion of the wires across the magnetic field induces a back-EMF that opposes the flow of current. This reduces the net current.

7. What can cause a spark when a motor's plug is pulled from an outlet?

The sudden change in the magnetic field can generate a back-EMF and cause a spark.

8. How does a sensitive balance use Lenz's law to stop its oscillation?

A piece of metal on the balance arm rides between the poles of a horseshoe magnet. When the balance arm swings, the metal moves through the magnetic field. Eddy currents generated in the metal produce a magnetic field that opposes the motion that caused the currents.

---

25 Study Guide

• • • • • • • • • • • • •

In your textbook, read how to find the direction of a current induced in a wire by a changing magnetic field.

Answer the following questions.

17. In the drawing on the right, in which direction does the current move?

The current moves down.

18. Which right-hand rule is used to find the direction of the current in the drawing on the right?

The third right-hand rule is used.

19. The drawing above represents five positions of one side of a wire loop as it turns in a magnetic field. The current produced when the wire loop is in position A is indicated on the graph below. Mark the approximate points on the graph that correspond to positions B through E.

In your textbook, read about alternating-current generators.

For each of the statements below, write true or rewrite the italicized part to make the statement true.

20. _true_ — In the United States, electric utilities use generators with a *60-Hz* frequency.

21. _varies_ — As the armature in a generator turns, the current *remains constant*.

22. _varies_ — The power associated with an alternating current is *constant*.

23. _true_ — The power of an alternating current is always *positive*.

24. _true_ — Alternating current and voltage are often described in terms of their *effective* current and voltage.

25 Study Guide

In your textbook, read about self-inductance.

Write the term that correctly completes each statement. Use each term once.

constant	EMF	magnetic field lines
current	increases	self-inductance
decreases	larger	zero

(9) **Current** through a coil of wire generates a magnetic field. If the current increases, the magnetic field (10) **increases** . This can be pictured as creation of new (11) **magnetic field lines** . As they expand, they cut through the coil of wires, generating a(n) (12) **EMF** to oppose the current increase. This generating process is called (13) **self-inductance** . The faster the current changes, the (14) **larger** the opposing EMF and the slower the current change. If the current reaches a steady value, the magnetic field is (15) **constant** and the EMF is (16) **zero** . When the current (17) **decreases** , the EMF generated helps prevent the reduction in magnetic field and current.

In your textbook, read about transformers.

Circle the letter of the choice that best completes each statement.

18. Transformers can change ___ with relatively little loss of energy.
a. power b. resistances (c.) voltages d. magnetic fields

19. A transformer has ___ coils, electrically insulated from each other, but wound around the same iron core.
(a.) two b. three c. four d. five

20. When the primary coil is connected to a source of AC voltage, the changing current creates a ___.
a. steady magnetic field (c.) varying magnetic field
b. potential difference d. resistance

21. In the secondary coil, the varying magnetic field induces a ___.
(a.) varying EMF b. steady EMF c. resistance d. charge

22. In a step-up transformer, the number of coils of wire in the primary coil is ___ the number of coils in the secondary coil.
a. equal to (b.) less than c. double d. greater than

23. In an ideal transformer, the electric power delivered to the secondary circuit is ___ the power supplied to the primary circuit.
(a.) equal to b. less than c. double d. greater than

26 Study Guide

Electromagnetism

Vocabulary Review

Write the letter of the choice that best completes each statement.

1. A wire that is connected to an alternating current source that forms or receives electromagnetic waves is a(n) ___.
a. receiver b. dish (c.) antenna d. cable

2. The combination of an antenna, coil and capacitor circuit, and amplifier is a ___.
(a.) receiver c. mass spectrometer
b. radio d. secondary antenna

3. Atoms that have the same chemical properties but different masses are ___.
a. nuclides (b.) isotopes c. isomers d. elements

4. Energy that is carried through space in the form of electromagnetic waves is ___.
(a.) electromagnetic radiation c. magnetic fields
b. electric fields d. electricity

5. Crystals that bend or deform when a voltage is applied across them show the property of ___.
a. conductance c. magnetism
b. electromagnetic waves (d.) piezoelectricity

6. An instrument that is used to find the masses of positive ions is a(n) ___.
(a.) mass spectrometer c. analytical scale
b. precise balance d. scintillation counter

7. Electromagnetic waves of relatively high frequency that are generated by accelerating electrons to high speeds using 20 000 or more volts and then crashing the electrons into matter are ___.
a. gamma rays (c.) X rays
b. infrared rays d. visible light rays

8. Electric and magnetic fields that move through space make up a(n) ___.
a. electric current c. static charge
(b.) electromagnetic wave d. electric wave

9. The type(s) of radiation with the longest wavelengths is(are) ___.
a. microwaves (c.) radio waves
b. light d. X rays and gamma rays

10. The type(s) of radiation with the highest frequency is(are) ___.
a. ultraviolet c. radio waves
b. light (d.) X rays and gamma rays

26 Study Guide

Section 26.1: Interaction Between Electric and Magnetic Fields and Matter

In your textbook, read about Thomson's experiment to measure the mass of an electron. *Refer to the diagram below. Write the term or letter that correctly completes each statement. Use each item once.*

cathode-ray tube   electric field   magnitude
charge-to-mass ratio   electrons   straight path
circular path   forces   velocity
direction   magnetic field

The **(1)** __charge-to-mass ratio__ of an electron was first measured in 1897 by J. J. Thomson. For his experiment, Thomson used a(n) **(2)** __cathode-ray tube__ with all of the air removed. An electric field accelerated **(3)** __electrons__ off the negatively charged cathode, labeled **(4)** __B__ in the diagram, toward the positively charged anode, labeled **(5)** __A__. Electrons that passed through a hole in the anode followed a(n) **(6)** __straight path__ toward a fluorescent screen, which glowed where the electrons hit.

Electric and magnetic fields in the center of the tube exerted **(7)** __forces__ on the electrons. The **(8)** __electric (or magnetic) field__ was perpendicular to the beam of electrons. The **(9)** __magnetic (or electric) field__ was at right angles to both the beam and the electric field. When the electric field was stronger, the electrons struck the fluorescent screen at the point labeled **(10)** __C__. When the magnetic field was stronger, the electrons struck the fluorescent screen at point **(11)** __E__. When the electric and magnetic fields were adjusted until the forces of the two fields were equal in **(12)** __magnitude__ and opposite in **(13)** __direction__, the electrons struck the screen at point **(14)** __D__. The magnetic and electric field forces were balanced only for electrons that had a specific **(15)** __velocity__. If the electric field was turned off, only the force due to the magnetic field remained, and the electrons followed a(n) **(16)** __circular path__.

Fluorescent coating

---

26 Study Guide

In your textbook, read about Thomson's experiment to measure the mass of a proton. *For each of the statements below, write true or false.*

__false__   **17.** Positively charged particles, when they are in an electric field, bend the same direction as electrons.

__true__   **18.** Positively charged particles, when they are in an magnetic field, bend the opposite way from electrons.

__false__   **19.** When electrons are pulled off hydrogen atoms, the hydrogen has a net negative charge.

__true__   **20.** The mass of the proton was determined from the charge-to-mass ratio.

__false__   **21.** The mass of the proton was determined to be 9.107×10^{-31} kg.

In your textbook, read about mass spectrometers. *Circle the letter of the choice that best completes each statement.*

22. When Thomson put neon gas into the tube, he found two dots on the screen instead of one, because neon has two ___.
a. atoms   b. isomers   (c.) isotopes   d. masses

23. The masses of positive ions can be measured precisely using a(n) ___, an adaptation of a cathode-ray tube.
a. ordinary balance   (c.) mass spectrometer
b. analytic scale   d. ion accelerator

24. Accelerated ___ strike the ion source of a mass spectrometer, knocking off electrons and thus forming positive gas ions.
(a.) electrons   b. protons   c. ions   d. atoms

25. In a mass spectrometer, a(n) ___ produces an electric field to accelerate the ions.
a. magnetic field   c. antenna
(b.) potential difference   d. magnet

26. The ions that are undeflected move into a region with a uniform magnetic field where they follow a(n) ___.
a. narrow path   b. straight path   (c.) circular path   d. elliptical path

27. The charge-to-mass ratio of the ion is determined by the equation ___.
(a.) $q/m = 2V/B^2r^2$ b. $r = mv/qB$ c. $KE = mv^2/2$ d. $q/m = 2V/Br$

28. In the mass spectrometer, the ions leave a mark when they hit a ___.
a. fluorescent screen   c. glass screen
b. cathode-ray tube   (d.) photographic film

29. Besides being used to measure the mass of positive ions, mass spectrometers can also ___.
a. make negative ions from atoms   (c.) separate isotopes of atoms
b. combine atoms   d. create isotopes of atoms

Section 26.2: Electric and Magnetic Fields in Space

In your textbook, read about electromagnetic waves.

For each of the statements below, write true or rewrite the italicized part to make the statement true.

true   **1.** A changing magnetic field can produce a changing electric field *without* a wire.

changing   **2.** Maxwell postulated that a changing electric field produces a *constant* magnetic field.

true   **3.** Either accelerating charges or changing magnetic fields can produce *combined electric and magnetic fields* that move through space, known as electromagnetic waves.

light   **4.** Electromagnetic waves move at the speed of *sound*.

decreasing   **5.** In order of *increasing* wavelength, the types of radiation are radio waves, microwaves, infrared, light, ultraviolet, and X rays and gamma rays.

In your textbook, read about production of electromagnetic waves.

Circle the letter of the choice that best completes each statement.

6. The alternating current source connected to an antenna produces a _____.
- **a.** constant current that produces a constant electric field
- **b.** constant current that produces a changing electric field
- **c.** changing current that produces a constant electric field
- **d.** changing current that produces a changing electric field

7. The changing electric field produced by an antenna generates a _____.
- **a.** wind
- **b.** constant magnetic field
- **c.** changing magnetic field
- **d.** charge

8. The magnetic field of an electromagnetic wave oscillates _____ the electric field.
- **a.** parallel to
- **b.** at lower frequency than
- **c.** at higher frequency than
- **d.** at right angles to

9. The electric field and magnetic field of an electromagnetic wave are _____ the direction of the motion of the wave.
- **a.** at right angles to
- **b.** opposite to
- **c.** parallel to
- **d.** independent of

10. An electromagnetic wave produced by an antenna is _____.
- **a.** energetic
- **b.** out of phase
- **c.** faster than the speed of light
- **d.** polarized

In your textbook, read about using a coil and a capacitor to generate high-frequency electromagnetic waves.

For each of the statements below, write true or rewrite the italicized part to make the statement true.

capacitor   **11.** When the battery is removed from a circuit containing a coil and capacitor, the *coil* discharges and the stored electrons flow through the coil, creating a magnetic field.

true   **12.** When the magnetic field of the coil collapses, a *back-EMF* recharges the capacitor in the opposite direction.

smaller   **13.** To increase the oscillation frequency, the size of the coil and the capacitor must be made *larger*.

true   **14.** Microwaves and infrared waves *cannot* be generated using a coil and capacitor and an antenna.

In your textbook, read about the pendulum analogy for the coil and capacitor circuit.

For each pendulum analogy, write the letter of the matching coil and capacitor property.

d   **15.** the pendulum bob

a   **16.** The pendulum bob moves fastest when its displacement from vertical is zero.

e   **17.** When the bob is at its greatest angle, it has zero velocity.

b   **18.** The potential energy of the pendulum is largest when its displacement is greatest. The kinetic energy is largest when the velocity is greatest.

g   **19.** The sum of the potential and kinetic energies and thermal energy losses of the pendulum is constant.

f   **20.** The pendulum will eventually stop swinging if it is left alone.

c   **21.** Gentle pushes applied at the correct times will keep a pendulum moving.

a. The largest current flows through the coil when the charge on the capacitor is zero.

b. When the current is largest, the energy stored in the magnetic field is greatest. When the current is zero, the electric field of the capacitor is largest.

c. Voltage pulses applied to the coil and capacitor circuit at the right frequency will keep the oscillations going.

d. the electrons in the coil and capacitor

e. When the capacitor holds the largest charge, the current through the coil is zero.

f. Oscillations of the coil and capacitor will die out if energy is not added to the circuit.

g. The sum of the magnetic field energy, the electric field energy, the thermal losses, and the energy carried away by electromagnetic fields is constant.

27 Study Guide

Quantum Theory

Vocabulary Review

Circle the letter of the choice that best completes each statement.

1. For light to cause the emission of an electron of a specific metal, its frequency must be at least the _____.
   - **(a.)** threshold frequency.
   - **b.** work function
   - **c.** de Broglie frequency
   - **d.** emission frequency

2. Discrete bundles of energy of light and other forms of radiation are _____.
   - **a.** quarks
   - **(b.)** photons
   - **c.** electromagnetic waves
   - **d.** isotopes

3. The emission of electrons when electromagnetic radiation falls on an object is the _____.
   - **a.** threshold frequency
   - **b.** Heisenberg principle
   - **c.** Compton effect
   - **(d.)** photoelectric effect

4. _____ states that the position and momentum of a particle cannot be precisely known at the same time.
   - **(a.)** The Heisenberg uncertainty principle
   - **b.** The third law of motion
   - **c.** The position uncertainty law
   - **d.** Compton's law

5. The energy needed to free the most weakly bound electron from a metal is the _____ of the metal.
   - **a.** threshold frequency
   - **b.** minimum energy
   - **(c.)** work function
   - **d.** weak electron energy

6. The wavelength of a particle is referred to as its _____.
   - **a.** photon
   - **(b.)** de Broglie wavelength
   - **c.** threshold wavelength
   - **d.** Compton effect

7. The increase in wavelength of X-ray photons when they are scattered off electrons is the _____.
   - **(a.)** Compton effect
   - **b.** Heisenberg uncertainty principle
   - **c.** X scatter effect
   - **d.** photon principle

8. Energy that exists only in packages of specific amounts is _____.
   - **a.** specified
   - **b.** pulsing
   - **(c.)** quantized
   - **d.** discontinuous.

9. A body that is so hot that it glows is _____.
   - **(a.)** incandescent
   - **b.** fluorescent
   - **c.** phosphorescent
   - **d.** radioactive

---

26 Study Guide

In your textbook, read about detection of electromagnetic waves.
Answer the following questions, using complete sentences.

22. Explain how electromagnetic waves are detected by an antenna.
When electric fields strike an antenna, they accelerate the electrons in it. An EMF across the terminals of the antenna oscillates at the frequency of the electromagnetic wave.

23. An antenna designed to receive radio waves is much longer than one designed to receive microwaves. Why is there a size difference?
The EMF across the terminals of an antenna is largest if the length of the antenna is one-half the wavelength of the wave. Radio waves have a longer wavelength than microwaves.

24. Describe two ways in which the detected EMF can be increased.
If two or more wires are spaced about one-quarter wavelength apart, electric fields generated in the individual wires form constructive interference patterns that increase the strength of the signal. At very short wavelengths, parabolic dishes can focus the waves on an antenna held on a tripod above the dish.

25. Explain how radio and television waves of a certain frequency can be selected. Describe briefly how selection works.
A coil and capacitor circuit is connected to the antenna. The capacitance is adjusted until the oscillation frequency of the circuit equals the frequency of the desired wave. Only this frequency can cause significant oscillations of the electrons in the circuit.

In your textbook, read about X rays.
Circle the letter of the choice that best completes each statement.

26. If electrons have _____ kinetic energy with a very _____ voltage, X rays are produced when the electrons are stopped suddenly by matter.
   - **a.** low, high
   - **(b.)** high, high
   - **c.** low, low
   - **d.** high, low

27. X rays can penetrate _____, but are blocked by _____.
   - **a.** lead, bone
   - **b.** bone, soft body tissue
   - **c.** bone, lead
   - **(d.)** soft body tissue, bone

28. When electrons crash into matter, _____ are converted into X rays.
   - **a.** the electrons
   - **(b.)** their kinetic energies
   - **c.** their potential energies
   - **d.** the atoms in the matter

27 Study Guide

Section 27.1: Waves Behave Like Particles

In your textbook, read about radiation from incandescent bodies.

For each of the following statements, write true or rewrite the italicized part to make the statement true.

1. **vibrating particles** — Hot bodies contain *charges*, which radiate electromagnetic waves.

2. **true** — Light and infrared radiation are produced by the vibration of particles within *an incandescent body*.

3. **a variety of frequencies** — Energy is emitted from incandescent bodies at *one specific frequency* that depends on the temperature.

4. **increases** — As the temperature of a hot body increases, the frequency at which the maximum energy is emitted *decreases*.

5. **true** — The total power emitted by an incandescent body *increases* with increasing temperature.

In your textbook, read about Planck's theory that energy is quantized.

Circle the letter of the choice that best completes the statement or answers the question.

6. Max Planck calculated the spectrum of radiation emitted from incandescent bodies based on his assumption that ___.
   a. energy is a wave
   b. energy is not continuous *(circled)*
   c. matter is a wave
   d. matter is a particle

7. In the equation $E = nhf$, which of the following is *not* a possible value of n?
   a. 0   b. 3   c. 5/4 *(circled)*   d. 6

8. Planck's theory depends on the fact that ___.
   a. atoms always radiate electromagnetic waves
   b. atoms always radiate electromagnetic waves when they are vibrating
   c. atoms emit radiation only when their vibration energy changes *(circled)*
   d. atoms emit radiation only if they have a source of electricity

9. If the energy of an atom changes from an initial energy to a final energy, the energy radiated is equal to ___.
   a. the initial energy
   b. the final energy
   c. the product of the initial energy and the final energy
   d. the change in energy *(circled)*

10. Because the constant h is extremely ___, the energy-changing steps are too ___ to be noticeable in ordinary bodies.
    a. small, small *(circled)*
    b. large, small
    c. large, large
    d. small, large

27 Study Guide

In your textbook, read about the photoelectric effect.

For each of the statements below, write true or rewrite the italicized part to make the statement true.

11. **emission of electrons** — The *absorption of energy* when electromagnetic radiation hits an object is called the photoelectric effect.

12. **the threshold** — Electromagnetic radiation of *any frequency* will eject electrons from a metal.

13. **true** — If the frequency of the incident light shone on a metal is below the threshold frequency, no level of *intensity* will cause ejection of electrons.

14. **true** — The *electromagnetic wave theory* cannot explain why electrons are ejected immediately even in dim light if the frequency of the radiation is at or above the threshold level.

In your textbook, read about Einstein's theories on the photoelectric effect.

Answer the following questions, using complete sentences.

15. How does Einstein's photoelectric-effect theory explain the existence of a threshold frequency?
    There is a minimum energy needed to eject an electron from a metal. If a photon has a frequency below the threshold, it will not have enough energy to eject an electron.

16. What does Einstein's theory say about conservation of energy?
    The incoming photon has energy hf. The energy not needed to free the electron from the metal becomes the kinetic energy of the electron.

17. Why will all of the photoelectrons ejected from the same metal not have the maximum kinetic energy?
    Not all electrons have the same energy, so they require different energies to escape. As a result, different amounts of energy are left over to become the kinetic energy of different electrons.

18. Briefly describe an experiment that supports Einstein's theory for the photoelectric effect.
    Light of a chosen frequency shines on a cathode, causing ejection of electrons. The anode connects to a variable potential difference, so that a negative charge on the anode can be controlled. This charge opposes movement of electrons from the cathode. When the potential difference across the anode is increased, it becomes more negative, and the electrons require greater kinetic energy to reach the anode. At some voltage, no electrons will have enough kinetic energy and the current will fall to zero.

27 Study Guide

Name _____

In your textbook, read about the kinetic energy of photoelectrons.
Refer to the graphs below that show the maximum kinetic energy of photoelectrons versus frequency for two different metals. Then answer the questions.

19. What is the numerical value of the slope of the line in graph A? In graph B?
The slope of the lines in both graphs is 6.6 × 10⁻³⁴.

20. To what constant are the slopes equal?
They are equal to Planck's constant.

21. How can you tell that these are graphs for two different metals?
They have different threshold frequencies.

22. What is the approximate threshold frequency in graph A?
~1.0 × 10¹⁵ Hz

23. What is the minimum frequency required to produce photoelectrons from the metal in graph B?
~1.25 × 10¹⁵ Hz

24. At what frequency do the photoelectrons produced from the metal in graph A have no kinetic energy?
~1.0 × 10¹⁵ Hz

25. Will a frequency of 1.0×10^{15} Hz eject electrons from the metal in graph B? Why or why not?
No; that frequency is lower than the threshold frequency.

26. What is the relationship between the frequency of the radiation and the kinetic energy of the photoelectrons?
At frequencies greater than the threshold frequency, the kinetic energy of the photoelectrons is proportional to the frequency of the radiation.

27. How would you use the graphs to find the work function of these metals? Compute the work function by multiplying
Read the threshold frequencies from the graphs. Compute the work function by multiplying the threshold frequency by Planck's constant.

27 Study Guide

Name _____

In your textbook, read about the Compton effect.
Answer the following questions, using complete sentences.

28. Which of Einstein's theories did Compton's experiment test?
Compton's experiment tested Einstein's theory that photons have momentum.

29. Briefly describe Compton's experiment.
Compton directed X rays of known wavelength at a graphite target and measured the X rays scattered by the target.

30. What were the results of Compton's experiment?
Some of the X rays were scattered without a change in wavelength. Other scattered X rays had longer wavelengths than the original radiation.

31. How is wavelength related to the energy of a photon?
The energy of a photon is inversely proportional to its wavelength.

32. What did Compton's results mean?
The increase in wavelength meant that the X-ray photons had lost both energy and momentum.

33. In later experiments, Compton observed that electrons were ejected from the graphite block. What hypothesis did Compton suggest to explain this?
The X-ray photons collided with the electrons in the graphite target and transferred energy and momentum to the electrons.

34. How did Compton test his hypothesis and what did he find?
He measured the energy of the ejected electrons and found that the energy and momentum gained by the electrons were equal to the energy and momentum lost by the photons.

35. How is a photon like matter?
A photon is a particle that has energy and momentum.

36. How is a photon not like matter?
A photon has no mass and travels at the speed of light.

27 Study Guide

Section 27.2: Particles Behave Like Waves

In your textbook, read about the wave nature of matter.

Write the term that correctly completes each statement. Use each term once.

de Broglie wavelength	electrons	waves	$\lambda = h/p$
diffracted	objects	X rays	$p = h/\lambda$
diffraction grating	particles		

Louis-Victor de Broglie was first to suggest that particles could behave like

(1) ___waves___ . He proposed that the momentum of a particle is represented

by the equation **(2)** $p = h/\lambda$. Therefore, the wavelength of a particle is

(3) $\lambda = h/p$. The wavelength of a particle is known as the

(4) ___de Broglie wavelength___ . One of the problems with de Broglie's theory was that effects such as

diffraction and interference had never been observed for **(5)** ___particles___ . Thomson

performed an experiment that showed that electrons are **(6)** ___diffracted___ just as light

is. In his experiment, he aimed a beam of **(7)** ___electrons___ at a very thin crystal. The

crystal acted as a **(8)** ___diffraction grating___ . Electrons diffracted from the crystal formed the same

pattern that **(9)** ___X rays___ of a similar wavelength formed. The wave nature of most

(10) ___objects___ is not observable because the wavelengths are extremely short.

In your textbook, read about the dual wave and particle description of light and matter.

Circle the letter of the choice that best completes each statement.

11. The spreading of light used to locate a particle can be reduced by _____ of the light.

   a. decreasing the wavelength   **c.** increasing the wavelength

   b. decreasing the frequency   **d.** increasing the intensity

12. The Compton effect means that, when light of short wavelengths strikes a particle, the _____ of the particle is changed.

   a. size   **b.** momentum   **c.** charge   **d.** identity

13. According to the Heisenberg uncertainty principle, it is impossible to measure precisely both the _____ and the _____ of a particle at the same time.

   a. charge, position   **c.** charge, mass

   b. position, momentum   **d.** wavelength, momentum

---

28 Study Guide

The Atom

Vocabulary Review

Write the term that correctly completes each statement. Use each term once.

absorption spectrum	excited state	quantum number
α particle	ground state	scintillation
coherent light	incoherent light	spectroscope
electron cloud	laser	spectroscopy
emission spectrum	quantum mechanics	stimulated emission
energy level	quantum model	

1. ___α particle___   A(n) _____ is a relatively massive, positively charged, fast-moving particle released by an atom.

2. ___ground state___   The lowest energy level for an electron is the _____ .

3. ___coherent light___   In _____ , the light waves are in step.

4. ___scintillation___   A small flash of light emitted by a detection screen is a(n) _____ .

5. ___absorption spectrum___   A(n) _____ has dark lines in an otherwise continuous spectrum.

6. ___laser___   A device that produces light by stimulated emission is a(n) _____ .

7. ___energy level___   A(n) _____ is a quantized energy state of an electron in an atom.

8. ___electron cloud___   The _____ of an atom is the region in which there is a high probability of finding an electron.

9. ___quantum mechanics___   A field of physics that uses the quantum model of the atom to make predictions about atomic structure and behavior is _____ .

10. ___incoherent light___   In _____ , the light waves are not in step.

11. ___emission spectrum___   A(n) _____ is the set of light wavelengths given off by an atom.

12. ___spectroscopy___   The study of the light given off by atoms is _____ .

13. ___stimulated emission___   When atoms in an excited state are struck by other photons, they release photons in _____ .

14. ___quantum model___   The _____ predicts the probability that an electron is at a specific location.

15. ___spectroscope___   A device used to study the light given off by an atom is a(n) _____ .

16. ___quantum number___   The principal _____ determines the values of r and E.

17. ___excited state___   An electron that has absorbed energy is in a(n) _____ .

28 Study Guide

Section 28.1: The Bohr Model of the Atom

In your textbook, read about the nuclear model of the atom.
The diagram below shows an experiment, with a close-up of the atoms in area C. Refer to the diagram to answer the following questions.

Rutherford's experimental apparatus

Atoms at C

Nucleus

1. What kind of material does container A hold?
   It contains a radioactive material, such as uranium.

2. What makes up ray B? What characteristics does the ray have?
   The ray is α particles–rapidly moving, relatively massive, positively charged particles.

3. What type of material is C?
   C is a sheet of gold foil.

4. What is D, and what role does it play?
   D is a circular fluorescent screen that emits scintillations when α particles strike it. It serves as a radiation detector.

5. What will happen to the particle labeled 1? Why?
   It will be strongly deflected at a large angle because it approaches the nucleus head-on, and is repelled by it because of the like charge.

6. What will happen to the particle labeled 2? Why?
   It will not be deflected because it does not come close to a nucleus.

7. What will happen to the particle labeled 3? Why?
   It will be slightly deflected because it comes close to a nucleus, and will be repelled less strongly than a particle that approaches head-on.

Physics: Principles and Problems

---

28 Study Guide

8. Will most of the particles that pass into object C behave like particle 1, 2, or 3? What does that tell us about atoms?
   Most will behave like particle 2, indicating that the atom is mostly empty space, the nucleus occupying only a small region within it.

9. From his experiment, what did Rutherford conclude about the atom and its component parts, including electrons?
   The atom has a nucleus that is positively charged but that occupies only a small region within it, and electrons revolve around the nucleus in planetary fashion.

In your textbook, read about spectra.
Circle the letter of the choice that best completes the statement or answers the question.

10. The spectrum of an incandescent solid is typically _____.
    a. a set of colored lines
    b. a single colored line
    c. a band of colors with dark lines
    d. a continuous band of colors

11. What information can an emission spectrum reveal about the elements present in a sample?
    a. their identities only
    b. their relative concentrations only
    c. both their identities and their relative concentrations
    d. neither their identities nor their relative concentrations

12. The Fraunhofer lines appear in the spectrum of _____.
    a. sodium
    b. all flames
    c. the moon
    d. the sun

13. Which element was discovered through study of the Fraunhofer lines?
    a. hydrogen
    b. helium
    c. lithium
    d. sodium

14. If the planetary theory of electrons were correct, at what wavelengths would light be released by an atom?
    a. at all wavelengths
    b. in a band at the red end only
    c. at certain specific values
    d. in a band at the violet end only

15. The visible spectrum of hydrogen consists of _____.
    a. two lines
    b. four lines
    c. a single narrow band
    d. a continuous wide band

16. The energy of a photon of light released by an atom is equal to _____.
    a. hc/λ
    b. $hc\lambda$
    c. λ/f
    d. $h\lambda/f$

Physics: Principles and Problems

Physics: Principles and Problems

17. What does the fact that an emission spectrum contains only certain wavelengths show about electrons?

   a. Their energy is continuous.

   c. They are present in the nucleus.

   (b.) Their energy is quantized.

   d. They have a negative charge.

In your textbook, read about the Bohr model of atoms.
For each of the statements below, write true or true or rewrite the italicized part to make the statement true.

do   **18.** Bohr hypothesized that the laws of electromagnetism *do not* operate inside atoms.

absorbs   **19.** An electron *releases* energy when it moves from the ground state to an excited state.

larger   **20.** The orbits of electrons in excited states tend to be *smaller* than those of electrons in the ground state.

true   **21.** According to the Bohr model, the energy of an *electron* in an atom is quantized.

ultraviolet waves   **22.** The electromagnetic radiation emitted by hydrogen when the electron drops into its ground state is *infrared waves.*

true   **23.** The electromagnetic radiation emitted by hydrogen when the electron drops into the second energy level from higher levels is *visible light.*

In your textbook, read about the symbols used in Bohr's calculations.
For each term on the left, write the matching item.

q	**24.** charge	λ
K	**25.** Coulomb's constant	E
mvr	**26.** angular momentum	h
r	**27.** radius of orbit	K
n	**28.** principal quantum number	mvr
h	**29.** Planck's constant	n
λ	**30.** wavelength	q
E	**31.** total energy	r

Section 28.2: The Quantum Model of the Atom

In your textbook, read about the shortcomings of the Bohr model of the atom and about the quantum model.
Circle the letter of the choice that best completes the statement or answers the question.

1. Which quantity equals a whole-number multiple of the wavelength of an electron?

   a. r **(c.)** 2π

   b. π **d.** πr^2

---

2. The modern quantum model of the atoms precisely predicts _____ for an electron at a given moment.

   (a.) the probability of being at a specific location

   c. position and velocity

   b. position and momentum

   d. direction and position

3. The probability of finding an electron in the electron cloud of an atom is _____.

   a. zero   **b.** low   **(c.)** high   **d.** infinite

4. A shortcoming of the Bohr model of the atom is its inability to _____.

   a. provide correct values for the lines in the hydrogen spectrum

   (b.) explain why angular momentum is quantized

   c. explain chemical properties of the elements

   d. predict the ionization energy for hydrogen

5. Application of the theories of electromagnetism to Bohr's model predicted _____.

   a. a positive charge for electrons

   c. great stability for the atom

   (b.) collapse of the atom

   d. a highly diffuse nucleus

6. Wavelength of a particle is equal to _____.

   a. h/c **b.** mv/h **(c.)** h/mv **d.** mvr

7. Which of the following is *not* true of quantum theory?

   a. It is based on the wave model.

   b. It predicts the probability that the electron is at a given radius.

   (c.) It proposes a planetary picture of the atom.

   d. It can be used to give details of the structure of molecules.

8. The circumference of the Bohr orbit equals _____.

   (a.) $2\pi r$ **b.** πr^2 **c.** λ **d.** $\lambda/2\pi$

9. Which of the following is true of n?

   a. It is always a negative number.

   c. It may take on any value.

   b. It cannot be expressed as a number.

   (d.) It is always a whole number.

In your textbook, read about the structure and operation of lasers.
Write the term that correctly completes each statement.

Light emitted by a(n) **(10)** **incandescent** source has many wavelengths and moves in all directions. Because the waves are out of step with each other, this light is **(11)** **incoherent** _____.

When an atom in an excited state is struck by a(n) **(12)** **photon** _____ with the correct amount of energy, the atom will emit another **(13)** **photon** _____ of identical **(14)** **wavelength** _____, which will be in step with the first one. In a laser, a flash of light

28 Study Guide

Name ___

that has a(n) (15) **shorter** wavelength than that of the laser is used to excite the atoms. As the atoms decay to a(n) (16) **lower** energy state, they lase, or give off light by (17) **stimulated** emission. As photons are produced, they strike other (18) **atoms**, which give off more photons. The photons are trapped inside a glass (19) **tube** capped at each end with parallel (20) **mirrors**, one of which is 100% (21) **reflective**. The other is only partially (22) **reflective** and allows some of the photons through. Because all the photons produced by the laser are in step, the light is (23) **coherent**. The beam produced is very narrow and thus very (24) **intense**. It also is all one wavelength, so it is (25) **monochromatic**.

In your textbook, read about applications of laser technology.
For each of the statements below, write true or false.

true 26. A hologram is a photographic recording of the phase and intensity of light.

false 27. Lasers are used in spectroscopy to remove atoms.

true 28. Fiber optics transmits lasers, using total internal reflection.

false 29. Laser beams spread out greatly over long distances.

true 30. Lasers can cut a wide variety of materials.

Date ___ Period ___ Name ___

29 Study Guide

Solid State Electronics

Vocabulary Review

Write the term that correctly completes each statement. Use each term once.

band theory	extrinsic semiconductor	junction transistor
conduction band	forbidden gap	n-type semiconductor
depletion layer	forward-biased diode	p-type semiconductor
diode	hole	transistor
dopant	intrinsic semiconductor	valence band

1. **conduction band** The lowest band that is not filled to capacity with electrons is the ___.

2. **p-type semiconductor** A semiconductor that conducts by means of holes is a(n) ___.

3. **intrinsic semiconductor** A(n) ___ conducts as a result of thermally freed electrons and holes.

4. **valence band** The highest band that contains electrons is the ___.

5. **junction transistor** A(n) ___ has a region of one type of doped semiconductor sandwiched between layers of the opposite type.

6. **extrinsic semiconductor** A(n) ___ is produced by adding impurity atoms to a semiconductor.

7. **dopant** An impurity added to a semiconductor is a(n) ___.

8. **hole** An empty energy level in the valence band is a(n) ___.

9. **diode** A(n) ___ consists of a p-type semiconductor joined with an n-type semiconductor.

10. **depletion layer** The region around a diode junction that has neither holes nor free electrons is the ___.

11. **transistor** Any simple switch made of doped semiconducting material is a(n) ___.

12. **n-type semiconductor** A semiconductor that conducts by means of electrons is a(n) ___.

13. **forbidden gap** A range of energy values that no atom can possess is a(n) ___.

14. **band theory** The ___ of solids explains electric conduction in terms of energy bands and forbidden gaps.

29 Study Guide

Section 29.1: Conduction in Solids

In your textbook, read about the band theory of solids.

For each of the statements below, write true or rewrite the italicized part to make the statement true.

true	**1.**	Electric charges are easy to displace in *conductors*.
affect	**2.**	When two atoms are brought close together, their electric fields *don't affect* one another.
broad	**3.**	When a large number of atoms is brought close together, their energy levels spread into *narrow* bands.
close together	**4.**	There are forbidden gaps of energy for atoms that are *far apart* in large numbers.
solids	**5.**	The band theory explains electric conduction in *gases*.
true	**6.**	The *inner bands* of atoms in a solid are full.
conduction	**7.**	The lowest band that is not filled to capacity with electrons is the *valence* band.
valence	**8.**	The highest band that contains electrons is the *conduction* band.
true	**9.**	In conductors, the valence band and the conduction band are the *same*.
true	**10.**	The size of the forbidden gap between a full valence band and the conduction band determines whether a solid is an *insulator*.

In your textbook, read about conductors and insulators.

Circle the letter of the choice that best completes the statement or answers the question.

11. _____ is a very good conductor of electricity.

  a. Silicon   **c.** Sulfur

  (**b.**) Aluminum   **d.** Iodine

12. A material that conducts electricity well tends to have _____.

  a. no valence electrons

  (**b.**) partially filled bands

  c. completely filled bands

  d. conduction and valence bands that are far apart

Physics: Principles and Problems

---

29 Study Guide

13. When an electric field is applied on a length of wire, _____.

  a. there is random motion but no overall drifting in one direction

  b. there is overall drifting in one direction, but no random motion

  (**c.**) there are both random motion and overall drifting in one direction

  d. there is neither random motion nor overall drifting in one direction

14. How is conductivity related to resistivity?

  a. The two are directly related.

  b. The two are equal.

  (**c.**) Conductivity is the reciprocal of resistivity.

  d. Their relationship can't be described in general terms.

15. What happens to the conductivity of metals as temperature increases?

  a. It remains the same.

  b. It increases.

  (**c.**) It decreases.

  d. It follows no general rule.

16. _____ is an insulator.

  a. Copper   **b.** Silicon   **c.** Gold   (**d.**) Table salt

17. In an insulating material, _____.

  (**a.**) the valence band is filled and the conduction band is empty

  b. the valence band is empty and the conduction band is filled

  c. both the valence band and the conduction band are empty

  d. both the valence band and the conduction band are filled

18. What is the effect if a relatively small electric field is placed across an insulator?

  (**a.**) No current flows.

  b. A small current flows.

  c. A large current flows.

  d. The insulator acts like a conductor.

In your textbook, read about semiconductors.

For each item on the left, write the letter of the matching item.

d	**19.**	a pure semiconductor
e	**20.**	an atom with four valence electrons
a	**21.**	any impurity added to a semiconductor
c	**22.**	an empty energy level in the valence band
b	**23.**	any semiconductor that conducts because of added impurities

  a. dopant

  b. extrinsic semiconductor

  c. hole

  d. intrinsic semiconductor

  e. silicon

---

29 Study Guide

2. Which way is conventional current flowing in each diagram, clockwise or counterclockwise?
Current flows counterclockwise in A, clockwise in B.

3. Which way are electrons flowing in each diagram?
Electrons flow clockwise in A, counterclockwise in B.

4. What differs in the *p*-type and *n*-type semiconductors?
A *p*-type semiconductor conducts by means of holes; an *n*-type semiconductor conducts by means of electrons.

5. What kind of biasing does each diode have? How you can tell?
A is forward-biased; the plus sign is on the *p* side and the minus sign is on the *n* side. B is reverse-biased; the plus sign is on the *n* side and the minus sign is on the *p* side.

6. Compare the depletion layer in the two diodes.
The depletion layer is wide in B and nonexistent in A.

7. Compare the quantity of current flow through the two diodes. Which is a conductor, and which is a large resistor?
Current easily flows through A but not much flows through B. A is a conductor; B is a large resistor.

In your textbook, read about transistors.
Circle the letter of the choice that best completes the statement or answers the question.

8. Transistors are used mainly as .
   a. resistors
   (b.) voltage amplifiers
   c. rectifiers
   d. insulators

9. How many layers of semiconductor are in a simple junction transistor?
   a. one
   b. two
   (c.) three
   d. four

10. What type of transistor has a center that is an *n*-type semiconductor?
   a. *n* transistor
   b. *p* transistor
   c. *npn* transistor
   (d.) *pnp* transistor

---

29 Study Guide

In your textbook, read about doped semiconductors.
Write the term that correctly completes each statement.

Dopants provide extra (24) **holes** or extra negatively charged
(25) **electrons** to a semiconductor. If an atom with five valence electrons replaces
an atom with four valence electrons, one electron is unneeded for (26) **bonding** .
The extra electron serves as a (27) **donor** electron. Adding a small amount of
(28) **energy** to the electron will move it into the (29) **conduction**
band. The resulting conductor is a(n) (30) **n-type** semiconductor; it carries
electricity by means of particles that have a(n) (31) **negative** charge. If an atom
with three valence electrons replaces an atom with four valence electrons, an extra
(32) **hole** forms. The atoms can accept electrons and can be used as a(n)
(33) **p-type** semiconductor. In either type of semiconductor, the net charge
on the semiconductor is (34) **zero** . As temperature increases, the electric
conductivity of semiconductors (35) **increases** and their resistivity
(36) **decreases** . This also happens to the electric conductivity of certain semiconductors when (37) **light** intensity upon them increases.

Section 29.2: Electronic Devices

In your textbook, read about diodes.
The diagrams below show a diode used with two kinds of biasing. Refer to the diagrams to answer the following questions.

1. What function does the battery serve?
It provides electrons and maintains a potential difference.

29 Study Guide

•••••••••••••

11. In an *npn* transistor, conventional current flows from the _____.
   (a) base to the emitter
   b. emitter to the base
   c. diode to the collector
   d. rectifier to the collector

12. In an *npn* transistor, electrons flow from the _____.
   (a) emitter to the base to the collector
   b. collector to the base to the emitter
   c. base to the collector to the emitter
   d. base to the emitter to the collector

13. What carries current in a *pnp* transistor?
   a. electrons   c. protons
   (b.) holes   d. nothing

14. Current through the collector is _____ than current through the base.
   a. a little smaller   c. much smaller
   b. a little larger   (d.) much larger

---

30 Study Guide

•••••••••••••

The Nucleus

Vocabulary Review

Write the term that correctly completes each statement. Use each term once.

activity   gamma decay   nuclear reaction
alpha decay   gluon   nuclide
antiparticle   grand unification theory   pair production
atomic mass unit   graviton   positron
atomic number   half-life   quark
beta decay   lepton   strong nuclear force
elementary particle mass number   transmute
force carrier   neutrino   weak boson

1. __nuclide__	The nucleus of an isotope is a(n) _____.
2. __activity__	The number of decays per second is the _____ of a radioactive substance.
3. __transmute__	During some types of radioactive decay, the radioactive element will _____, or change into another element.
4. __force carrier__	A member of the family of fundamental particles that carry forces between matter is a _____.
5. __quark__	The _____ family of fundamental particles includes protons, neutrons, and mesons.
6. __lepton__	The electron and neutrino are examples of the _____ family of fundamental particles.
7. __antiparticle__	A particle of antimatter is a(n) _____.
8. __pair production__	Energy can be converted to matter when a gamma ray passes close by a nucleus and _____ occurs.
9. __grand unification theory__	Physicists are trying to create a _____ that connects the electromagnetic, weak, strong, and gravitational forces.
10. __gluon__	The particle that carries the strong force that holds the nucleus together is the _____.
11. __alpha decay__	The emission of an α particle is _____.
12. __neutrino__	The little neutral particle emitted during beta decay is the _____.
13. __strong nuclear force__	The attractive force between protons and neutrons that are close together is the _____.
14. __beta decay__	The emission of a β particle is _____.

30 Study Guide

15. **weak boson** — The particle involved in the weak nuclear interaction is the ___.
16. **graviton** — The particle that carries the gravitational force is the ___.
17. **positron** — An antielectron, or ___, has the same mass as an electron but a positive charge.
18. **atomic number** — The number of protons in a nucleus is the atom's ___.
19. **half-life** — The time required for one-half of a radioactive sample to decay is the ___ of that element.
20. **mass number** — The sum of the number of protons and neutrons in a nucleus is the ___.
21. **gamma decay** — A nucleus emits a gamma ray during the process of ___.
22. **nuclear reaction** — Whenever the number of protons or neutrons in a nucleus changes, a(n) ___ occurs.
23. **atomic mass unit** — The mass of one proton, 1.66×10^{-27} kg, is equal to one ___.
24. **elementary particle** — A fundamental unit of matter that does not appear to be divisible into smaller units is a(n) ___.

Section 30.1: Radioactivity

In your textbook, read about the atomic nucleus.
For each of the statements below, write true or false.

true 1. The only charged particle in the nucleus is the proton.
false 2. Most of the mass of an atom comes from the mass of protons.
false 3. The weak nuclear force overcomes the electrical force between protons to hold the nucleus together.
false 4. Neutrons are not affected by the strong nuclear force.
true 5. All nuclides of an element have the same number of protons but different numbers of neutrons.
true 6. The mass of an individual atom is close to a whole number of mass units, while the atomic mass of an average sample of that type of atom is not, because it contains a mixture of isotopes.
false 7. One mass unit is now defined on the basis of the mass of a proton.
true 8. In the notation $^A_Z X$, A is the mass number, Z is the atomic number, and X is any element.

---

30 Study Guide

In your textbook, read about radioactive decay.
Circle the letter of the choice that best completes each statement.

9. Photographic plates that Becquerel had near uranium compounds were exposed because ___.
   a. their coverings had a light leak
   b. uranium reacted chemically with the photographic plates
   c. uranium emits light rays
   (d.) uranium undergoes radioactive decay

10. Three types of radiation produced by radioactive decay are ___.
    (a.) alpha, beta, and gamma
    b. gamma, X ray, and light
    c. ultraviolet, light, and infrared
    d. alpha, beta, and delta

11. A thick sheet of paper can stop ___.
    a. X rays
    b. gamma rays
    c. β particles
    (d.) alpha radiation

12. α particles are ___.
    a. high-speed electrons
    (b.) the nucleus of a helium atom
    c. high-energy photons
    d. low-energy photons

13. β particles are emitted when ___ during radioactive decay.
    a. a proton changes to a neutron
    (b.) a neutron changes to a proton
    c. an electron changes energy levels
    d. a valence electron is ejected

14. When a nucleus emits a gamma ray during gamma decay, ___.
    a. both the mass number and the atomic number change
    b. the atomic number increases by one and the mass number stays the same
    (c.) neither the mass number nor the atomic number changes
    d. the mass number decreases by four and the atomic number stays the same

In your textbook, read about nuclear reactions and equations.
For each of the statements below, write true or rewrite the italicized part to make the statement true.

15. **nuclear reaction** — A *chemical reaction* occurs whenever the number of neutrons or protons in a nucleus changes.
16. **Some** — *All* nuclear reactions occur with a release of energy.
17. **true** — Nuclear reactions can release excess energy in the form of *kinetic energy* of emitted particles.
18. **can** — Nuclear reactions *cannot* be written in equation form.
19. **true** — The total number of nuclear particles *stays the same* during a nuclear reaction.
20. **true** — In a nuclear equation, the sum of the atomic numbers on the right side must *equal* the sum of the atomic numbers on the left side.

30 Study Guide

In your textbook, read about particle detectors.
For each of the statements below, write true or rewrite the italicized part to make the statement true.

4. **true** — Exposure of *photographic film* is one way to detect radiation from radioactive decay.

5. **true** — The *Geiger-Mueller tube* detects radiation because high-speed particles emitted during radioactive decay ionize matter they bombard.

6. **bubble chamber** — In a *Wilson cloud chamber*, trails of small vapor droplets form in a liquid held just above the boiling point.

7. **true** — Modern experiments use *spark chambers* in which a discharge is produced in the path of a particle passing through the chamber.

8. **neutral** — Because *charged* particles do not produce charges and leave tracks, the laws of conservation and momentum in collisions are used to detect production of the particles in spark chambers.

In your textbook, read about elementary particles.
Complete the table by marking quark, lepton, or force carrier for each particle.

Table 1

Particle	Quark	Lepton	Force Carrier
9. electron		X	
10. photon			X
11. neutrino		X	
12. muon		X	
13. charm	X		
14. down	X		
15. gluon			X
16. bottom	X		

In your textbook, read about particles and antiparticles.
Circle the letter of the choice that best completes each statement.

17. The wide range of energies of electrons emitted during beta decay suggested that another particle, later found to be the _____, was emitted with the β particle.
a. photon   (b.) antineutrino   c. electron   d. muon

18. A proton within the nucleus can change into a neutron with the emission of a _____ and a neutrino.
(a.) positron   b. antineutrino   c. muon   d. photon

---

30 Study Guide

In your textbook, read about the half-lives of radioactive elements.
Refer to the graph below to answer the following questions. Use complete sentences.

Amount of radioactive atoms (mg) vs. Time (years): 12.3 24.6 36.9 49.2 61.5

21. What fraction of the original amount of radioactive atoms remains after 24.6 years?
One-fourth of the radioactive atoms remain.

22. How many milligrams of radioactive atoms remain after 12.3 years?
Ten mg remain.

23. Define half-life.
The half-life is the time required for half of the atoms in a given quantity of a radioactive isotope to decay.

24. What is the half-life of the element in the graph?
The half-life is 12.3 years.

25. At what time will the activity of the sample be one-eighth of the original activity?
The activity of the sample will be one-eighth of the original activity after 36.9 years.

26. Based on Table 30-1 in your textbook, what is the identity of the element represented in the graph?
The element is hydrogen-3.

27. According to Table 30-1, what type of radiation is produced by this element?
Beta radiation is produced.

Section 30.2: The Building Blocks of Matter

In your textbook, read about nuclear bombardment and nuclear accelerators.
Answer the following questions, using complete sentences.

1. Why are neutrons often used to bombard nuclei?
Neutrons are uncharged and not repelled by the nucleus.

2. Explain how a linear accelerator accelerates protons.
The first tube has a negative potential, and protons accelerate into it. The potential of the second tube is negative in relation to the first, resulting in an electric field gap between the tubes that accelerates the protons into the second tube. This process continues, with the protons accelerating between each pair of tubes.

3. Why can synchrotrons be smaller than linear accelerators?
Synchrotrons use a magnetic field to bend the path of the particles into a circle.

30 Study Guide

19. The existence of beta decay indicates that there is a force, called the _____, acting in the nucleus.
   a. strong nuclear force
   c. transient nuclear force
   b. beta force
   d. (✓) weak nuclear force

20. When a particle and an antiparticle collide, the two can annihilate each other, resulting in _____.
   a. (✓) conversion of matter into energy
   c. pair production
   b. creation of energy
   d. creation of matter

21. Matter and antimatter particles must be produced in pairs to satisfy the law of conservation of _____.
   a. energy   **b.** matter   **c.** (✓) charge   **d.** quarks

In your textbook, read about quarks and leptons.
Answer the following questions.

22. Which quarks make up a proton? A neutron? How do they differ?
A proton is made of two up quarks and one down quark. A neutron is made up of one up quark and two down quarks. They differ by only one quark.

23. Why can't individual quarks be observed?
The strong force that holds them together becomes larger as the quarks are pulled farther apart.

24. Describe the steps that occur during beta decay using the quark model.
One d quark in a neutron changes to a u quark, emitting a W– boson. Then the W– boson decays into an electron and an antineutrino.

In your textbook, read about unification theories.
Write the term that correctly completes each statement.

The force between charged particles is carried by **(25)** __photons__ . The electric force acts over a long distance because a photon has **(26)** __zero mass__ . The weak force acts over short distances because a boson has **(27)** __large mass__ . In the high-energy collisions produced in accelerators, the **(28)** __electromagnetic__ and weak interactions have the same strength and range. Astrophysical theories indicate that, during massive stellar explosions, the two interactions are **(29)** __identical__ . These theories unify the electromagnetic and weak forces into a single **(30)** __electroweak force__ . Physicists are trying to create a grand unification theory that includes the **(31)** __strong force__ as well.

31 Study Guide

Nuclear Applications

Vocabulary Review

For each term on the left, write the letter of the matching item.

d **1.** the part of a nuclear reactor that absorbs neutrons and controls the rate of the chain reaction

a **2.** the difference between the energy of the assembled nucleus and the particles in it

i **3.** the union of small nuclei to form larger ones

j **4.** liquefied fuel enclosed in tiny glass spheres and imploded by laser beams

b **5.** a nuclear reactor that produces more fuel than it uses

k **6.** the difference between the mass of the nucleus and the masses of the particles in it

m **7.** a proton or a neutron

e **8.** necessity for safe use of energy from fusion

l **9.** the substance in a nuclear reactor that slows fast neutrons

h **10.** a division of a nucleus into two or more fragments

o **11.** reactions that take place when nuclei have large amounts of thermal energy

c **12.** the process in which neutrons released by one fission induce other fissions

g **13.** a neutron released by a fission reaction and moving at a high speed

n **14.** a neutron that has been slowed by a moderator

f **15.** a process that increases the number of fissionable nuclei

a. binding energy
b. breeder reactor
c. chain reaction
d. control rod
e. controlled fusion
f. enrichment
g. fast neutron
h. fission
i. fusion
j. inertial confinement fusion
k. mass defect
l. moderator
m. nucleon
n. slow neutron
o. thermonuclear reactions

Use with Chapter 31.

31 Study Guide

••••••••••••••

Section 31.1: Radioactivity

In your textbook, read about what holds the nucleus together.

For each of the statements below, write true or rewrite the italicized part to make the statement true.

strong nuclear force   1. The force that overcomes the mutual repulsion of the charged protons is the *electromagnetic force*.

less   2. An assembled nucleus has *more* energy than the separate protons and neutrons in it.

true   3. The binding energy comes from the nucleus's converting some of its *mass to energy*.

less   4. Because mass is converted to energy to hold the nucleons together, the mass of an assembled nucleus is *more* than the sum of the masses of the nucleons that compose it.

difference   5. The mass defect is the *total* of the sum of the masses of the individual nucleons and the actual mass.

true   6. The binding energy is calculated using the equation $E = mc^2$ to compute the energy equivalent of the experimentally determined mass defect.

In your textbook, read about how the nuclear binding energy relates to nuclear reactions.

Circle the letter of the choice that best completes each statement.

7. Nuclei whose atomic masses are larger than that of iron are _____ strongly bound and are therefore _____ stable than iron.

   a. more, less   **c.** more, more

   (**b.**) less, less   **d.** less, more

8. A nuclear reaction will occur naturally if energy is _____ by the reaction.

   (**a.**) released   **c.** used up

   b. absorbed   **d.** conserved

9. When a nucleus undergoes radioactive decay, the resulting nucleus is _____ the original nucleus.

   a. less stable than   **c.** as stable as

   (**b.**) more stable than

10. At atomic numbers below 26, reactions that add nucleons to the nucleus make the nucleus _____.

   a. lighter   (**c.**) more stable

   b. more reactive   **d.** less stable

---

31 Study Guide

••••••••••••••

Section 31.2: Using Nuclear Energy

In your textbook, read about the production of artificial radioactivity.

Write the term that correctly completes each statement.

In 1934, Irene Joliot-Curie and Frederic Joliot bombarded aluminum with

(1) **α particles** _____, producing phosphorus atoms and neutrons.

(2) **Positrons** _____ were also produced, even after the alpha bombardment stopped. The positrons came from the new (3) **phosphorus isotope** _____. Radioactive isotopes arise from stable isotopes bombarded with α particles, (4) **protons** _____, neutrons, electrons, or gamma rays. The resulting unstable nuclei may emit alpha radiation,

(5) **beta radiation** _____, gamma radiation, and positrons.

In your textbook, read about artificial radioactivity used in medicine.

Answer the following questions, using complete sentences.

6. Explain how tracer isotopes are used in medicine.

Patients are given radioactive isotopes that are absorbed by specific parts of the body. The detection of the decay products of these isotopes allows doctors to trace the movement of the isotopes and of the molecules to which they are attached.

7. Name an instrument that can detect the decay products of tracer isotopes.

Answers may vary. Two examples are the Geiger-Mueller counter and the PET scanner.

8. Explain how a PET scanner works.

A solution injected into a patient's body carries a positron-emitting isotope. The isotope decays, releasing positrons. A positron annihilates an electron and two gamma rays are emitted. The PET scanner detects the gamma rays and pinpoints the location of the positron-emitting isotope. A computer makes a three-dimensional map of the isotope distribution.

9. How can $^{60}_{27}$Co be used in medicine?

It can destroy cancerous cells.

Name _____

31 Study Guide

In your textbook, read about nuclear fission.
Complete each statement.

10. The division of a nucleus into two or more fragments is ___**fission**___.

11. In a fission reaction, the total mass of the products is ___**less**___ than the total mass of the reactants, and energy is produced.

12. Repeated fission reactions, or a ___**chain reaction**___, takes place when neutrons produced by earlier fission reactions cause the fission of other nuclei.

In your textbook, read about nuclear reactors.
Circle the letter of the choice that best completes each statement.

13. Most of the neutrons released by the fission of ${}^{235}_{92}$U atoms are ___.
   a. moving at slow speeds
   b. slow neutrons
   c. in pairs
   (d.) moving at high speeds

14. When a ${}^{238}_{92}$U nucleus absorbs a fast neutron, it ___.
   (a.) becomes a new isotope
   b. fuses with another atom
   c. starts moving at a high speed
   d. undergoes fission

15. Slow neutrons are more likely to be absorbed by ___ and to make a chain reaction possible.
   a. ${}^{235}_{92}$U
   b. ${}^{239}_{94}$Pu
   c. ${}^{238}_{92}$U
   d. ${}^{92}_{36}$Kr

16. When Fermi produced the first controlled chain reaction on December 2, 1942, he used ___ as a moderator.
   a. hydrogen
   b. water
   c. heavy water
   (d.) graphite

17. Enrichment increases ___ in the fuel for nuclear reactors.
   a. the amount of gold
   (b.) the number of fissionable nuclei
   c. the number of fusionable nuclei
   d. the number of slow neutrons

Name _____

31 Study Guide

In your textbook, read about the nuclear reactors used in the United States.
Refer to the drawing to answer the following questions.

Write labels for the drawing.

18. ___**containment structure**___
19. ___**steam turbine**___
20. ___**control rods**___
21. ___**steam**___
22. ___**condenser**___
23. ___**reactor**___
24. ___**steam generator**___
25. ___**pump**___
26. ___**lots of water**___
27. ___**pump**___

28. What type of reactor is shown in the drawing?
   The drawing shows a pressurized water reactor.

29. What purposes does water serve in this reactor?
   Water is the moderator and transfers the thermal energy from the fission of uranium.

30. Describe how the reactor produces electric energy.
   Energy released by the fission heats the water surrounding the uranium rods. This water is pumped to a heat exchanger, where its heat boils other water, producing steam that turns turbines. The turbines connect to generators that produce electric energy

31. Why do fuel rods glow blue when they hit water? What is this effect called?
   When electrons that have kinetic energy from the fission reaction and are moving at the speed of light in a vacuum enter water, their speed exceeds the speed of light in water. This causes a blue glow, called the Cerenkov effect.

In your textbook, read about the products of fission reactions.
For each of the statements below, write true or rewrite the italicized part to make the statement true.

32. ___**are**___ Old rods that can no longer be used in a reactor *aren't* radioactive.
33. ___**true**___ Plutonium could be removed from radioactive waste and *recycled* to fuel other reactors.
34. ___**limited**___ The world's supply of uranium is *unlimited*.

31 Study Guide

• • • • • • • • • • • • • • •

35. _____**true**_____ From some reactors, *more fuel* can be recovered than was originally present.

In your textbook, read about nuclear fusion.
Circle the letter of the choice that best completes each statement.

36. In nuclear fusion, nuclei with _____ combine to form a nucleus with _____.

   a. small masses, a larger mass   **c.** large masses, a larger mass

   b. low velocities, a higher velocity   **d.** low energy, a higher energy

37. In the sun, _____ hydrogen nuclei fuse to form one helium nucleus.

   a. two   **b.** three   **c.** four   **d.** six

38. The energy released by a fusion reaction _____.

   a. is the energy equivalent of the mass difference between the products and the reactants

   b. depends on the temperature at which the reaction takes place

   c. transfers to the potential energy of the resultant particles

   d. is very small compared to other types of reactions

39. The reaction $^1_1H + \underline{\qquad} \rightarrow\, ^3_2He + \gamma$ is one possible step in the proton-proton chain of fusion in the sun.

   a. ^1_1H **b.** ^2_1H **c.** ^2_1He **d.** ^4_2He

40. In a thermonuclear bomb, the high temperature necessary to produce the fusion reaction is provided by _____.

   a. dynamite   **b.** an atomic bomb   **c.** a conventional bomb   **d.** electricity

In your textbook, read about controlled fusion.
Answer the following questions, using complete sentences.

41. If energy could be produced economically by the fusion of deuterium and tritium, what would be two benefits?

There would be an almost limitless source of energy from seawater without the formation of radioactive wastes.

42. What are two problems that prevent fusion reactions confined with magnetic fields from being used as an energy source?

The energy produced by fusion has been only a tiny fraction of the energy required to create and hold the plasma. Instabilities in the magnetic field allow the plasma to escape.

43. Explain what happens during inertial confinement fusion.

Deuterium and tritium are liquefied under high pressure and confined in tiny glass spheres. Multiple laser beams hit the spheres, and their energy makes the pellets implode, squeezing their contents. This raises the temperature to levels needed for fusion.

Physics: Principles and Problems

Notes

Notes

Notes